Generating Sound
& Organizing Time

Thinking with gen~ Book 1

Graham Wakefield and Gregory Taylor

DEDICATION

This book is dedicated to our friend and colleague Darwin Grosse, who helped us shape this text and championed it from the beginning.

Thanks for everything, man.

Table of Contents

Chapter 1:
Patching One Sample at a Time

This book is all about the astonishing things you can do—and the insights you can find—when you work at the atomic sample-by-sample structure of digital audio.

The immense possibilities of digital signal processing (DSP) are often inaccessibly black-boxed in music software, and sometimes also shrouded in a mystique of complexity. In this book we'll use gen~, which lets us work directly at the sample level through visual patching (or by coding if you prefer to) and hear the results immediately at every edit. Our aim is to crack open these black boxes, revealing how working at the sample level is not only easier to reason about, but also far more open to experimentation.

Whether you are a musician, sound designer, composer or some other sonic experimentalist, we hope that demystifying a wide selection of musical signal processing techniques, and showing how they are put together from a few common structures, will make it easier for you to imagine and explore variations, hybrids and completely new directions of your own. This book is therefore also about developing *useful things to think with*: design patterns, techniques and subcircuits to help you approach sonic signal processing at the sample level and bring amazing new things to life. Starting from the simplest beginnings we'll develop things like:

- algorithmic rhythm generators, beat slicers, Euclidean sequencers,
- morphing LFOs, wave shapers, bit-crushers and gliding quantizers,
- chaotic systems, stepped and smoothed noise and chance operations,
- a wide palette of filters and delay effects,
- a plethora of phase and frequency modulation algorithms,
- formant, pulsar and polyphonic granular synthesizers of various kinds,
- bandlimited virtual analog and wavetable oscillators capable of intensive modulation,

...and more in the extensive software package provided with the book.

Before we dive into exploring these topics and projects, we think it is helpful to share a couple of insights into the nature of digital signal processing of sound. In all digital audio systems, time passes in discrete steps. Throughout this book, we'll refer to those discrete steps as *sample frames*. These sample frames divide and represent time in terms of the audio *sample rate* — typically 44,100 or 48,000 sample frames per second of real time, which is fast enough to represent pretty much any sound humans can hear. Every digital audio signal is therefore just a stream of numbers.

Within a typical audio plugin for example, these audio streams pass in a flurry through sequences of a few math, logic and memory operations, to produce transformed signals at the output. To make signal processing efficient, these operations will have been pre-compiled from a language like C++ into native code. However, this also makes them less flexible: it's not possible to change the operations inside and hear the results right away (and you would also need to learn a language like C++). Moreover, they are processed in batches of time, sometimes called "buffers" or "blocks" or "signal vectors" of sample frames. This means you can't join them up in feedback circuits shorter than this signal vector size. As we'll see in this book, feedback circuits are fundamental to most audio algorithms, and building feedback circuits as short as a single sample frame is essential to many filters, oscillators, physical models, chaotic processes, and more. The gen~ patching environment was designed to resolve these problems.

What is gen~?

At first glance, **gen~** is just another object that can be added to a Max or RNBO patch, where it can send and receive audio from other objects you connect it to. What makes a **gen~** object different is that *you can open it up* to view its internal circuits and edit what they do, right down to the lowest details of sound signal processing at each passing sample frame. As such, gen~ is also a distinct patching environment (and language) devoted to audio processing and musical programming at the sample frame level.

At the same time, the gen~ environment retains the benefits of flexible patching and native efficiency. With every edit as you work, behind the scenes it is immediately generating and compiling efficient native CPU code for the whole patch. That means can you hear and interact with new sample-level programs and algorithms as you develop them on the fly. It also means that gen~ lets you work at this level without needing to use a complex language like C++, but it can still give you the high performance of compiled C++ code.

What's more, *and what this book is really about*, it means we can think about and develop sonic signal processes at the very level of sample-by-sample operations they are made of. Working at this level means we can define processes—including feedback down to a single sample frame—that are either very difficult or simply impossible any other way. We also think that it makes reasoning about and exploring sonic signal processing much easier. Starting from a humble set of operators you can build up a very flexible library of useful subcircuit "abstractions" that you can combine into powerful yet efficient patches. We'll be doing this throughout the book.

(And, although this isn't the focus of this book, it's worth mentioning that if you make patches that you like, you can also take these algorithms with you. The entire contents of a gen~ object in a Max or RNBO patch can be embedded in a Max for Live Device, or it can also be exported as C++ code for use elsewhere. A RNBO patch that has gen~ objects inside it can also be exported into targets such as audio plugins and embedded hardware devices, or as web-native or C++ code.)

Using this book (and the software that comes with it)

This is a book full of many different circuits and projects, as well as insights and habits of thought. We don't assume that all readers will read from start to finish, so we've tried to structure chapters and sections in ways that will help you to find areas that are of specific interest to you. At the same time, we have provided links and cross-references throughout the book to connect between foundations and possibilities and reinforce the ideas and techniques from the part you're currently reading.

We designed this book to serve equally well whether as a companion for self-study or as a resource for educational situations. We have written it so that you don't need much knowledge of math at all, and we don't expect you to be a coder or even an experienced gen~ user, but the book does assume that you have a little experience of patching with Max or RNBO and know how to create and edit a gen~ patcher. If you've never used gen~ before or you're feeling uncertain, the "gen~ for Beginners" tutorial series on the Cycling '74 website (**https://cycling74.com/tutorials/gen-video-tutorial-series**) will provide you with all you need.

The book also comes with a Max Package including all the patches we build in this book, and more. You can download it from:

cycling74.com/books/go/resources

All you need to do is unzip the downloaded file and place the result in your Max Packages folder (e.g., "Documents/Max 8/Packages" or "My Documents/Max 8/Packages").

A Bestiary of signals and operators

Before we dive into exploring projects and patches, we think it is helpful to recall the nature of sonic signal processing as a combination of signal streams and operations, which within a gen~ patch all happens one sample at a time.

That means:

- ○ Every patch cord is a *signal* that is updated with every sample frame of passing time.[1]
- ○ Similarly, every *operator* also updates at this same sample rate, one sample frame at a time.
- ○ Moreover, *the entire patch* also moves forward one sample frame at a time. This is what lets us perform essential "single-sample" feedback processing, which we do all the time.

For the remainder of this chapter, we would like to introduce the most common kinds of signals and operators we use as building blocks to generate and organize ephemeral digital sound. You can think of it as a bestiary or cast of likely characters if you like. We hope that this will help you to better understand just about everything else in the rest of this book.

Signals

Patch cords can carry *audible* signals, but they don't have to: signals can carry any numeric values, and their behavior and purposes can be quite varied. So, when you think about a signal, it's often helpful to consider its main characteristics:

- *Rates* of change

    - ○ Does the signal change at audible rates, more slowly, or not at all?
    - ○ Are those changes periodic, sporadic, complex, or stochastic (random) over time?

- *Shapes* (and *slopes*) of change

    - ○ Does the signal move in stepped, sloped, or curved segments, or does it have a more complex shape? How steep are the slopes, and how tight are the curves?

- *Ranges* of values

    - ○ What are the lower and upper limits of the signal (if any)?[2] Is the range composed of only positive values (unipolar), or does the range include negative values (bipolar)?
    - ○ Can the signal take any numeric value in this range, or is it limited to whole numbers only ("integers"), to a handful of specific values, or only 0.0 or 1.0 ("logic signals")?

- *Kinds* of value

    o   Does the value represent a linear or cyclical idea? Values such as clock-face time and angles, as well as the phase of an oscillator or a metric rhythm, are all cyclical—when you pass the upper limit, you wrap back to the lower limit (e.g., an angle of 365° is the same as an angle of 5°).
    o   Do the values correspond to specific units such as time (milliseconds), frequency (Hz), loudness (decibels), MIDI note numbers, etc.?[3]

Let's take a closer look at some of the most common variants of the signals we work with in terms of their rates, shapes of change, ranges, and kinds of value.

Audio signals

An audio signal is one that we can potentially hear. This means that the signal oscillates up and down hundreds or thousands of times per second.

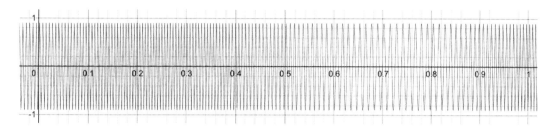

This graph shows a sine wave oscillating up and down at 100-200Hz (100 to 200 oscillations per second), which could be created using a **cycle** operator. (The term "Hz" is short for Hertz, which is a standard representation of frequency. So, 100Hz simply means 100 oscillations per second.)

All audible signals are in motion, jumping up and down one way or another. It is primarily the repetitive periodicity of their movement that imparts pitch and their distribution of shapes that colors how they sound (their timbre).

Normally, audio signals move in a bipolar way (which means, they can swing both negative and positive), ranging from -1.0 to +1.0 at their loudest or over a narrower range for quieter sounds. If audio signals go below -1.0 or above 1.0, they may be clipped or distorted by your audio hardware.

The fastest audio signal a digital system can represent is one half of the sampling rate (since it takes two samples per period to make an oscillation!)—this is called the Nyquist limit. At a frequency of 48,000Hz, the Nyquist limit of **samplerate/2** is 24,000Hz, which is higher than humans can hear.

Low frequency oscillations (LFO)

If we slow oscillations down well below around 30Hz, we will no longer hear them directly, but these kinds of signals can be extremely useful for animating parameters of operations—common musical examples include vibrato and tremolo. LFOs are also often bipolar but do not need to be, nor do they need to stay within -1.0 to 1.0 limits.

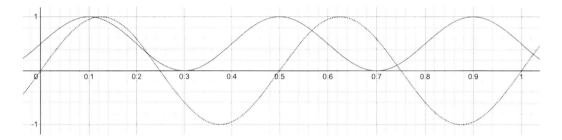

The dotted line in the previous illustration shows a bipolar sine wave oscillation at 2Hz (two cycles per second), which could be created using a **cycle 2** operator. The solid line is a *unipolar* sine wave (sweeping between 0.0 and +1.0) at 2.5Hz.

Unipolar ramp (phasor)

A special unipolar function is the ramp from 0.0 up to +1.0 (or in reverse, from +1.0 down to 0.0). These kinds of ramps can be thought of as a universal primitive of repeating change and are used in almost every section of this book, but especially in Chapter 2.

This graph shows a ramp repeating at 4Hz, as produced by a **phasor 4** operator:

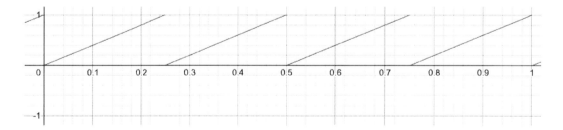

Unipolar envelopes (and windows)

The unipolar range is very useful as a multiplier for any other signal, since multiplying with the upper limit of +1.0 will preserve the signal; multiplying with the lower limit of 0.0 will silence it; and anywhere in between will attenuate the signal (make it quieter). Accordingly, a smooth ramp up to +1.0 and then back down to zero is often used to "envelope" or "window" the dynamics of a sound event, smoothly shaping and containing its activity.

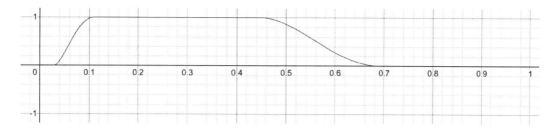

Just like this graph, natural envelopes usually rise faster and fall more slowly, but not always. We'll look at ways to create envelopes and windows in Chapters 3, 4, and 11.

Stepped signals

By "stepped signals," we mean a signal that flatly holds a steady value for a while and only occasionally changes to a new value. (Remember, operators and signals always run at the sample rate, so even a stepped signal is still a continually running stream of samples—it's just that within one step all the sample frames have the same value.)

In this graph, the solid line is a signal that holds a value of 0.4 for a while, then jumps to 0.8 for the remainder, while the dashed line holds a value of zero throughout:

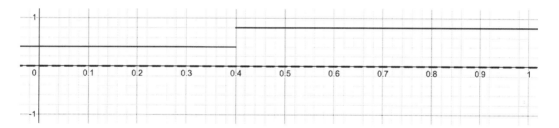

A flat signal has a conceptual frequency of zero (sometimes called "bias" or DC, following the concept of "direct current" in electronics). We can't hear flat signals, but any non-zero constant should be kept out of audio paths because they effectively change the centerline of an oscillation and limit the available "headroom" between -1.0 and 1.0. But stepped signals are extremely useful for all kinds of *control* of a patch, as well as for sequencing rhythms and pitch patterns (as we see in Chapter 5).

Whole number (integer) signals

If a signal can *only* take whole number values, it is considered an integer. You can convert any continuous signal into a whole number signal by passing it through a **floor** operator (which rounds down), **ceil** operator (which rounds up), or **round** operator (which rounds to the nearest whole number). Integer signals can be useful for selecting between modes, picking harmonics frequencies, or quantizing a pitch sequence, etc.

Unipolar logic signals (gate)

Unipolar logic signals are stepped integer signals that can only ever have a value of 1.0 (meaning *true/on*) or 0.0 (meaning *false/off*). Here is a logic signal that is "on" for one-tenth of a second and off for four-tenths, etc.

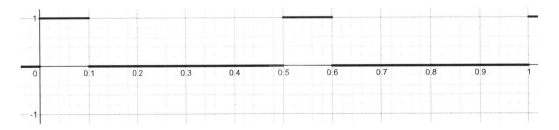

These kinds of signals are produced from the outputs of logic operators, such as < (less than), == (equal)[4], **not** (logical inversion), and so on. This can be very useful for things like turning other processes on or off.

But for operators with logical *inputs,* such as the condition input of a **switch** operator, you can plug in *any* signal at all, not just zeroes and ones. In these cases, gen~ uses an existential convention in which 0.0 represents a false/off value, and *any other non-zero value* represents a true/on value.[5]

Bipolar logic (sign) signals

In certain cases, we may want to know the polarity of a signal, which we can get using a **sign** operator. This is a tri-value logic signal, which is either positive (nominal value of +1.0), negative (nominal value of -1.0), or zero (0.0). Bipolar logic signals can also represent *direction* without indicating *speed*: for example, a **change** operator will give the polarity of a signal's slope: (+1.0 for rising signals, -1.0 for falling signals, or 0.0 for flat signals).

Single-sample impulse (trigger) signals

This is a special kind of logic signal that is nearly always zero but occasionally spends a single sample frame with a non-zero value, typically 1.0. For example, this graph shows a stream of triggers every tenth of a second, with all other values at zero.

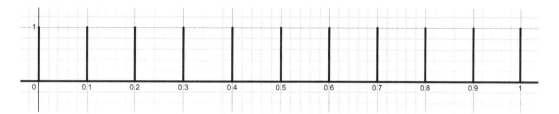

Periodic triggers like this are sometimes called "clock" signals, but in Chapter 2 we will show why we recommend using unipolar ramps for this purpose instead. We use triggers to synchronize the timing of events, starting, stopping, resetting a process, or letting you know the exact sample frame at which some threshold has passed. For example, sending a trigger to the right inlet of a **latch** operator makes it sample the left input and hold that value at the output until the next trigger.

Stochastic (random) signals

Stochastic or random signals vary over time but without discernible repetitions. The **noise** operator produces a new evenly distributed random value between -1.0 and +1.0 for every sample frame of passing time.

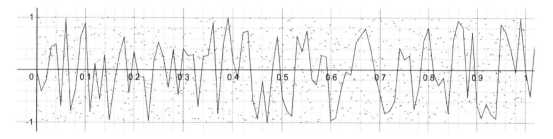

The dotted graph above shows this pure noise, and the solid line shows another stochastic signal *derived* from noise; these and many other extensions and applications of the unpredictability of chance and chaos are explored in Chapter 4.

A signal can be any of these and something else, too

This isn't a strict taxonomy. There are no hard and fast rules that define the "differences" between signals — they can be used in many ways at once, carry multiple meanings, or may often morph from one to another. This can be a liberating idea! For example:

- An envelope isn't just for shaping amplitude; it could be driving a crossfader or a frequency modulator or anything else
- An audio oscillator can be slowed down to used as an LFO, and vice versa

- A unipolar ramp could be the heart of an LFO, be used to drive a crossfader, determine a tempo-related rhythm, and as you will see in this book, so much more
- A trigger signal could have values other than 1.0, perhaps also being bipolar, to carry more information within it.
- A stream of zeroes could be silent audio, a logical false, an absence of triggers, or just a zero-valued step, etc.

In philosophical terms, all signals have the same flat ontological importance; what's important is not what they are, but what an operator can do with them. As much as possible therefore we try to design circuits to handle unexpected signal behaviors, such that plugging A into B in an unplanned way may lead to something interesting!

Operators

The gen~ environment provides you with a small number of operators to harness, process, and redirect the flow of signals and, in this way, quickly create complex and efficient patches. They can be divided into a few basic categories:

- Operators that interface with the environment outside (**in, out, param**, **buffer,** etc.)
- Operators for fundamental audio signal generation (**noise**, **cycle**, etc.)
- Operators for working with ranges of signals (**scale, clip, wrap, fold, max,** etc.)
- Operators for working with rates or slopes of signals (**delta, accum, phasor,** etc.)
- Operators for storing data over time (**history, latch, delay, data**, etc.)
- Routing operators to control signal flows (**mix, switch, selector,** etc.)
- Math operators such as **+, *, pow, sin**, **round,** etc. and logic operators such as **and, not, ==, >,** etc.
- Operators that perform common numeric conversions (**radians, sampstoms, mtof, atodb**, etc.), and operators that provide commonly used numbers (**pi, sqrt2,** etc.) or that relate to the audio engine (**samplerate**, **elapsed,** etc.)
- Structural operators for code (**expr, codebox**) or to embed patches within patches (**gen** and abstractions)

For some operators, it will be fairly obvious what they do (e.g., a + operator just adds two signals together, and similarly for other math operators such as **pow, sin, round**, etc), but it might not be immediately clear for many others. Some share names and inspiration with Max and RNBO objects and operators you may be familiar with, though there may also be differences to better fit the gen~ environment.

Aside from the documentation available within Max and online[6], in this book, we'll introduce and demonstrate different operators as we need them. But first, we'd like to introduce you to a handful of the most frequently used ones. You'll see these used over and over throughout this book, and understanding how they work and why they're important will help you develop patches with greater ease.

The param operator

You can use the **param** operator to add control parameters that you can modify outside your gen~ patch. Each **param** operator must be named with its first argument, and this name corresponds to *messages* you can send in the parent patcher to your **gen~** object to change that parameter's value.

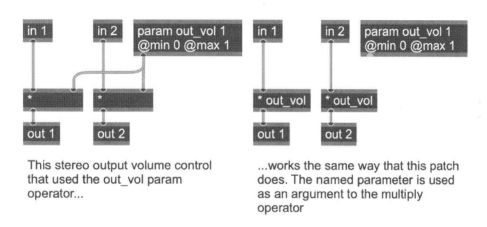

This stereo output volume control that used the out_vol param operator...

...works the same way that this patch does. The named parameter is used as an argument to the multiply operator

As you can see, you can also use a parameter's name when performing calculations in other operators within the same gen~ patch. You can also set a **param's** initial value with a second argument and limit a param's range by giving it **@min** and **@max** attributes.

Unlike the **in** and **out** operators, which allow continuous audio-rate signals into and out of the gen~ patch, the value of a **param** operator is updated at best at the current signal-vector rate (as defined in Max's Options: Audio Status window). That is, a **param** operator outputs a stepped signal.

The history operator (and delay)

Most operators perform work on the value at their input and immediately give the result at their output. The **history** operator is a little different: it stores the value at its input and outputs it *one sample frame later.* That means it can function as a single-sample delay. But more importantly—and this is the killer feature—you can route that output through some processing and back to the input in a single-sample feedback loop. This is exactly what is needed to build a multitude of audio processing tasks, including practically all filters[7] and many oscillators, as well as all kinds of nonlinear, chaotic, and cybernetic feedback systems.[8] In fact, many of the other operators in gen~ are really just equivalent to a combination of a **history** operator and one or more logic or math operators.

You can also give a **history** operator a name with its first argument, and then it will behave like another **param** operator. A second argument will set its initial value.

A **delay** operator is like a series of many **history** operators *in series* that you fill one sample at a time and read values out at different delay times. Like the **history** operator, it also lets you patch feedback loops, and we'll look at this in depth in Chapter 7.

The scale operator

We talked earlier about thinking of a signal's *range of values*. Frequently, we need to map a signal from one range of values to a different range of values[9], and the easiest way is to use the **scale** operator. All you need to know is a pair of corresponding points. For example, you could create a Fahrenheit to Celsius converter using **scale 32 212 0 100**, since the freezing and boiling points of water are 32° F and 212° F respectively at the input, corresponding to 0° C and 100° C at the output.

Here are some more relevant examples that we very frequently use in this book:

- To convert a bipolar normalized signal (-1.0 to +1.0) to a unipolar normalized signal (0.0 to +1.0), use **scale -1 1 0 1**. To convert the other way, just reverse the inputs and outputs: **scale 0 1 -1 1**.
- To turn a unipolar signal upside down (which is also called inverting it), we can pass it through a **scale 0 1 1 0** operator.

For a more involved example: A modular synthesizers sometimes use a convention to represent pitch called "volt per octave" where increasing a value by +1.0 means going up by one octave, which is the same as going up 12 semitones in MIDI note numbers. If our reference value of 1.0 corresponds to MIDI note number 24 (note C1), then a value of 2.0 indicates MIDI note number 24 + 12 = 36 (note C2), and we can use a **scale 1 2 24 36** operator.

A **scale** operator with no arguments will have a series of additional inlets to dynamically set the input and output ranges with input signals (defaulting to 0.0 to 1.0 ranges if not connected).

The wrap, fold, and clip operators

These operators are all useful ways to set limits or boundaries of a signal in their left inlet. You set the lower and upper bounds in the operator's arguments or other inlets, and any input value that is outside these bounds will be transformed so that it remains within them.

With the **wrap** operator, any value that exceeds the upper bound will automatically wrap back to the lower bound value, and vice versa. This creates a kind of *circular* number space, a bit like the way an angle of 365° is the same as an angle of 5°, or that 13:00 is the same as 1pm.

This turns out to be incredibly useful, and we'll see it in many forms in this book, such as:

- Creating a ramp oscillator from a **history**, a +, and a **wrap** operator
- Building modular arithmetic for tempo manipulations and Euclidean rhythms
- Operating on musical pitch spaces
- Pulling out the fractional part of a number for interpolation purposes

The **wrap** operator has several close relatives that differ in handling out-of-range inputs. The **fold** operator reflects any signals outside the range back in, whereas the **clip** operator (also known as **clamp**) holds the value at the limit. So, for example, if the input signal is 1.2, a **clip 0 1** operator would output 1.0, a **fold 0 1** operator would output 0.8, and a **wrap 0 1** operator would output 0.2.

The accum (and phasor) operators

The **accum** operator (also known as the += operator) can be used whenever you want to keep a running count. If you send it a signal of occasional triggers of 1.0, it will count how many triggers it received. If you send it a constant signal of 1.0, it will add one for every passing sample frame and thus count how many sample frames have elapsed. But the **accum** operator doesn't have just to count in ones, it can add up *any* input values at all. (In mathematical terms, it performs stepwise integration.) It can also reset its count to zero whenever its right inlet receives a non-zero signal. With an **accum** operator, you can:

- Measure elapsed time (in whole number samples or other units of time)
- Index samples for playback from an audio buffer
- Build slope generators for envelopes and other modulations
- Combine with a **history** and **wrap** operator to create a cycling **phasor**

A **phasor** operator is another accumulator that counts in tiny increments from 0.0 to 1.0 over and over, creating the kinds of repeating ramp signals we use at the core of oscillators and rhythms, as we will see in Chapter 2.

The delta (and change) operators

We noted earlier how important it is to think about the *rates of changes* of signals. The **delta** operator tells you how much a signal changes in value from one sample frame to the next, whether positively or negatively. To take an analogy from physics, if the signal represents a position, then the **delta** gives you the velocity. (This is like the stepwise differentiation of calculus: it is the difference quotient of the signal per sample frame. In that sense, it's the opposite of the **accum** operator!)

It's really just the input minus the previous input, which provides you with the *slope* of a signal. This deceptively simple slope-per-sample measurement lets you do some amazing things:

- You can use the magnitude (absolute value) of a **delta** operator's output (or a filtered version of it) for things like onset detection in waveform processing.
- When a **delta** operator is combined with a **wrap -0.5 0.5** operator, you can get the slope of a phasor ramp without "jumps." And from *that,* you can derive the phasor's frequency and many other features, as we explore in Chapter 2.
- Connecting two **delta** operators together lets you detect kinks and curves in an input signal: the rate of change of the rate of change, or *acceleration* of the signal.
- The **sign** of the **delta** operator's output is a bipolar logic value that tells you whether an input is rising (sign = 1), falling (sign = -1), or staying the same (sign = 0). This is also exactly what the **change** operator does.
- Chaining two **change** operators together will give you a bipolar trigger when a signal switches direction, picking out only its peaks and troughs.

The latch operator

The **history** operator lets you hold a value from one sample frame's worth of calculations to the next, but it then immediately forgets it because signals are always flowing through it. If you want to hold on to a value for longer and only let it update when you say so, you want a **latch** operator.

The right inlet expects a trigger or logical control signal to activate the **latch**. A non-zero trigger at this inlet will "sample" the left inlet's value, passing it through to the outlet. A zero value at this inlet means that the previously sampled value will continue to be held and output. This behavior is often called "sample and hold."

However, suppose the signal at the right inlet is a logic signal rather than a trigger. In that case, any non-zero value (meaning "on") at the latch operator's right inlet will let signals pass from the left inlet right through to the outlet. Still, with a zero at the right inlet (meaning "off"), the **latch** operator will keep outputting the previous value, effectively freezing the signal. This is sometimes called a "track and hold" operation.

The **latch** operator's simplicity belies its usefulness. For example:

- If you feed the control input a trigger signal, the output will be a stepped control signal. In this way, you can *slow down the rate of change* of a process, which can be handy in bringing fast changes down to human-readable time frames.
- A triggered **latch** operator can also be used to synchronize one process to another, such as updating a process parameter only when it has been cross faded out or holding parameters constant throughout a grain's envelope.
- A set of interconnected **latch** and **history** operators can form the basis of a "shift register," which we use in several places in this book, including creating smoothed random signal generators in Chapter 4 (p. 93) and building algorithmic sequencers in Chapter 5 (p. 123).

The mix (and switch) operators

As you might guess, you can use the **mix** operator to crossfade between two signals. Send a unipolar (0.0 to 1.0) signal in the right "mix" inlet to crossfade from the left inlet (with the mix at 0.0) to the middle inlet (with the mix at 1.0) or any blended point in between. But don't let your imagination stop at crossfading audio signals. There's a world of interesting things we'll do throughout this book with **mix** operators:

- A **mix** and a **history** operator in a feedback loop will give you a running average, which you can use to smooth out stepped signals, or to lowpass filter audio,
- You can also use it to find weighted averages between data points and, with a couple of **latch** operators and a **phasor**, create a sequence of ramp segments,
- You can use a **mix** operator as a linear interpolator between points, such as mixing smoothly between quantized values (and possibly with different curves),
- We will also see the **mix** operator used to compute sub-sample waveform points for antialiased (band-limited) oscillators!

If you don't need to crossfade and just want to switch between two inputs, you can use the **switch** operator (also known as the **?** operator). The **switch** operator performs basic logic if-then-else routing: *if* the left input is true (any non-zero value), *then* it passes the middle inlet through; else, it passes the right inlet through.

The buffer and data operators

These two operators let you work with stored collections of sequential values, such as from audio files, which can either be mono or multi-channel.

A **buffer** operator in gen~ lets you access the data of a regular **buffer~** object in the parent Max or RNBO patch. You do this by giving them the same name (the first argument).

The underlying data is *shared*: if you write to the **buffer** in gen~, it will also be changed in parent's **buffer~**, and vice versa; if you load a new audio file into the **buffer~** in Max, the **buffer** in gen~ will also change.

In contrast, a **data** operator's storage is local, meaning it belongs only to the gen~ patch and cannot be accessed from outside. You must give the **data** operator a name and declare its length (and optionally also specify the number of channels). The **data** operator is like a collection of **history** operators in parallel, which you can read from and write to however you like.

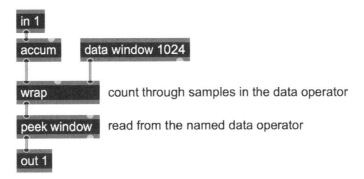

The **buffer** and **data** operators don't do any signal operations themselves; they just output their total length in samples and their number of channels. To write a value to a **buffer** or **data**, use a **poke** operator with a matching name argument, and set the new value and sample position via its inlets.

To read values from a **buffer** or **data**, use **peek** or **sample** operators with matching name arguments and send them a sample position (for **peek**) or a 0.0 to 1.0 phase (for **sample**) at the inlet. We'll see **peek** and **sample** in the next chapter and go into them much more detail in Chapter 9.

The codebox operator

Gen~ is primarily a visual programming environment, but it also offers a way to write algorithms with text-based code when you want to, using a simple language called GenExpr within **codebox** operators. You'll the **codebox** used for patches in this book from time to time, but we use it sparingly and only when it's necessary for the tasks we're working on. Here are some of the reasons that we usually prefer visual to textual programming:

- You can place comments anywhere and lay out the algorithm spatially to convey what it does, add assistance comments on **in** and **out** operators, etc. This means the patch can be easier to understand when you return to it months later and make more sense to others when you share it.

- You can make more efficient use of reference resources (by Option-clicking [Macintosh] or alt-clicking [Windows] the operators, or using the reference sidebar)
- Errors in textual code are much easier to make, harder to understand, and can break your workflow. It's almost impossible to make a syntax error with visual patching.
- Using a **codebox** operator does not make your patch any more efficient.

The last point may surprise some readers, as there seems to be some mystique among the community to the contrary. There is <u>absolutely no difference</u> in terms of performance between using visual patching compared to utilizing a **codebox** operator to do the same thing. The gen~ environment always converts all the visual patching into GenExpr anyway (and you can see that GenExpr code by looking into the sidebar of the patch marked with a C symbol). Everything in the patch—whether it be visual patching or **codebox** operators— gets merged into a single representation. The gen~ environment then uses that representation to generate and compile fast native code on-the-fly.

On the other hand, there are a few situations where there are very good reasons for using a **codebox** operator in your patch, and you'll see us using a **codebox** in these situations:

- If you had done textual coding first, then on your first encounter with visual programming you might have asked, "how do I write an if/else or a for loop?" The **codebox** operator is necessary if you need to perform procedural branching and looping with `if()`, `for()`, or `while()`. It's the only way to include those kinds of procedural operations. However, it can still be better to avoid using these if you can.[10]
- The **codebox** operator gives you precise control of the order of reads and writes for working with delays and operations on **data** and **buffer** operators. While you can mostly achieve this with visual patching, there will be some cases where you want to lay out a specific order for these operations, and a **codebox** operator may be your best choice.
- Using a **codebox** *might* make it easier to translate some other code or a math expression found "in the wild" into the context of your patch.

The gen operator (and abstractions)

If you have a sequence of operators that achieve a single task together, grouping them into a subpatch (a patch within your patch) can make sense. Within a **gen~** patcher we can use a **gen** operator to create a subpatch—just double-click the **gen** operator to open and edit it. subpatch. Within the subpatch, you can use the **in** and **out** operators to create inlets and outlets of the **gen** operator. Encapsulating bits of patching into a **gen** subpatch can be a great way to organize your patches for clarity. We recommend you also give the **gen** operator a **@title** attribute to remind you what it does when you return to it later!

But what if you created a patch that does things that would be useful in other patches? Any handy gen~ patch (or subpatch) can be saved to an external file using **Save As…** from the File menu, which saves the patch as a *.gendsp* format file. These *.gendsp* files can then be reused as "abstractions" in other gen~ patching contexts just by typing their name into a new operator box as if they were just another **gen** operator. This means *you're not limited to the set of operators provided*. Building up a library of handily reusable abstractions allows you to design your own set of tools with the needed features.[11]

The "go" library

Throughout this book, we frequently solve problems with bits of patching made of a handful of operators, and we have saved these as reusable abstractions. These abstractions are all named with the prefix "*go.*" (from "**g**enerating" and "**o**rganizing…" in the book's title[12]), and you can find them in the "patches" folder of the software that accompanies this book.

If you have placed the software in your Max package folder, you'll be able to use these "go" anywhere you want to. They provide subcircuits for common tasks for working with signals, including shaping them, detecting specific changes or other logic, generating complex control sources, applying filters to audio, and other starting points for higher-level patch functionality. For example, the ***go.ramp2trig.gendsp*** abstraction outputs a trigger signal that spikes whenever an input ramp signal completes its cycle, which is something we need very often! You can add one to a gen~ patch simply by creating a new operator named **go.ramp2trig**. We'll build this abstraction and use it extensively in the next chapter.

Chapter 2:
Modular (Arithmetic of) Time

There are many ways to think about time. There are pasts, presents, and futures, or perhaps nested sets of shorter and more enduring moments. There are births, lifetimes, and decays, with moments imagined and forgotten. And there are repetitions and measures of time, from the natural cycles of heartbeats and seasons to the rhythms and beats of music and the oscillations and resonances of sound.

In this chapter, we're going to look at how we keep count of time. We'll show you how we handle both linear and cyclic time in gen~ and how widely that can be applied–for oscillators, sample players, loopers, rhythm generators, LFOs, and more. We'll model cyclical time as a ramp whose positions along a repeating timeline can be thought of as *phase* and how representing musical time as a set of ramp functions provides you with more information and greater flexibility and opens up more powerful ways to modulate musical time.

Counting by sample frames (accum)

In our everyday lives, we measure time by counting intervals (minutes, hours, days, years, etc.) as well as measuring in comparison to those known rates—minutes per hour, days per week, etc. The act of counting time is also central to much of the work we do in gen~ and is a recurrent theme of this book. Like other digital signal processing (DSP) environments, the passing time of a signal is sliced into *sample frames* at a rate defined as the *sampling frequency* or **samplerate**: the number of sample frames that pass per second.

This rate is typically faster than we can hear (44,100 or 48,000 samples per second are common sample rates), fast enough that we can compute and generate sounds up to the highest frequencies that we can hear. Since the operators in a gen~ patch are always working, *they perform their function once for every passing sample frame*. In the gen~ world, each operator performs its operation in turn within a single "sample frame" so that the entire patch moves forward as a whole, one sample frame at a time.

The *counter_simple_timer.maxpat* patch shows the simplest form of counting time by samples; we create a patch that adds one to itself on each sample frame. This needs only two operators: a + (plus) operator to do the sample-by-sample addition and a **history** operator to keep track of the result from one count to the next. We've also added some patching that lets us see how much time has elapsed.

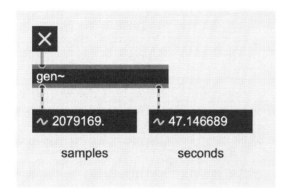
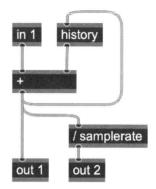

counter_simple_timer.maxpat

In this example, we use a **toggle** object to enable the counting. Remember that signals are always flowing in the gen~ world. That means everything is always on *unless you make it do nothing*. For example, the **in 1** operator in the gen~ patch above continuously outputs numbers. When the **toggle** object is turned on, it sends a value of 1.0, so the **in 1** operator outputs a continuous stream of 1.0s. This sets things going, counting in ones. Turning the **toggle** off sends a zero, which sets the **in 1** operator to output a continuous stream of zeroes. This appears to "pause" the counting, but really, the patch is working away—we're just adding zeros with each tick of the sample clock, so the total doesn't change.

You may notice that the count gets very large, very quickly. That's because our accumulator is working at very high speed, adding one for every passing sample frame. At a typical sample rate of 44,100Hz or 48,000Hz, that means we are counting by adding one, tens of thousands of times every second.

If we want to work in other measures of time beyond the single sample frame — such as seconds or milliseconds or beats, etc. — we need to specify *how many samples* constitute these longer spans of time and use that value when we do our calculations. The **gen~** object automatically keeps track of the sample rate currently being used by the parent patcher and provides a constant operator (**samplerate**) that lets us perform calculations based on this rate.[1] For example, in the patch above, we divided our sample count by the **samplerate** to calculate the elapsed time in seconds.

What we have made here is a *timer*. The output of this patch will tell you how much time (in sample frames and in seconds) elapsed while you had the toggle turned on.[2] We can also think of the count as a position along a timeline. When the output count is zero, we are at the start. As the output count increases, we are moving through the timeline. Compare this to the transport control in a sequencer or wave editor: with the toggle input, we can *pause* and *resume* playback.

What if we want to *rewind* back to the start? We can add the ability to *reset* our accumulator by adding a **switch** operator and a second inlet for the reset input.

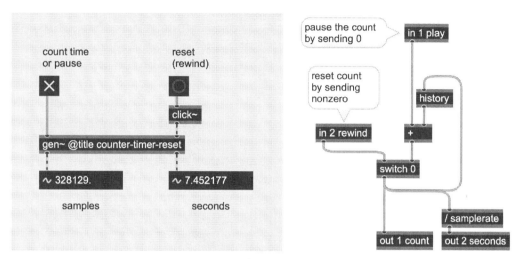

counter_timer_reset.maxpat

What does the **switch 0** operator do here? If the left inlet is "false" (which means a zero value), it routes its right inlet to the output (in this case, our current count). Otherwise, if the left inlet is "true" (which means any non-zero value), it will route its middle inlet or argument (in this case, the argument **0**) to the output.[3] Since this switch is now in our accumulator feedback loop, when it outputs a zero, the running count will be reset back to zero. In our parent patch, we use the **click~** object to produce a single-sample trigger (a signal that has a value of 1 for a single sample frame and then returns to zero again) to perform this reset.

This simple patch is so useful that it exists as a built-in operator, called **accum**, which you'll see in wide use throughout this book. Both of the following patches do the same thing.

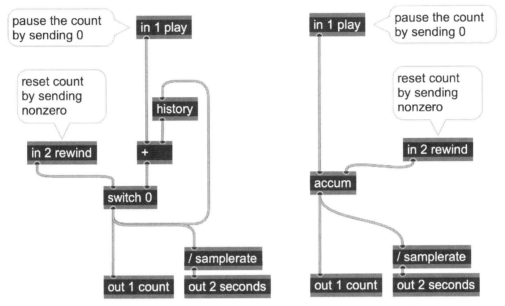

counter_timer_reset.maxpat (left) and counter_accum.maxpat (right)

On every sample frame of passing time, an **accum** operator will keep adding up whatever you send to its left inlet and outputs the running count from its outlet. You can reset this count back to the start by sending a non-zero value to the **accum** operator's *right* inlet.[4]

Playing a sound file

As a simple example, let's use a count of elapsed samples to play back the content of an audio file, sample by sample.

First, we'll need to bring a sound file into the parent patch, using the **buffer~** object, with a name we can refer to it by, such as "mybuf". If we have an audio file in Max's search path or want to use one of Max's built-in sound files, such as "duduk.aif", then we can have **buffer~** auto-load this file using arguments in the object box (**buffer~ mybuf duduk.aif**). Or we can also use the **buffer~** object's *replace* message to load a different audio file, and it will also automatically resize our **buffer~** length.

To access this data from inside of a gen~ patch, we'll need to add a **buffer** operator inside of the gen~ patch. We can <u>link</u> the gen~ **buffer** to the parent patch **buffer~** by giving both the same name, e.g., **buffer mybuf**.[5]

Now that we've associated our gen~ **buffer** with the **buffer~** object in our paren Max or RNBO patch, we need a way to read sample data out of it. The simplest way is to use the **peek** operator, which requires the name of the buffer to read from; in our case, **peek mybuf**. Since our accumulator will count every sample of audio in the buffer and do so one sample at a time, all we need for playback is to take the current sample count output from our **accum** operator, send it to the **peek** operator's first inlet to fetch the corresponding sample value from the buffer, and then route the **peek** operator's outlet to send that audio to our patch's output.

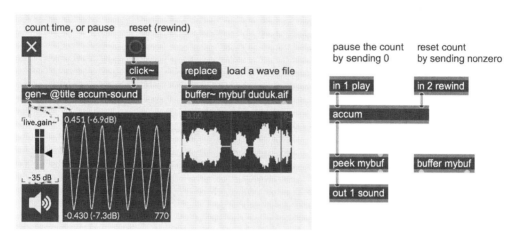

counter_play_a_buffer.maxpat

The counter now rewinds and the wave file plays again whenever we hit the reset button. We have built the simplest retriggerable sample player.

Looping with modular arithmetic

As a timeline, the count of an **accum** operator goes on forever (or until you reset it). But the wave itself file is a finite number of sample values; pretty soon, the timeline has gone past the end of the wave file's data, and there's no more sound. What if we want to work with a *looping* timeline to make the sound file repeat?

We can easily turn our linear counter into a looping counter by feeding our accumulator through a **wrap** operator. The **wrap** operator lets us set low and high limits for a signal, and whenever the input goes above the higher limit, it is "wrapped" back down and starts again from the lower limit. Similarly, if we count down and cross the lower limit, our count is "wrapped" around up to the upper limit. This kind of mathematics is known as *modular arithmetic*.[6] We use it all the time with clocks, angles, sawtooth waveforms, and rhythms.

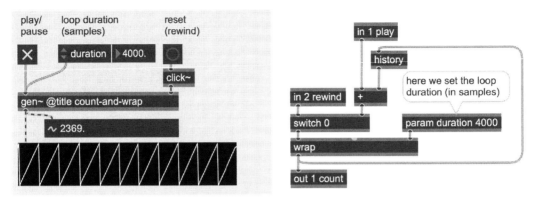

counter_and_wrap.maxpat

In this patch, we started with our initial accumulator-based patch. We inserted a **wrap** operator inside of the feedback loop, using a **param duration 4000** operator to specify the limit to which we wish to count. The lower limit inlet was left unconnected, so it will default to 0. Our accumulator works as we expect — it outputs number values between 0 and 3999, producing a nice ramp output, and restarts counting from zero every time we click on the button.

We can use this looping counter to loop the playback of a **buffer** wave file. All we need to know is how long the file is. Fortunately, the **buffer** operator in gen~ outputs the number of samples in any associated **buffer~** object from its left outlet (and this will automatically update any time we change the **buffer~** object's content in the parent patch). So, all we need to do is to connect the **buffer** operator's left outlet to the right-hand inlet of the **wrap** operator.

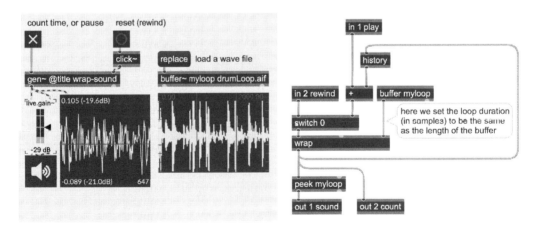

counter_and_wrap_buffer.maxpat

Thinking in rates and changes of phase (phasor)

What if we want to play audio files at different speeds, not just 1:1, with their original sampled rate? Perhaps we want to play a sound file at different speeds to change its pitch, or maybe we want to synchronize several different sound files to all loop at the same tempo, regardless of how many samples they contain.

We can change the playback speed by changing how much we accumulate every sample frame of passing time. For example, if we added two on every sample, our playback would run twice as fast, and if we added 0.5 on every sample, our playback would run at half speed.

If we count by fractional numbers, our counter will output fractional sample counts. However, here we run into a problem. If, for example, our sample count is 1.5, then which sample slice should the **peek** operator fetch from the **buffer**? Since the **peek** operator can only read a whole number (integer) position from a sound file by default, the fractional information will be ignored.

For example, if we count by steps of 1.2 to play back at 1.2x speed, then every 5th sample point will be skipped (indicated by the grey boxes in the following table).

real time (sample frames)	1	2	3	4	5	6	7	8	9	10
accum count	1.2	2.4	3.6	4.8	6.0	7.2	8.4	9.6	10.8	12
peek index	1	2	3	4	6	7	8	9	10	12

Unfortunately, this will cause an audible distortion (a kind of aliasing or nonlinear harmonic distortion). The usual solution to this problem is to apply some kind of *interpolation* when reading from the buffer. Interpolation just means estimating what the waveform's position would be between sample frames.

The most convenient solution we can choose for now is to use a different buffer reading operator that automatically performs interpolation[7] when reading data: the **sample** operator. (We'll be returning to problems related to aliasing distortion later in the book).

The **sample** operator also has another important difference. Rather than sending it a sample index to read from a buffer, we send it a *phase.* This simply means a floating-point number *between zero and one* that represents the relative position from the start to the end of the buffer. It doesn't matter how many samples the **buffer** contains. It could be a hundred, or it could be a hundred thousand.

From the **sample** operator's point of view, the phase is *always* just a normalized value between 0.0 and 1.0. Ensuring the 0.0 to 1.0 range is easy: we can modify our accumulator to use a **wrap 0 1** operator.

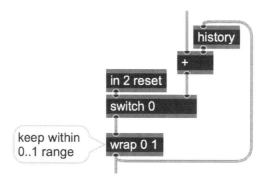

There is a very important implication for this change. It means that the duration of the loop is no longer determined by the amount of data in the **buffer**; it's determined only by how we count. And that's great because it means we can now set our looping to work with time scales we're more comfortable with — say, in terms of seconds or milliseconds, or in terms of beats at a certain tempo, or as a frequency in Hz.

A phasor (using Hz)

If we're no longer counting in samples, how do we know what to count *by*? Let's look at an example working from a frequency in Hz. Remember that our accumulator is adding something to every passing sample frame of real-time. The number of sample frames of time in one second is simply the sample rate, which we can implement using either the **samplerate** operator or simply saying "samplerate" as an argument to another operator. If our sample rate is 48000 samples per second, and we want a loop that lasts exactly one second long; then, we want to add in steps that would reach 1.0 after 48000 sample frames. That means adding in steps of 1/48000. But if we wanted *two* loops per second (2Hz), we would need to count *twice as fast*, which means adding in steps of 2/48000.

So that's our answer: for a given rate in Hertz, the amount our accumulator counts by (the change of phase per sample frame) is calculated as the ratio between our desired playback frequency and the system's sampling rate: *frequency / samplerate*. This value is sometimes called the normalized frequency or the phase increment. In this book, we'll often just call it the *slope* for short. We can now modify our patch to compute the slope from an input frequency by the sample rate using a **/ samplerate** operator.

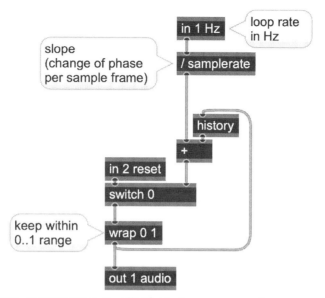

phasor_counter.maxpat—effectively the same as a phasor operator

The circuit we have just created is so useful that it also exists as a built-in operator: the **phasor**. The output looks like a sawtooth shape but is unipolar, rising from 0.0 to 1.0. In this book, we call these *ramp signals* or *phasor signals.*

Here is a ramp signal at 2Hz (two cycles per second).

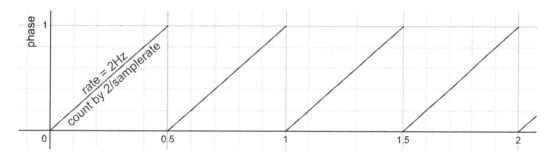

If we directly plug this patch (or an equivalent **phasor** operator) into a **sample** operator, we can get an oscillator whose waveform is defined by a **buffer** of data—sometimes called a wavetable oscillator.

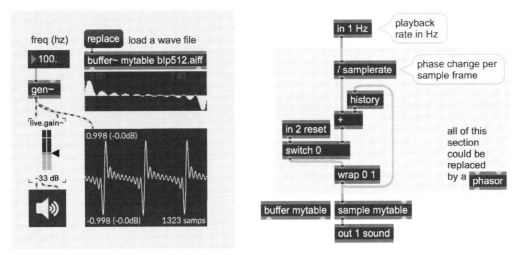

phasor_basic_table_oscillator.maxpat

It doesn't matter how many samples are in the **buffer~**; the oscillator will always play at the frequency we set at our **in 1**. We can also dynamically replace the buffer~ contents, and this fundamental frequency will be maintained. Although this table-based oscillator is very simple, it is already very flexible. We'll look at more powerful wavetable oscillators in Chapter 9.

A drum loop (using BPM)

The patch above uses a very short sound file, just a single cycle of a waveform. But we can replace the audio file with anything else that could loop, such as a breakbeat sample. Send a *replace drumLoop.aif* or *replace jongly.aif* message to the **buffer~ mytable** operator. You'll probably notice that the playback will seem very rapid or sound quite complex and noisy. The **phasor** patch is working perfectly fine, but the looping frequency is too high to hear the breakbeat. If we drop the playback frequency down to around 0.2-0.5 Hz, we should start to hear a drum pattern looping nicely.

But it's much more common to think of tempo in terms of BPM (beats per minute). If you want to specify a tempo in beats per minute, we need to convert a *per-minute* value (we'll use a **param bpm** operator to set that value) into a *per-second* frequency for our ramp. Since there are 60 seconds in a minute, this just means dividing our BPM value by 60.

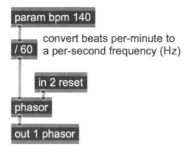

However, our drum loop or breakbeat might represent four, eight, sixteen, or some other number of beats. To get our desired looping rate, we also need to slow the phasor further by dividing the frequency by the number of beats per loop:

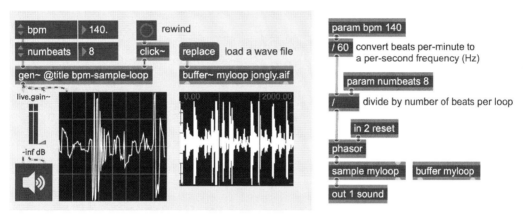

phasor_bpm.maxpat

Ramps as cyclical time

Let's step back for a moment and consider how we represent rhythm as a signal.

Rhythms are often described as patterns of *events*. The events typically tell us when to hit a drum, start a new note, etc., relative to an underlying metric pulse, grid, or "beat" that is a regular and potentially endless sequence of evenly spaced instants, rather like the ticks of a clock. Here, for example, is the characteristic "Clave Son" pattern of five events over a grid of 16 pulses.

It's easy to see why we might also gravitate toward thinking of musical pulse as a series of ticks or with empty space between them. This is how timing signals work in a variety of systems, from MIDI clocks, various forms of synchronization (DIN/SMPTE), as well as analog synthesis "clock triggers". But is this really the best way to work with musical time?

Rhythm *endures* through time—not just when we hit things—just as time passes between the moments when the second hand ticks. In this book, we're going to explore a different way of thinking about rhythmic pulse by expanding upon the phasor ramps we've already built in this chapter. We hope to show how phasor ramps can better capture the cyclic quality of rhythmic pulse as a signal.

To begin to explain why, let's compare the two representations.

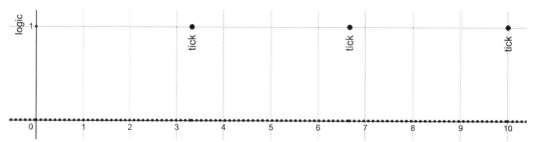

Trigger-based clock: a periodic train of occasional single-sample impulse spikes (the "ticks"), with zero values filling all the durations between them.

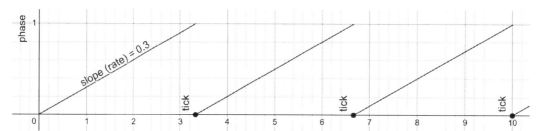

Ramp-based clock: a continual signal at a given slope, in which the pulse is marked by when the ramp wraps around from 1.0 to 0.0.

Cycling ramp functions provide a precise, signal-based way of representing the continual passage of time. Unlike trains of ticks, a repeating ramp function conveys timing information at all moments between pulses, not just when the spike happens. This information includes:

- The *phase*, which tells us exactly where we are between pulses,
- The *rate* or *tempo* (the slope of the ramp). This includes whether it is going in reverse (when the slope is negative) or is paused (a zero slope).

This information is also crucial when dealing with changing tempos. For example, in the following trigger-based graph, the tempo starts at about 20 triggers per second at the start and ends up at about 10 triggers per second at time = 1.0, but you don't know how the tempo is changing until the next trigger comes in earlier or later than expected. Processes synced with this clock may also become sloppy.

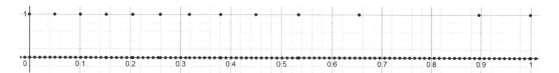

In contrast, the ramp signal pictured in the following graph gives you an accurate representation of changing tempo *all the time*. The tempo is exactly proportional to the *slope* of the **phasor**. the steeper the slope, the faster the clock. And as you can see, this also includes representing clocks running backward (where the slope is negative, running downward instead of upward):

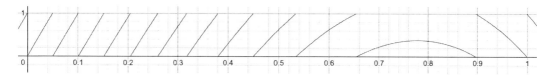

This is just one benefit. Knowing how time passes between beats was also essential for making our sample playing patch, and as we will see in this chapter, working with cycling ramps also allows a rich palette of signal-based transformations of rhythm that are far more difficult or impossible to achieve using triggers alone. (Later in the book, we will also see how cycling ramps can provide audio-rate timing accuracy that is better than sample-accurate—and why that is important.)

Exploration

To demonstrate, let's start from the same breakbeat looping patch from a few pages ago (***phasor_bpm.maxpat***), which has a phasor clock that spans the entire loop (8 beats). We're going to do some processing to the looping ramp at the heart of this patch before it reaches the sample operator for playback.

No matter what we do, the final ramp signal must still stay within the 0.0 to 1.0 range, so we'll add a **wrap 0 1** operator to ensure that.

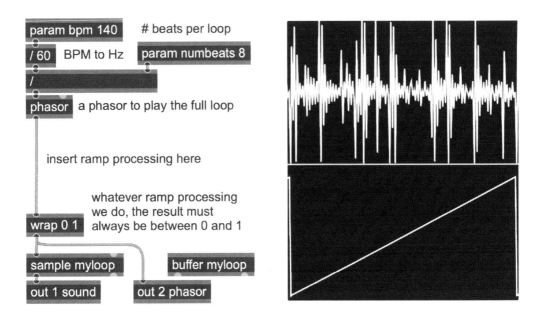

phasor_loop_processing.maxpat

Between the **phasor** and the **wrap 0 1** operators, we can explore a wide range of different ramp clock manipulations. For example, we can try multiplications and additions.

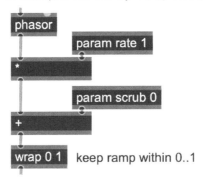

Adding (or subtracting) allows us to "scrub" the playback back and forth, but the playback tempo remains the same. Adding an offset to the phase like this is a really simple way to derive shifted rhythms like hocketing. Meanwhile, multiplying the clock signal lets us make things play faster or slower. Multiplying by two makes it loop twice as fast; multiplying by eight makes it loop eight times in the same period; multiplying by -1 makes it play in reverse. Multiplication is a really simple way to derive related pulses.

Example: beat slicing

Let's plug these ideas together and build an algorithmic beat slicer. Imagine if the *jongly.aif* wave stored in the **buffer** is divided into 16 even slices:

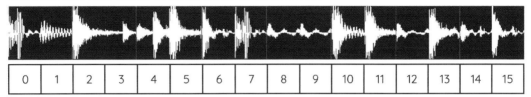

0	1	2	3	4	5	6	7	8	9	10	11	12	13	14	15

We can define the number of slices using a **param slices 16** operator (we can add an **@min 1** to this operator since we can't have less than one slice!)

These 16 slices span 8 beats of time over the whole loop. Now, every 16th of a loop (every half beat), we'd like to offset our sample playback to start at a different one of those slices. In order to fire events at every 16th of the loop time, we can run a second ramp 16x as fast as the loop phasor just by multiplying the loop phasor by the **slices** parameter and using a **wrap 0 1** again to bring that back to the 0.0 to 1.0 range. This creates a ramp that loops 16 times as often, but since it also makes the slope 16x steeper, unfortunately, it also plays the sample 16 times faster too.

To get the original slope and sample playback speed back, we need to divide by the number of slices again.

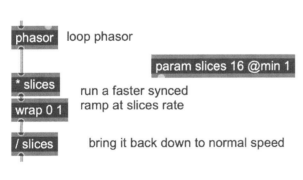

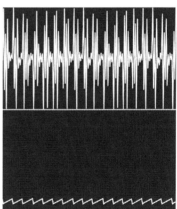

Now the ramp doesn't go from 0 to 1. It goes only up to 1/16, and what you can hear is the first 16th slice of the waveform playing over and over. a 16th note repetition of the opening kick. Here we can bring the scrubbing idea back. If we add to our ramp before dividing by the "slices" parameter, we can select a different 1/16th slice of the waveform.

For example, picking an offset of 12 will jump 12/16ths into the waveform, repeating a high-hat sound.

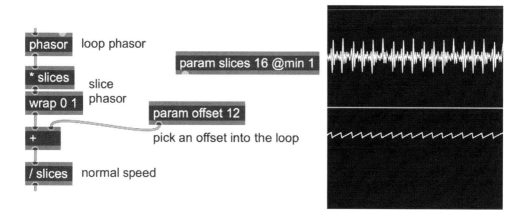

To get a precise slice, the offset should be a whole number (an integer). That's easy to do by adding a **floor** or **round** operator after the **param offset**. You might notice that scrolling around the offset parameter can create a lot of clicks and noise as it continuously changes. To avoid this, we could use a **latch** operator to limit when parameter changes are passed through, and in this way, lock changes to the beat. The **latch** operator needs a trigger input to work but getting triggers from a ramp is simple: we are just looking for the moment when the ramp wraps around, which is the moment when the ramp's change is very large.

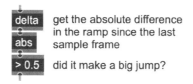

The simplest way to find this moment is to check how much the signal has changed since the last sample frame, which we can get from the **delta** operator. During the ramp's rise, this delta is a very small number, but at the moment it wraps, it is almost -1.0 (or almost +1.0 if the ramp was going backward). We don't care if the ramp was forward or backward, so we feed the result through an **abs** operator to ignore the sign. Then we can use a **> 0.5** comparator operator to detect when this delta is large and thus output a trigger signal with a value of 1.0 (true) when the ramp wraps and 0.0 (false) everywhere else; just what the **latch** operator needs.

Now all we need for our algorithmic beat slicer is to replace the param offset with some process to generate the slice offset automatically. There are lots of different kinds of signals we could plug in here! For example, we could jump through the slices at different rates by further multiplying the phasor.

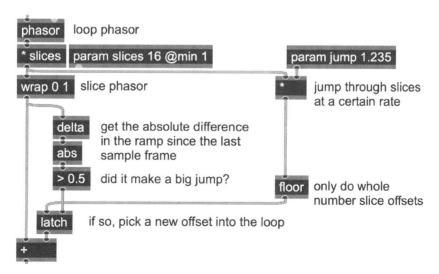

35

If the **param jump** is set to 0, we will be back to a single repeating slice. If the jump is set to 1, we'll get a continuous playback of the whole loop. With **param jump** set to other values, we get different patterns of slices. Even fractional values do interesting things. We can add a little randomization to this, too—by mixing in a small amount of a noise operator to our jump signal. We'll add the chance that we might pick the slice immediately before or after instead, adding some refreshing variation to the pattern. Here is our final patch:

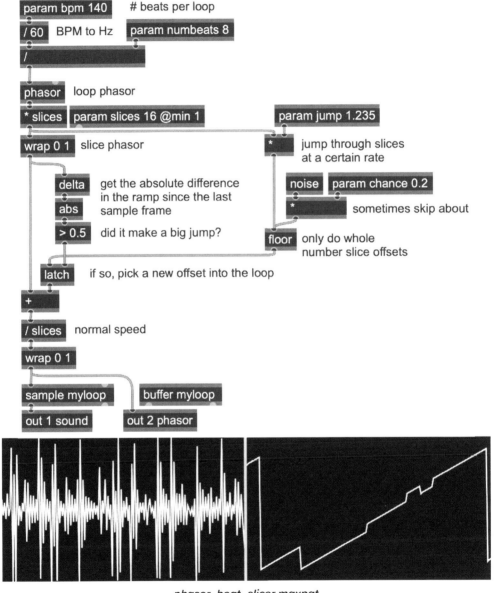

phasor_beat_slicer.maxpat

36

A collection of ramp processors

In the process of building the beat slicer, we encountered a few things that are worth looking into in more detail, which we'll do over the next sections. Along the way, we'll build up more abstractions that we will use throughout the book.

A phasor as a clock source

First, let's build ourselves a primary clock generator. As we saw in the last section, we can use a **phasor** operator to generate a ramp at a certain BPM by dividing the BPM by 60 to get a frequency in Hertz.

When we built our counter-accumulator at the start of this chapter, we could pause its progress by setting its counter increment to zero. Pausing a phasor operator is just as simple: we can pause our clock by momentarily setting its frequency to zero (so that internally, it is counting by adding zeros). A simple way to do this is to multiply the frequency by a logic signal, which is either 1 to keep the original frequency or 0 to set the frequency to zero and pause the clock. We can turn any signal into a logic signal using a **bool** operator; if the input is 0, it outputs 0. If the input is any other value, it outputs 1. So, we added a **param enable** operator, converted it to logic using a **bool** operator, and multiplied this with the frequency to pause or continue the clock:

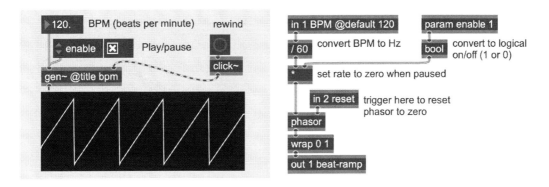

ramp_from_bpm.maxpat

Now that we have a basic clock source, let's look at ways in which we can process the modular time of phasor-based clocks to do some more interesting things.

Ramp clock multiplication

Ramp multiplication is convenient when you want to derive multiple related clocks from a common source, such as measures and beats, polyrhythms, ratchets, and so on. Multiplying a ramp by any number greater than one will stretch it vertically: the period remains the same, but the amplitude, and the slope, are increased. For example, if you take a normalized phasor ramp, which runs from 0.0 to 1.0 (as with the dashed line below), and multiply the ramp by 4, the result is a ramp that runs from 0.0 to 4.0 and whose slope is also 4x steeper (as indicated by the solid line).

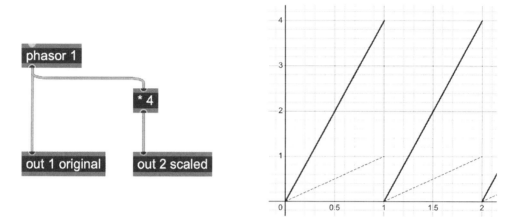

We can pass this scaled signal through a **wrap 0 1** operator to recover a normalized phase range of 0.0 to 1.0.

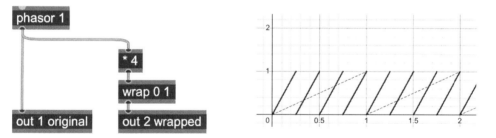

The slope is still 4x steeper, but now the period is 4x shorter. This makes sense: since the *slope of a phasor is what gives its rate,* increasing the slope means speeding it up, which means shortening the period.

In this way, ramps make it really simple to create precise substeps of any clock source, as opposed to a trigger-based clock world, in which clock multiplication requires quite complex and imprecise estimation.

We can use this to modify our ramp from the BPM patch to output both beats and measures. Let's add a **param beats** operator to define how many beats there should be per measure (the upper number of the time signature in staff notation). Just as we did with the sample looper, we'll divide our frequency by the number of beats to compute the phasor frequency *per measure* rather than per beat. Then, we can multiply the phasor output by the number of beats and feed that through a **wrap 0 1** to get back our per-beat ramp.

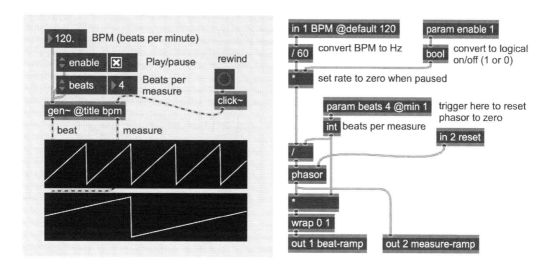

ramp_from_bpm.maxpat and go.ramp.frombpm.gendsp

If the input phasor is per beat or some other event level, then multiplication is an easy way to create ratchets. If the multiplier is a power of 2, you will get standard divisions (halves, quarters, eighths, etc.). If this is then scaled by 3/2, you will get triplet ratchets. Here is a variety of ratchet patterns produced by the ***ramp_ratchets.maxpat*** as an example:

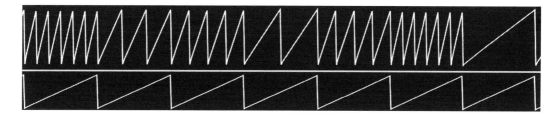

Using ramps as clocks also makes stranger fractional ratios of clock multiplications really simple. However, whatever fractional multiplier you use, it will be reset to the start when the input phasor wraps (whether this is the next measure, next beat, or otherwise). We will look at more free-running polymetric systems later in the chapter.

From ramps to steps

If we take a multiplied ramp through a **floor** operator, we will split it into a step function. For example, in the following graph, the ramp function (dashed line) is multiplied by *4,* and then the floor taken to produce a step function of 0, 1, 2, 3, 0, 1, 2, 3 (indicated by the solid lines).

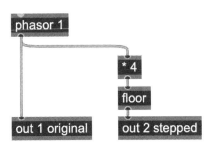 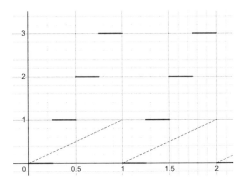

In this way, we can produce clock-synchronized step counts, which could be the basis for arpeggiation or other sequencing processes. For example, we used a variation of this in our beat slicing patch to compute the jump offset steps from a secondary ramp. If you want to normalize the steps to within a 0.0 to 1.0 range, just divide the step function by 4 again:

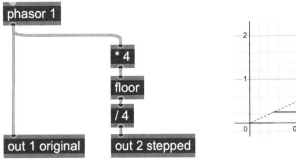 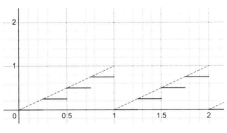

This sequence of *multiply N, floor, and divide by N* is at the heart of many quantization algorithms, and we'll see it again in Chapter 5 (p. 151) among other places.

Putting all of these together, we have the very handy **go.ramp2steps** abstraction.

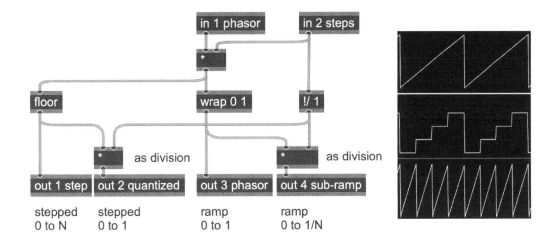

go.ramp2steps.gendsp

The ***ramp_steps.maxpat*** patch shows an example of adding two of these step functions together to generate an arpeggiated melody and multiplying percussion with steps to create accent rolls.

Shifting ramps (phase rotation)

One of the simplest manipulations we can make is to shift a ramp in time simply by adding or subtracting a phase delay (**in 2** in the following patch) and then using another **wrap 0 1** to bring it back into the 0.0 to 1.0 range. In the image below, the bold line is the original phasor, and the softer line is the same phasor delayed by 0.25 (25%) of a cycle:

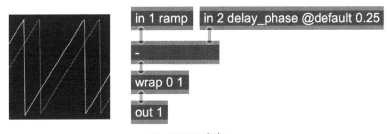

go.ramp.rotate

A phase offset by subtracting 0.25 will create a phasor that is 25% delayed. However, since phase is a <u>circular</u> concept, a phase offset of 0.25 can also be seen as 75% ahead (just as a 90-degree turn clockwise is the same as a 270-degree turn anticlockwise). Ramp shifting is, therefore, really phase rotation.[8]

The ***ramp_rotate.maxpat*** patch shows an example of driving two percussion patterns, one shifted relative to the other using a **go.ramp.rotate** abstraction. If the rotation amount is a very slow phasor, this can recreate the "phasing rhythms" characteristic of early Steve Reich compositions.

Getting the slope, frequency, period, and direction of a ramp

We can get the rate of change of a signal using the **delta** operator, which just subtracts the previous input from the new input (in mathematical terms, it is a discrete differentiator). If the input is a phasor or any normalized ramp signal, then this is almost all we need to get its normalized frequency (its "slope").

There's just one subtlety, which we can solve by applying a **wrap -0.5 0.5** operator.

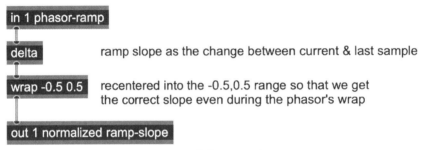

go.ramp2slope.gendsp

Why are we using the **wrap** operator here? Consider a looping **phasor** whose slope is +0.01 and whose bounds wrap at zero and one. When this phasor moves from 0.99 + 0.01 => 1.00, it will wrap back to 0.00, resulting in an apparent delta of -0.99. But **wrap**ping that -.99 value between -0.5 and 0.5 will give us a value of 0.01, thus recovering our original correct slope. This also works for reversed ramps!

Now that we have the slope, we can derive all kinds of useful values from it—at any point in time!

- Would you like the rate in Hertz (cycles per second)? Just multiply the slope by the **samplerate**.
  Do you want the rate as a BPM? Multiply the frequency in Hertz by 60.
- Do you want the period of the clock in samples? It is the reciprocal (one divided by, or **!/ 1**) of the slope.
  If you want the period of the clock in seconds, it is one divided by the frequency (or feed the slope into a **!/ samplerate** operator).

- Multiply the period by the clock ramp, and it will tell you how much time has elapsed since the last wrap (assuming the rate is not changing). Multiply by clock **- 1** to estimate how long until the next wrap.
- Do you want to know if the clock is running forward, backward, or paused? Look at the **sign** of the slope. It will be +1.0 for forward, -1.0 for backward, and zero when paused.

Here are all of these things together in the **go.ramp2freq.gendsp** abstraction.

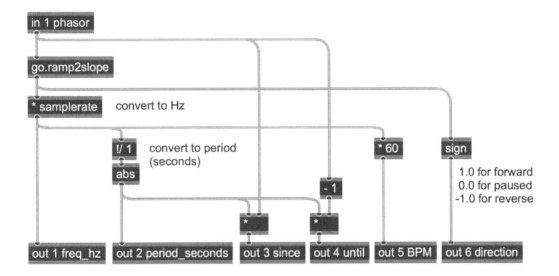

Getting triggers from a cyclic ramp

If you need triggers, perhaps to reset an **accum** operator for example, it is easy to get them from a ramp. It just means looking for the moment when the ramp wraps around. The simplest way to find this moment is to check how much the signal has changed since the last sample frame, which we can get from the delta operator. During the ramp's rise, this delta is a very small number, but at the very moment it wraps, it is almost -1.0 (or almost +1.0 if the ramp was going backward). We don't care if the ramp was forward or backward, so we feed the result through an **abs** operator to ignore the sign.

We can then use a **> 0.5** comparator operator to detect when this delta is large and thus output a trigger signal with a value of 1.0 (true) when the ramp wraps and 0.0 (false) at all other times.

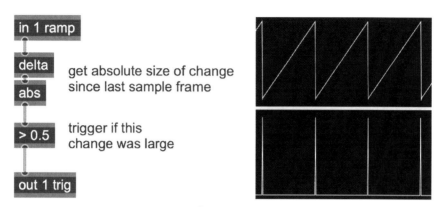

ramp_to_trig.maxpat

This concept is incredibly useful, and we use it throughout this book, so we created an abstraction for it called **go.ramp2trig**. But if you look inside **go.ramp2trig,** you'll see the patch is more complex to handle a few subtleties. Let's look at each one in turn.

The first subtlety is that resets to the input phasor do not always cause triggers. If the ramp happened to be reset during the first half of its duty cycle, the magnitude of change is not large enough to cause a trigger at that moment. We could perhaps reduce the threshold to something much smaller, such as 0.001 (which would detect resets so long as they are not in the first 1/1000th of the cycle), but then we run into the limitation that any ramp running faster than **samplerate** * 0.001 will start to generate spurious triggers. That might not be such a problem for tempo clocks, but it certainly can be for other processes!

Another challenge with this patch is that it will not give a trigger when a clock starts from the beginning. If you pause the clock, rewind it, then unpause, there should be a trigger at the moment of unpausing, but since at this moment the delta is very small, there will be no trigger.

We can address both problems by approaching wrap detection in a slightly different way. Rather than looking at the *magnitude delta* of the ramp signal, we can look at its *proportional change*. That means that instead of using the **delta** operator to get the difference between the current and previous sample frame's magnitude, we get the proportional change by dividing their difference by their sum.

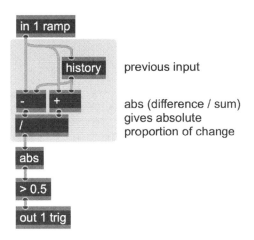

If the absolute proportional change is greater than the 0.5 threshold, we know that the input ramp is changing significantly, and so we send a trigger. In this way, any sudden kinks or significant changes in the slope of an input (such as happens when a phasor wraps) will output a trigger. In fact, a triangle wave will also cause a trigger. It also gives a trigger when the phasor begins from a rewound state.

The next subtlety is to prevent a trigger from being followed on the immediately next sample frame with another trigger. Here, we use a **change** operator into a **> 0** operator to only output a trigger at the moment when the comparator switches to true.

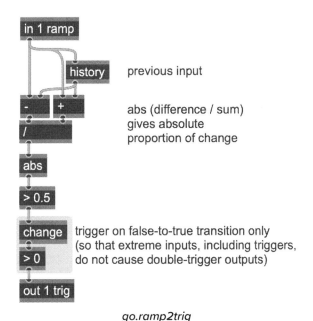

go.ramp2trig

This will prevent a sharp reset on the input from causing a double-trigger on the output, and also means the patch can process trigger-like inputs too!

Ramp/clock division

Earlier in this chapter, we saw how multiplication can create faster (shorter duration) ramps. In a similar way, division (or multiplication with a magnitude below 1.0) can be used to create slower (longer duration) ramps. However, we can't simply scale the ramp itself, as it will never reach 1.0.

For example, if we scale a ramp by dividing by two, it will only run from 0.0 to 0.5. Instead, we have to create a second ramp accumulator and drive it with a *divided slope*.

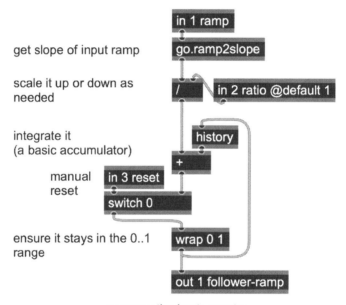

get slope of input ramp

scale it up or down as needed

integrate it
(a basic accumulator)

manual reset

ensure it stays in the 0..1 range

go.ramp.div.simple.gendsp

We take the rate of change of the incoming phasor, derived by using the **go.ramp2slope** abstraction, and integrate this slope via the same **history, +, switch** and **wrap** loop we saw earlier in this chapter. If the ratio is 2, then the output ramp will have twice the period (half the rate, which is to say, the clock divided by two) of the input ramp.

In fact, this patch serves a similar role as clock dividers in modular synthesizers, except that it works with ramps rather than pulses and thus can also clock divide at fractional rates with perfect precision.[9] Moreover, if the incoming ramp gradually changes slope, the derived slope immediately also changes accordingly; if the incoming phasor jumps, our derived slope will also jump by exactly the right amount.

Unlike the ramp multiplication we explored earlier in this chapter, we can work with divisions that are longer than the input ramp without being reset. However, even with simple divisions, with this patch, there's no guarantee that the output ramp's cycle will remain phase-synchronized with the input ramp. Even if they start synchronized, modulations to the ratio can cause them to drift. That might be desirable for some musical applications, but in the cases where it isn't, the tricky part of clock division is how to sync the derived ramp: *When* should we perform the sync, and what do we sync *to*?

The **go.ramp.div** abstraction in the software included with this book tries to address this in a pragmatic way. This is a more complex algorithm than we've seen so far, but let's go through how it works.

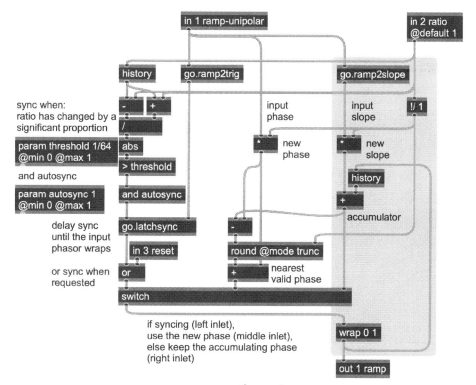

go.ramp.div.gendsp

The core circuit, shaded in grey, remains the same. We take the slope of the input ramp using **go.ramp2slope**, scale it by the divisor ratio to derive the new slope, and feed that into an accumulator built of **history**, **+**, **switch**, and **wrap 0 1** operators. The main differences are the condition of *when to sync* and the determination of *what to sync to*.

When to sync: In addition to the manual reset input at **in 3**, this patch can also resync automatically if the **in 2 ratio** input changes by a significant amount. This is detected as a proportional change (in much the same way as we did for **go.ramp2trig**) by taking the absolute division of the difference and sum current and previous sample frame's ratio values and comparing them to a threshold value (here via the **> 1/64** operator). In this way, any gentle modulations of the ratio for tempo curves and so forth will not trigger a resync, but any sudden changes of ratio such as selection from a list will. (This can also be bypassed by setting the **param autosync** to 0 (off) via the **and autosync** operator.)

A request to resync here will not take place immediately, however. It is held inside the **go.latch.sync** abstraction until triggered by the **go.ramp2trig** abstraction when the ramp at **in 1** cycles. This means that if you are working from a tempo clock input, the resync will happen at the start of the next beat or bar.

What to sync to: Rather than simply restarting the ramp at zero, we calculate what the real phase should be when the sync occurs by scaling the input ramp's phase by the division ratio. That means we can even resync mid-cycle.

However, when dividing a ramp, there may be more than one viable place it could sync to. For example, a ramp divided by 4 has four possible beats it could align with. The **go.ramp.div** patch attempts to find the nearest viable alignment to minimize the change. In this patch, the trio of **-**, **round,** and **+** operators make it jump to whichever viable sync value is nearest.

Ramp multiplications and divisions with musical ratios

Musicians with training in Western systems may be in the habit of describing durations in terms of note values—as quarter notes, dotted eighth notes, triplets, and so on. This is easy using **go.ramp.div**.

Here are some examples of how to translate a ramp-per-beat (equivalent to **4n** in Max time syntax) into different note durations:

go.ramp.div ratio	Output ramp	Max time syntax
4 / 1	Whole note (semibreve)	**1n**
2 / 1	Half note (minim)	**2n**
1 / 1	Quarter note (crotchet)	**4n**
1 / 2	8th note (quaver)	**8n**
1 / 4	16th note (semiquaver)	**16n**
3 / 2	Dotted quarter note	**4nd**
3 / 4	Dotted eighth note	**8nd**
3 / 8	Dotted 16th note	**16nd**
2 / 3	Triplet over two quarter notes	**4nt**
1 / 3	Triplet over two 8th notes	**8nt**
1 / 6	Triplet over two 16th notes	**16nt**

In the *ramp_division.maxpat* example we stored a list of common time divisions in the parent patch using a **umenu** object to select the desired division and a **coll** object to store the ratio parameters. This lets you choose common note values and shows you the numerator and denominator of the resulting ratios before feeding them to a **go.ramp.div** abstraction.

As an alternative, if you look at the first column of the table of ratios above, you can see it all comes down to simple integer ratios (simple whole number numerators and denominators). Moreover, there's a simple pattern to them. Starting from a quarter note, we can multiply or divide by each power of 2 to get whole notes, half notes, eighth notes, sixteenth notes, etc. Then, to get a dotted note, scale by 3/2, or to get a triplet, scale by 2/3. For example, to get a dotted 16th note, we must scale by $(1/4) * (3/2)$, which is $3/8$.

If we could do these calculations within a gen~ patch it would allow you to make these selections algorithmically (and with sample accuracy). Here's how these calculations might look:

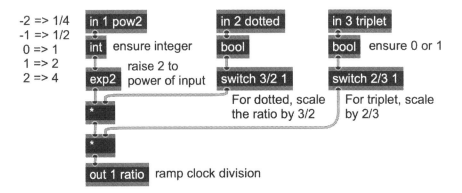

Once you understand the connection between note durations/tempo divisions and integer ratios, it's easy to extend this idea to wider ranges of N-tuplets and other numeric patterns simply by choosing different numerators and denominators of a ratio directly. Working with simple integer ratios like this turns out to be very useful not only for calculating rhythms but also for other things like quantization, carrier & modulator frequencies for FM synthesis, and other processes we will see in later chapters.

Modular arithmetic with rhythms

We've now seen a couple of different ways that multiplying a ramp can produce related polymeters by subdividing a measure. But what if we want to break up a measure into sections of different durations?

For example, the 8-step pattern below, sometimes called the Tresillo rhythm, is one of the most widely observed rhythmic motifs spanning many cultures of music worldwide:

1	2	3	1	2	3	1	2
3/8			3/8			2/8	

Amazingly, we can produce this easily with a bit of modular arithmetic. First, we multiply the measure's ramp by 8 for the eight steps in the pattern and then use the wrap operator to get the remainder after division by three steps. That will produce ramps from 0.0 to 3.0, which we can normalize back to a 0.0 to 1.0 range by dividing by 3.

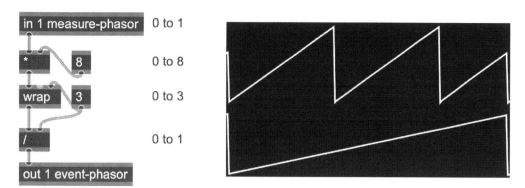

ramp.modulo.rhythm.maxpat [10]

We can refine that patch beyond the 3:8 pattern to a more general N:D (numerator:denominator) pattern with **param** operators, as below. With this patch, you can explore a variety of different grouping patterns.

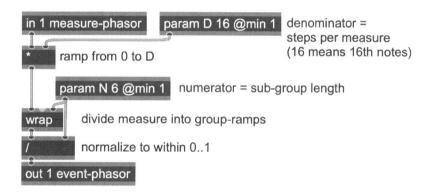

It gets even more interesting if you nest groups within groups: applying one modulo **wrap** operation for a first grouping level and then applying another, *smaller* modulo **wrap** operation for a sub-group level.

These parameters can be fun to modulate, so in the following patch, we also added **latch** operators to ensure that parameter changes are synced to the beat.

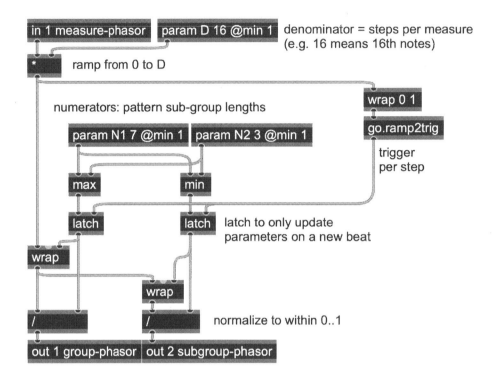

ramp_modulo_rhythm.maxpat

With the default parameters of 3:7:16, the resulting pattern looks like this:

1	2	3	4	5	6	7	1	2	3	4	5	6	7	1	2
1	2	3	1	2	3	1	1	2	3	1	2	3	1	1	2
3/16			3/16			1/16	3/16			3/16			1/16	2/16	

Since these are all working with ramp signals, all the other things we can do with ramps work too. Here are the measure, group, and sub-group signals with a little swing added, using a shaping function we'll introduce in the next chapter.

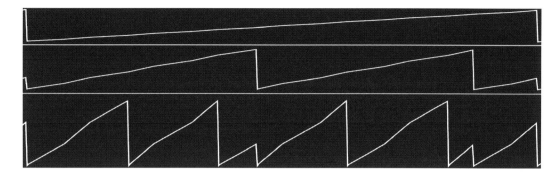

You can also feed this kind of ramp into the beat slicer to have more structured control! With a combination of the operations we've seen in this chapter and others we will meet in the following chapters, we can build up quite complex polyrhythms, and polymeters all derived from an underlying clock, and apply them to schedule all kinds of operations that work with triggers, step functions, or ramps, from triggering sound file playback, notes or other events, to driving LFO curves and sequencers, and so on. And everything is sample-accurate. Ramp signals really are one of the most versatile tools in your toolbox.

Modulating ramps with ramps

As a final example, let's try something a bit more experimental. The **go. ramp.div** abstraction provides an easy way to stretch or compress the time of a phasor ramp. The ratio doesn't have to be constant and can even be modulated continuously. What would happen if we modulated this ratio using another related phasor?[11] It may surprise you.

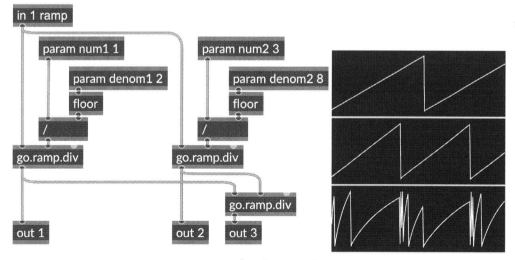

ramp_bursts.maxpat

The resulting waveform has become curved and tends to burst rapidly and then slow down, burst again, and so on.

If we wanted to get triggers from these bursty shapes, we could just route them through **go.ramp2trig** abstractions. To detect the *kinks* in the output (changes of slope), we could use a **delta** into a **delta** operator series, which gives us the equivalent of the *acceleration* of the waveform. This will provide us with spikes that are louder if the kink angles in the waveform are larger (and negative if the angular change goes down rather than up).

If we wanted to exclude the big phase wraps at the end of each ramp from this (since **go.ramp2trig** already finds those), we can use a **go.ramp2slope** into a **delta** operator.

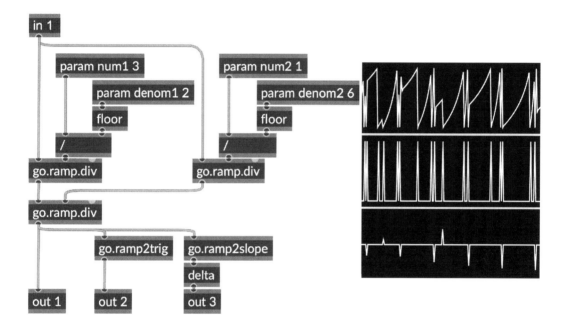

go.ramp_bursts2trigs.maxpat

To take the experiment to the next level, let's insert a couple of LFO waveshaper operations just before our final **go.ramp.div**. We'll add two pairs of unit shaper abstractions: a **triangle** operator with a skew **param** operator (to let us morph between positive ramps, negative ramps, and triangle waveforms) whose output is sent to a **go.unit.lfo** abstraction with a shape **param** operator (to let us morph between triangle, sine, and square wave outputs - we'll build up this **go.unit.lfo** abstraction in the next chapter).

Here is a simple example of our now highly morphable waveform, and the very complex outputs it generates.

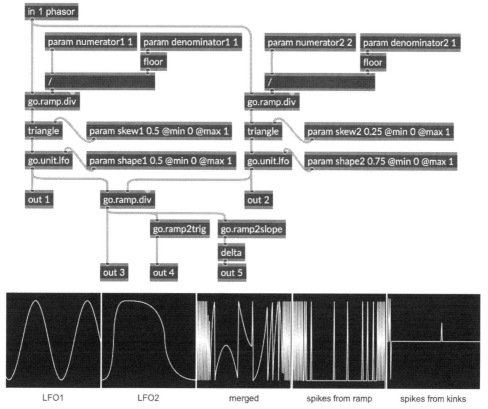

go.ramp_bursts_shaped.maxpat

Chapter 3: Unit Shaping

In Chapter 1, we saw how useful it can be to think about ranges of values and how we can use a **scale** operator to transform between one range and another. Internally, the **scale** operator first maps the input to a unipolar (0.0 to 1.0) range and then maps that unipolar value to the desired output range. This is an example of why the unipolar range is so useful as a kind of common intermediate format for many kinds of transformations. In the last chapter, we also saw how changing the *slope* of a unipolar ramp can be so powerful for articulating timing.

We also talked about the importance of thinking about the *shapes and curvatures* of signals—which can impart a great deal of the expressive character of melodic glides, envelopes, and other dynamics, as well as the timbre of audio. In this chapter, we'll be looking at a variety of functions to apply *shapes and curvatures* to unipolar signals and a few of the ways they can be useful. We call these functions "unit shapers." Briefly, here are some of the many ways they can be used:

- To change a robotic metric tempo into one with swing.
- To create more interesting oscillator and LFO shapes and morph between them.
- To create more interesting interpolations, including animation-inspired easing functions, for natural slew and parameter movement.
- To create a variety of interesting envelope shapes.
- To apply waveshaping distortion to bipolar signals (especially audio)
- To apply hard or smooth quantization (e.g., dividing octaves into scale or chromatic steps), as we see in Chapter 5 (p. 151).
- To shape the distribution of a noise generator, as discussed in Chapter 4 (p. 99).
- To apply window functions for granular and formant synthesis, explored in Chapter 10.

To be more specific, the term "unit shaper" in this book refers to any function that can take a linear input from 0.0 to 1.0 and produce at the output some other curved or nonlinear shape that still starts at 0.0 and ends at 1.0. We built a collection of unit shapers in the repository of patches included with this book, all prefixed with "go.unit". Some of these shapers also take additional parameter inputs to further control their shape.

Here are a few examples:

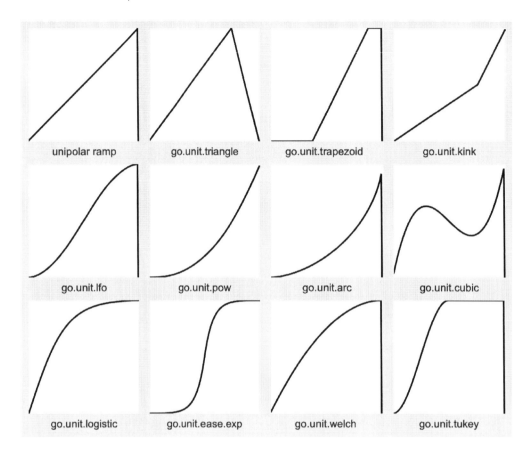

Swing and warping time

If we are working from ramp-based timing as we saw in the previous chapter, then we can use unit shaper functions to warp the time between beats to produce a variety of rhythmic effects, such as swing. In broad terms, adding swing to a rhythm usually means that every other ⅛th note (or half-beat) is delayed by some amount. Put another way; it means stretching and shrinking the times between the downbeat and the upbeat without changing the total duration between downbeats. Creating swing by unit shaping ramps doesn't just move the upbeats and downbeats; it also warps every other moment in between accordingly.

For example, let's use the **go.unit.kink** abstraction to break up a per-beat ramp into two line segments of different slopes. The **go.ramp.kink** abstraction makes these line segments that meet at a coordinate X and Y in the middle. The first inlet is for the ramp, and the second and third inlets set the X and Y coordinates, respectively (though the X coordinate is inverted by a **!- 1** operator to make the shape work more naturally alongside other unit shapers).

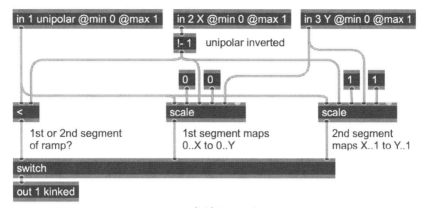

go.unit.kink.gendsp

It might look complex, but really, it's very simple. First, we check whether we are in the first half of the ramp (ramp < *X*) or the second half (ramp > *X*). For the first segment, the input range 0.0 to *X* is mapped to the output range 0.0 to *Y*, and for the second segment, the input range *X* to 1.0 is mapped to the output range *Y* to 1.0.

Let's plug that unit shaper into a BPM-based ramp generator along with a bipolar parameter **param swing_bi** to choose the intensity of the swing (so that 0.0 means no swing).

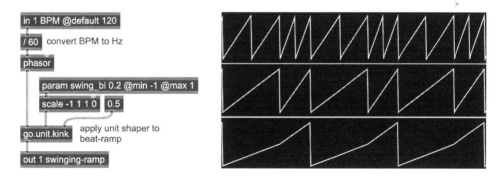

The bottom scope in the image above shows the kinked ramp per beat; the middle scope shows the ramp per half beat (revealing the swing action of delaying every other event), and the top scope shows the ramp subdivided by two, showing how it still follows the kinked ramp.

If we use different unit shaping functions, the time between each beat could be warped and curved in many different ways, each giving a different feel. For example, here are four different swing vibes:

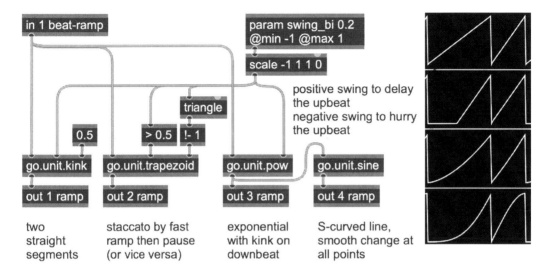

two
straight
segments

staccato by fast
ramp then pause
(or vice versa)

exponential
with kink on
downbeat

S-curved line,
smooth change at
all points

ramp.swing.maxpat

If we want to apply the swing warping to a ramp that spans multiple beats, such as a ramp-per-measure, we can use the general method of splitting a scaled ramp into steps and ramps using **floor** and **wrap 0 1** operators respectively, applying the warping to the ramped portion only and recombining them through addition into a multi-warped ramp per measure (as shown in the bottom scope in the following image).

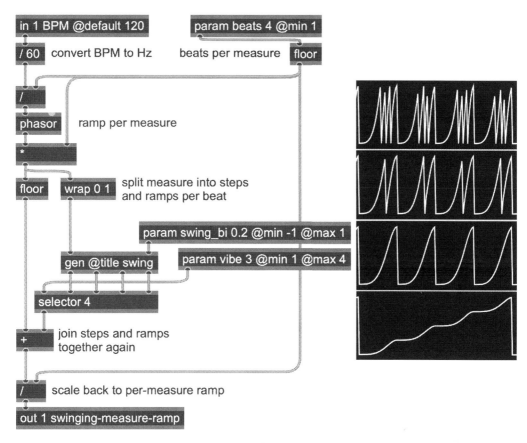

ramp.swing.maxpat

From ramps to LFOs

One of the great things about working with a common unipolar range is that we can chain one unit shaper with another to create more articulated shapes. Through the application of unit shapers, we can turn any low-frequency unipolar ramp into more complex LFO (low frequency oscillator) modulation signals.

Some of the most commonly used LFO shapes include rising and falling ramps, triangle-shaped waves, sinusoids, and square waves (or pulse waves with different duty cycles). In this section, we'll build up a simple LFO patch that uses a unipolar phasor ramp as the basic starting point, applying different unit shaping functions to build up many common (and some less common) LFO shapes. By controlling the unit shaper parameters, we can also morph LFO shapes over time. Moreover, if the input ramp is a tempo clock, then these will automatically be tempo-synced LFOs!

Triangles

Let's start with triangles. The triangle operator provides an easy way to convert a phasor ramp into several LFO waveforms. By default, it will map a 0.0 to 1.0 ramp input (left inlet) into a rising & falling triangle shape waveform, also in the 0.0 to 1.0 range. However, by changing the duty cycle parameter (right inlet), it can blend smoothly between a falling ramp, a skewed triangle, and a rising ramp.

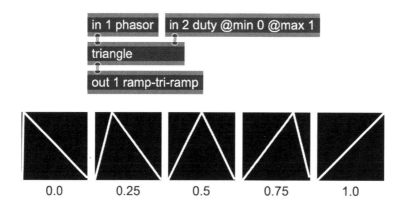

Looking carefully at the scopes, you may notice that with the **triangle** operator, the trough of the graph always remains in place, and the peak moves left to right as the duty input is changed. If you require the opposite movement (i.e., the peak remains in place, the trough moves right and left), you can use the **go.unit.triangle** abstraction, which routes a triangle operator through a **scale 0 1 1 0** operator to turn it upside down within the unipolar range. For example, this may be preferable when using the triangle as the basis for envelope shapes.

You may notice that modulating the **in 2 duty** can quickly produce jumps or clicks in the output. This occurs if we are controlling the duty using a user interface such as a number box, which updates its values more slowly than audio rate, resulting in stepped changes of the waveform. But even some modulations at full audio rates can cause large value jumps that produce unwanted effects.

One way to solve these problems is by controlling *when* the parameter of the **triangle** operator is updated. Specifically, if we only update this control when the LFO waveform loops, the glitchy noise will disappear. Since the waveform loops when the input phasor ramp wraps around, we can use the **go.ramp2trig** abstraction we built in the last chapter and a **latch** operator to synchronize the parameter changes.

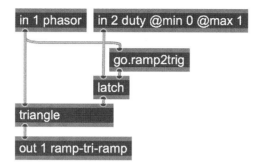

The **latch** will "sample" its left input when the right input is non-zero, such as when it receives a trigger from **go.ramp2trig**, and then the **latch** will "hold" that value until the next trigger (when the phasor next loops). You'll see this again in other patches in this book.

One of the nice things about using a **triangle** operator is that it has turned one unipolar ramp into a combination of two unipolar ramps (just that one of them goes down rather than up). That means any shaping that we could apply to a phasor ramp, we can also apply to our **triangle** output, and we can skew the result just by changing the triangle's duty parameter. It's great when we can produce several different outputs from the same circuit, and even better when it can continuously morph between them for almost no cost in complexity or performance! Now that we've got a morphing ramp-to-triangle generator, let's extend our patch to generate more LFO waveforms from the same circuit.

Sinusoids

Let's start with sinusoids. We can quite easily generate a unipolar sinusoidal output from a unipolar triangle input by mapping through a simple mathematical function.

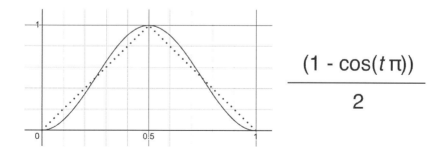

$$\frac{(1 - \cos(t\,\pi))}{2}$$

The dotted waveform is the triangle input "t"; the solid waveform is a derived sinusoidal function output: `(1 - cos(t*pi))/2`

As with most mathematical environments, the **sin** and **cos** operators expect angles in radians, which run from negative -**π** (**-pi**) to positive **π** (**pi**).[1] So, to compute our sinusoidal function as above, we can convert our triangle operator's output into radians using a * **pi** operator and then apply a **cos** operator. That already gives us a sinusoidal shape at the output, but it doesn't look similar to our triangle yet.

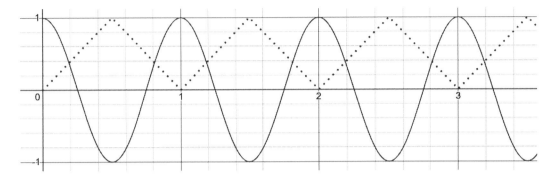

As you can see, the output of the **cos** operator is a *bipolar* signal between -1.0 and 1.0, but we want a unipolar output from 0.0 to 1.0. The cosine is also upside down relative to our triangle waveform (the peak of the triangle is at the trough of the cosine). Morphing between these waveforms would be more useful if they had the same direction.

In the mathematical equation above we corrected this by subtracting from 1 and dividing by two, but we got the same result in the following patch using a **scale** operator (**scale 1 - 1 0 1** both inverts the input and converts a bipolar signal into a unipolar signal).

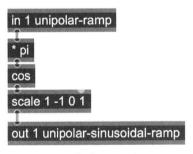

go.unit.sine.gendsp

This trio of operators is a common need for unit shaping, and so we saved that as the **go.unit.sine** abstraction. Just remember — to get a full sinusoid out of this, feed it with a triangle wave.

Here we combined it with the triangle generator from the last section to get both triangular and sinusoidal waveforms with the same duty parameter:

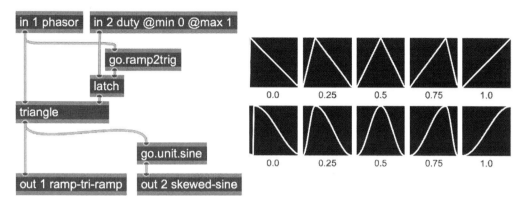

Now that we have both triangular and sinusoidal outputs, we could easily switch between them. But since we made our sinusoid have the same peak, range, and skew as our **triangle**, why not morph instead of switching?

We can smoothly morph between the linear ramp/triangle output and the cosine waveforms by crossfading using a **mix** operator. To control this crossfade, we need another input (**in 3 sinusoid** in the following patch), and again we've added the **go.ramp2trig** and **latch** operators to make sure that it only updates the **mix** when the phasor wraps to avoid unintended clicks.

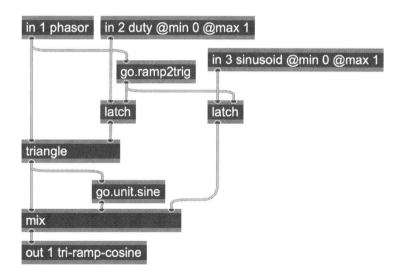

Pulse waves

Next, let's get a square wave/pulse output from our phasor ramp. A pulse wave is a logical signal—either +1.0 (true) or 0.0 (false)—and so naturally, we can use a logical condition such as a > ("more than") comparator operator to convert a ramp signal to a logical signal. For example, taking our original phasor through a > **0.5** operator will produce a neat square wave that is 0.0 for the first half of the period and 1.0 for the second half. As an alternative, we can pass the phasor through a - **0.5** operator to shift the phasor down by half a cycle and then test with a > **0** operator to see when the shifted phasor rises above the zero line.[2]

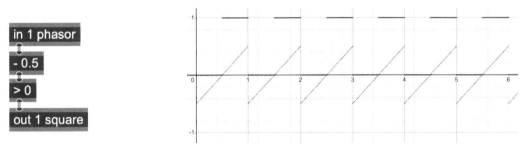

Dotted line: shifted phasor - 0.5; solid line shows the logical comparison > 0.

And if we change the argument to the subtraction operator, we will get different duty cycles. We could just map the **param duty** here to get variable pulse width, but it doesn't quite work the way we might like it to. As the param duty *increases*, the pulse width of the output *decreases*. We can fix that really easily just by sending the **param duty** value through a **!- 1** (subtract from one) operator, which inverts the 0.0 to 1.0 range into a 1.0 to 0.0 range. Now when the **param duty** is 0.75, we get a pulse wave that is high for the first 75% of the period and low for the remainder.

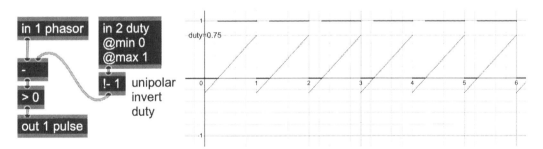

Dotted line: shifted ramp. Solid line: output pulse wave, with duty cycle (dashed line) = 0.75

In this way, we have built a pulse wave LFO with a pulse-width modulation (PWM) control due to the **param duty** operator.

Trapezoids

There's another neat thing we can do with our shifted phasor. If we multiply it by some number greater than one, we will make the slope get steeper. The bigger the number we multiply, the steeper it gets until it also starts to look like the pulse wave shape. Of course, this will also make it burst beyond the 0.0 to 1.0 range, but we can fix that very easily by sending the result through a **clip 0 1** operator. Finally, we can also recenter the phasor after this multiplication, simply by adding back on the inverted duty we had subtracted. The result of these changes is a trapezoidal wave.

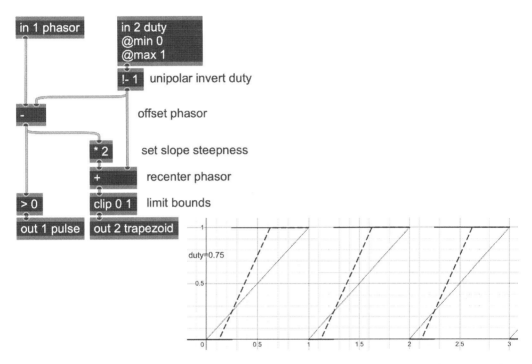

*Dotted line: input ramp. Solid line: pulse wave with duty cycle = 0.75. Dashed line: trapezoidal waveform, using a multiplier of * 2.*

You might notice how the trapezoidal waveform connects the middle of the bottom pulse wave segment to the middle of the top pulse wave segment. If the multiplier was * **4**, then it would blend from a quarter of the way into each segment. The bigger the multiplier gets, the steeper this line becomes until it begins to look just like the pulse wave. And, going the other way, the closer the multiplier gets to 1.0, the more it begins to look like the original phasor. We now have an algorithm that can smoothly morph between ramps and pulse waves!

It would be neat if we could control this morph with another unipolar parameter, such as an **in 3 shape @min 0 @max 1** operator. All we need is a bit of math to neatly compute the multiplier from the **in 3 shape**. The smallest multiplier we could use is 1.0, which leaves the ramp unchanged. The largest multiplier we could imagine would be something almost infinite, which would turn the ramp into a step. There's lots of different math functions that can map a range of 0.0 to 1.0 into a range of 1.0 to infinity; here we'll use the simple expression `1.0 / (1.0 - shape)`; which we can achieve very compactly using a **scale 1 0 0 1 -1** operator.

There's just one catch: We can't actually compute the infinite slope when the **in 3 shape** is exactly 1.0. But, in this case, our trapezoid would be exactly the same as a pulse wave, so we can simply use a **switch** operator accordingly.

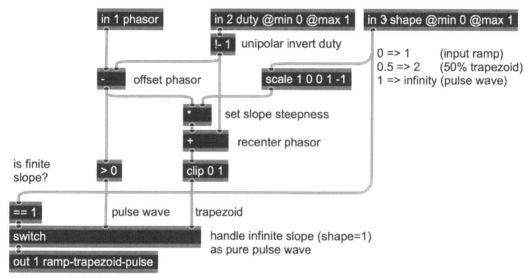

go.unit.trapezoid.gendsp

We now have a pretty simple function that can morph from a ramp, through a rising trapezoid ramp, to a pulse, and we can modify the pulse width duty cycle of them. We saved this as the **go.unit.trapezoid** abstraction. To get a trapezoid that can both rise and also fall, all we need to do is feed the **go.unit.trapezoid** abstraction with a triangle wave, whether from the **triangle** operator or from a **go.unit.triangle** abstraction.

Moreover, when the trapezoid shape input is zero, it passes the triangle through unchanged, so we can also combine it with the morphing to sinusoid from earlier to get an LFO that can morph between ramps, sines, pulses, and trapezoids, with a variety of intermediate shapes and duty cycles.

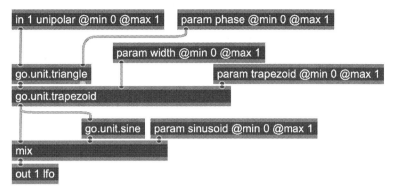

go.lfo.multi.gendsp

Here is a selection of some of the different waveforms we can get out of this patch:

Trapezoid	Sinusoid	Phase	Width	Shapes	Notes
0	0	**0.0 — 1.0**	N/A		ramps and triangles
0	1	**0.0 — 1.0**	N/A		sine and skewed wave
0.5	0	**0.0 — 1.0**	0		sharp envelope attack to decay
0.5	0	0.5	**0.0 — 1.0**		variable width trapezoids
0.5	1	0.5	**0.0 — 1.0**		windows and ducking
0.5	1	1	**0.0 — 1.0**		soft envelope variable hold
1	N/A	**0.0 — 1.0**	0.5		pulse phase modulation
1	N/A	0	**0.0 — 1.0**		pulse width modulation

That's a very useful set of LFO waveforms using very few operators and very few parameters. Moreover, we already know we can modulate the frequencies and phases of the input ramp using **go.ramp.div**, **go.ramp.rotate**, etc., and these will modulate the LFO output equivalently!

The output of all of these morphable waveforms are in the 0.0 to 1.0 range ("unipolar-normalized"), but sometimes we want a bipolar-normalized signal in the range of -1.0 to 1.0 for LFOs, just like audio signals. You can use a **scale 0 1 -1 1** operator again here to do this or other **scale** operator inputs to map to any arbitrary range you need.

Shaping smooth-stepped interpolation for LFOs and smooth glides

In Chapter 1, we saw that a **mix** operator performs a linear crossfade from value A (first inlet) to value B (second inlet), according to a control parameter (third inlet). A linear crossfade is also known as a linear interpolator, as we'll explore in Chapter 6 (p. 162). Since the **mix** operator's control input expects a unipolar signal from 0.0 to 1.0, we can drive it with a regular phasor ramp, but more interestingly, we can also apply any kind of unit shaper functions to this ramp to create nonlinear crossfades and interpolations.[3]

To put this into practice, we're going to introduce a little "smooth-stepped" patching pattern that we reuse in many different patches in this book.

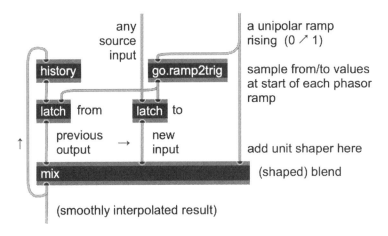

The core idea is to use a unipolar rising ramp (such as created by a **phasor** operator) driving a **mix** operator's control inlet to glide smoothly (interpolate) from one value to another. The target point of the glide is sampled from some external source signal—which could be anything at all—when the phasor wraps by using a **latch** operator and **go.ramp2trig** abstraction. The start point of the ramp is also sampled using a **latch** at the sample moment by taking the patch's own output, fed back through a **history** operator. In that way, the ramp always moves to a new position from wherever it was before.

For example, by using a simple **noise** operator as the source signal, we will get a series of connected random glides, all synchronized to a driving **phasor** operator. We also added a second outlet to that patch, so you can see how the **phasor** output (bottom scope) drives the line segments of the main output (top scope).

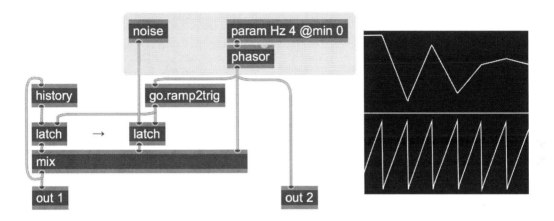

Since the driving phasor ramp always runs from 0.0 to 1.0, regardless of what the input and output signal values are, we can use any unit shaper to more interestingly curve our way between one value and another simply by inserting the shaper into the **mix** control. For example, we reused the **go.unit.sine** abstraction we built earlier in this chapter here.

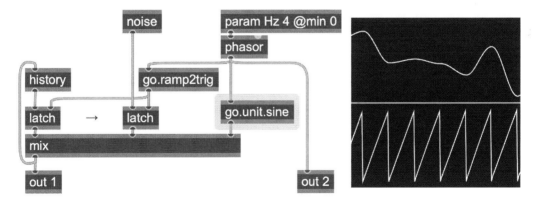

LFOs from smoothed steps

We can use this to build another LFO by feeding it with a pulse wave that alternates between 0.0 and 1.0 with each ramp cycle. There are a few different ways we could do this, but to keep things simple and flexible, we're going to do it with a triangle shaper (**go.unit.triangle**) and simply invert the falling section of the triangle wave so that we get two rising segments.

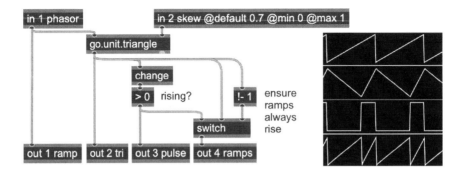

The **change** operator tells us if the triangle wave is rising (+1.0) or falling (-1.0). If it is not rising, then the **> 0** operator returns false, and the **switch** operator instead routes a copy of the falling segment that has been inverted (turned upside down) via the **!- 1** operator. In this way, our ramp segments are ensured to be always rising, which we will need for the smooth-stepping patch to work. As you can see, using the **go.unit.triangle** abstraction also gives us control over the pulse width via the **in 2 skew** operator. Let's use this subpatch to feed our interpolator template and apply a unit shaper to the ramps before they reach the **mix** control input. Here we used the **go.unit.arc**[4] unit shaper, giving us another parameter to generate more interesting LFO shapes.

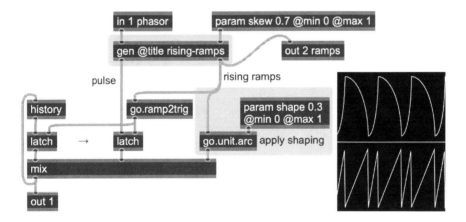

There's a few more things we can add to this to open up more LFO shapes.

You might notice that the output has a somewhat "sharktooth" character in that the curvature is different whether the ramp is rising or falling. If instead you want a symmetric curvature, all you need to do is invert the shape parameter while the output is falling. We can tell if the output should be falling simply by comparing the two latches (the *from* and *to* values for the interpolation) using a greater-than-or-equal (>=) operator, and we can use that to drive a **switch** and **!- 1** operator pair to do the conditional inversion, just as we did earlier.

We can also add a **param symmetric** operator to enable and disable this inversion through an **and** logical operator, so that inversion only happens if the ramp is falling *and* the **param symmetric** is enabled (non-zero).

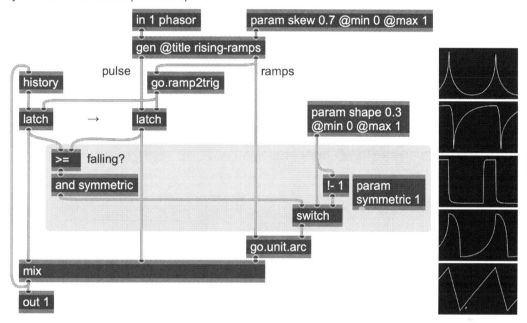

We don't have to limit this patch to using only unipolar pulse wave inputs; we could take our input from any external signal using an **in 2** operator.

We made this change in the next patch, as well as encapsulating the shape symmetry logic into the "symmetry" subpatch to keep things organized.

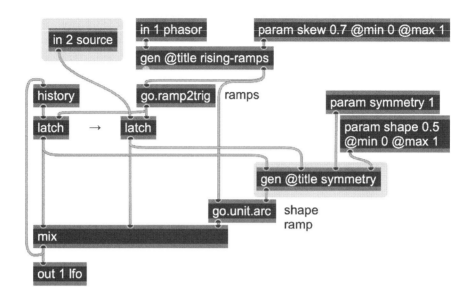

Here are some examples of the kinds of signals it can give when sampling from a bipolar **noise** generator. We'll see more variants of this kind of smoothed stepped random generation in the next chapter (p. 93).

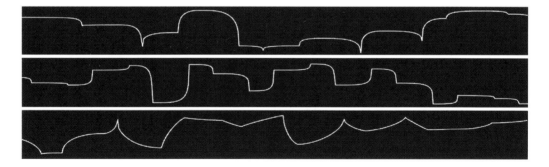

Alternatively, we could strike a balance between our pulse wave and noise and between unipolar and bipolar. We could use another **mix** operator to blend the pulse with a little **noise** operator, made unipolar with an **abs** operator. Moreover, it's very easy to convert the unipolar range of the pulse/noise mix to a bipolar range using a **scale 0 1 -1 1** operator. We can put this under more dynamic control of a **param bipolar** by setting the lower output bound of a **scale** operator to either -1.0 (for bipolar) or 0.0 (for unipolar).

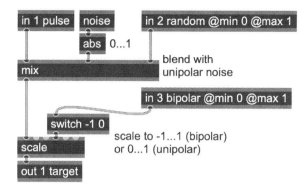

Let's add this to our patch as a "target selection" subpatch. Finally, just as we did with our first LFO in this chapter, we can use a **go.ramp2trig** abstraction with **latch** operators to ensure that parameter updates only happen when the driving phasor wraps so that modulating parameters does not cause unwanted clicks. Here is the final patch with those changes added:

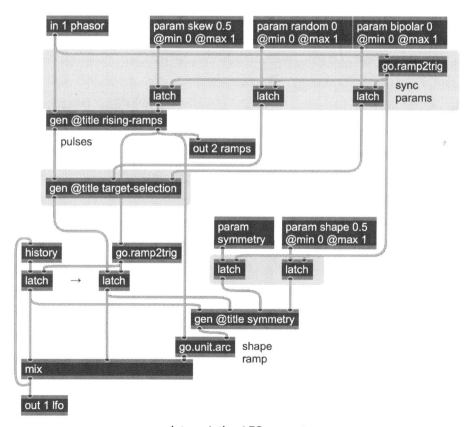

interpolating-LFO.maxpat

A slightly modified version of this patch is also available for your use as the **go.lfo** abstraction.

Glides and portamento

A **phasor**-driven smooth-stepped interpolator makes sense when you have control over repeating shapes. But we can use smooth-stepped interpolation for any arbitrary non-repeating input, to add for example smooth glides to sporadically stepped pitch changes. In this case, rather than driving the **mix** operator interpolator from a **phasor**, we can drive it from a "one-shot" ramp that is retriggered whenever the input changes.

As we saw in Chapter 2 (p. 19), we can easily create an endlessly rising ramp with an **accum** operator. If we want to stop it once it gets to a goal of 1.0, we can do that by sending it through a **clip 0 1** operator. Any non-zero trigger to the **accum** operator's second inlet will restart the ramp from zero again. That gives us a "one shot" ramp that rises from zero to one and stops there.

This ramp can now smoothly interpolate between any two **latch** values by driving a **mix** operator just as we did before. The first **latch** operator represents our location when the ramp started, and the second **latch** operator is the target goal we are trying to reach. Whenever the input signal changes (as detected by a **change** operator), we can update these two **latch**es and restart the accum operator's ramp from zero, to begin a new glide.

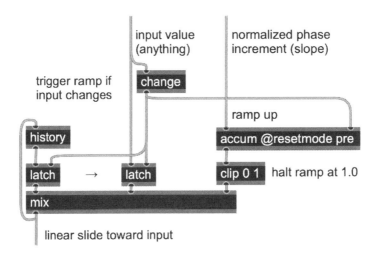

All we need to set the glide duration is a way to compute the required slope for the **accum** operator. For example, given a ramp duration in milliseconds, we can convert it to a ramp duration in sample frames using the **mstosamps** operator; and then take the reciprocal of that via a **!/ 1** operator to get the slope per sample frame. Or, we can combine both of these operations into one using a **!/ 1000/samplerate** operator.

Now, whenever the input changes, we will begin a glide from wherever we are, even if we were mid-ramp, toward the new input value, and we always arrive after a fixed duration or "lag". In fact, what we have built here is also known as a lag generator, which we will explore in more detail in Chapter 6 (p. 195).

As with the smooth-stepped LFO, we can add a unit shaper of our choice before the mix operator's control inlet to drive the curvature of the change. Notice how the ramp (in the lower scope) always rises from 0.0 to 1.0 and then holds there, regardless of what the input is:

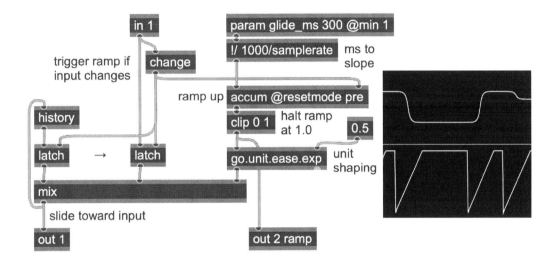

For a more complex example with randomized curvatures, see the *interpolating_glides.maxpat* patch.

Easing functions

In the previous patch, the unit shaper we used is based on an "easing function." Easing functions are drawn from a history of classic motions in animation, described in terms of three variants: an "ease in" that starts slow and speeds up, an "ease out" that starts suddenly but smoothly arrives at its destination, and an "ease in-and-out" that combines both for smooth start and arrival.

This book's software repository contains several examples of common easing functions as unit shapers including **go.unit.ease.pow**, **go.unit.ease.pow**, **go.unit.ease.exp**, **go.unit.ease.circle**, **go.unit.ease.back**, **go.unit.ease.elastic**, and **go.unit.ease.sine**. For all of these we generalized the easing variants under a single "shape" parameter, where shape=0 means "ease in", shape=1 means "ease out", shape=0.5 means "ease in-and-out", and any other value is a gradual blend between these. We'll use these easing function unit shapers in many patches throughout this book.

All but one of these follow a common patching template structure, as shown below. You can place any other unit shaper within this structure to create new easing functions.

Most of the classic animiation easing functions follow a common structure.

The first part converts the input ramp into a rising and falling section according to the value of the "shape" input. This is actually exactly equivalent to a [triangle] operator.

The middle part applies some curvature function to the triangle shape -- any unit shaper can be used here.

The final section scales the ramps and flips the second part, so that it rises to a value of 1.0 at the end, with a symmetrical shape between skewed by the shape parameter.

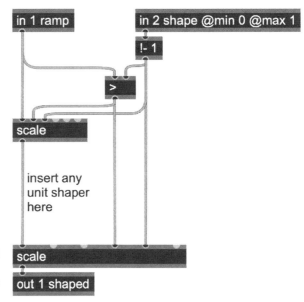

Window envelope functions

A window function is a function that rises from zero to one, then falls back to zero, to provide the period and amplitude bounds of an event in a signal. In that sense, they are also a kind of envelope function. However, most often windows are symmetric in time.

We can create a symmetric rising & falling window shape simply by driving any unit shaper with a unipolar triangle wave:

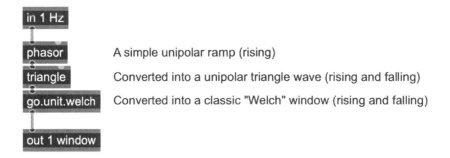

There are many window shapes used in signal analysis, granular synthesis, and related methods, and the book's software package includes many of the most widely used as unit shapers, including **go.unit.hamming**, **go.unit.hann**, **go.unit.blackman**, **go.unit.blackmanharris**, **go.unit.blackmannutall**, **go.unit.nutall**, **go.unit.flattop**, **go.unit.welch**, and **go.unit. parzen**.

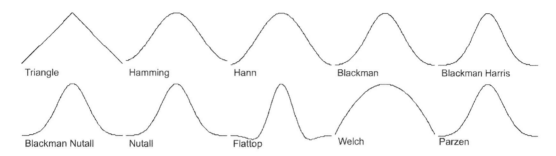

The software package also includes several widely used parametric window shapes, including **go.unit.trapezoid, go.unit.tukey, go.unit.plancktaper, go.unit.gauss**, and **go.unit.raisedcosine**.[5]

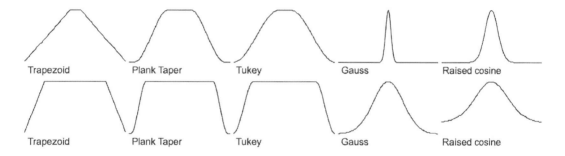

Of course, you can also use any other unit shapers for different windowing responses.

You can also create an asymmetric window or envelope shape simply by changing the second input of the **triangle** operator. For example, a **triangle 0** operator will produce decay-only shapes. Or, you could extend the **triangle** operator into a trapezoid shape (such as generated by **go.unit.trapezoid**) for windows and envelopes with extended "hold" or "sustain" sections.

Waveshaping bipolar signals

So far, we have looked at ways of shaping based on unipolar inputs and outputs, but there are some specific cases—particularly when processing audio signals—where bipolar shaping makes more sense. This shaping of audio signals is often called *waveshaping*. It is a kind of distortion synthesis which can be useful to make a simple oscillator more complex, or to add soft limiting, overdrive, or other harmonically rich complexity to an audio signal.

We can build bipolar waveshapers from any of our unipolar unit shapers merely by applying a little extra patching to handle bipolar input and produce bipolar output. Here are two options:

1. **Asymmetric:** We could stretch the unit shaper over the whole bipolar range. Use a **scale -1 1 0 1** operator to shrink the bipolar signal to a unipolar range, apply the unit shaper to this unipolar signal, and then stretch back to bipolar with a **scale 0 1 -1 1** operator.

2. **Symmetric:** As an alternative, we can apply a symmetric mirror image of the unit shaper for the positive and negative signals. First, we take a copy of the signal and throw away any negative sign using an **abs** operator. This mirrors negative parts of the signal into the positive region, which is called full wave rectification. Then we apply the unit shaper to this rectified signal, then multiply the result by the **sign** of the input, so that the parts that were originally negative go back to being negative.

Both of these methods are shown in this patch, where we use a **go.unit.spline** unit shaper to make an input signal more complex.

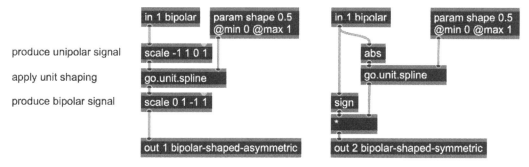

bipolar_waveshaping_unitshapers.maxpat

The results look like this:

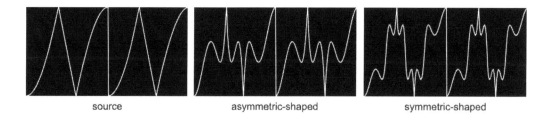

Of course, you can use any input signal and any unit shaper—the following patch uses the **go.unit.ease.pow** shaper for example. Moreover, you can also easily explore a **mix** between the asymmetric and symmetric options if you wish:

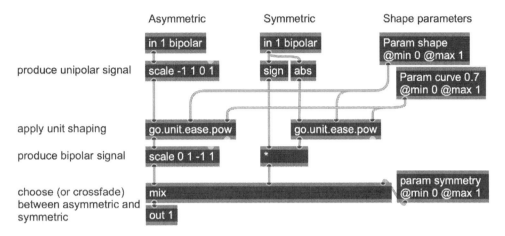

bipolar_waveshaping_unitshapers.maxpat

Audio waveshaping

As the last example showed, waveshaping can turn relatively simple waveforms into more complex waveforms. When processing audio signals, wave shaping imparts a timbral change to most input waveforms, and in this sense is comparable to filter-based signal processing (as we will explore in Chapter 7). However, there are a few interesting differences.[6]

- Where most filters *reduce* the spectral complexity of a signal, waveshaping tends to *increase* it, adding more harmonics to the signal. For this reason, simpler waveforms such as sine and triangle waves are good choices for input. On the other hand, a plain square or pulse wave is not a good choice of input, as it has practically no slope in its waveform for a waveshaper to complexify.
- Where the timbral response of most filters remain the same whether sounds are quiet or loud, the timbral response of a waveshaper is very dependent on the amplitude of the input: in many cases, the quieter the input, the less timbrally bright or complex the result. This correspondence of "louder" being "brighter" also tends to be the case for physically produced sounds, which means that waveshapers often respond in a perceptually satisfying way to enveloped inputs.

The specific effect of waveshaping on the spectrum of a signal is generally a nonlinear process, and for most shaping functions it is hard to predict precisely.

It can also sometimes produce harsh aliasing frequencies, particularly when using sharp piecewise linear shaping functions such as **go.unit.kink** and **go.unit.trapezoid**. Smoother functions of sigmoid, and polynomial, or sinusoidal nature are much less problematic. Let's take a closer look at those.

Polynomial shapers

If you take a sine wave, and square it, you will get a waveform with twice the frequency (the second harmonic frequency). If you raise it to the power of 3, you will get a waveform with components up to three times the frequency (up to the 3rd harmonic). This continues for powers of 4, 5, 6 and so on.

Mixing an original signal with a slight amount of these power signals can be a relatively cheap way to add a bit of harmonic sizzle to audio. This is part of how exciter effects work. It's also a relatively cheap way to create a kind of additive harmonic synthesis.

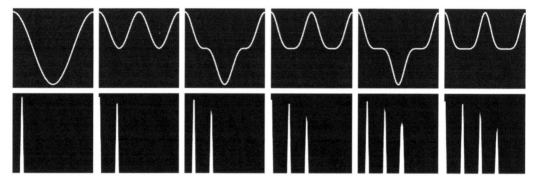

Top row: a sine wave raised to the power of 1, 2, 3, 4, 5, and 6.
Bottom row: the corresponding spectra showing the resulting frequency components.

We can mix these signals together, scaling each one by a different weight, to create a *polynomial* function. In mathematical terms, a polynomial just means a weighted mix of integer powers of the input signal *x*, and is notated as:

$$a_0 + a_1x + a_2x^2 + a_3x^3 + \text{... etc. up to } a_nx^n.$$

or in code:

```
a0 + a1*x + a2*pow(x, 2) + a3*pow(x, 3); // etc
```

The degree of a polynomial is its highest power exponent (so, in the function above, the degree is 3), and this also tells you the highest harmonic it can produce from a sine input. So, if the input signal is a sinusoid, then the process above will have no frequencies higher than the 3rd harmonic.[7]

You may have noticed that raising a sine wave to a single integer power does not produce a single harmonic, but a mixture of harmonics. Unlike simple power functions, a special class of polynomial functions called Chebyshev functions produce only single harmonics from a sine wave input, so long as the sine wave is at unity gain. That is, if you feed them a sine wave of amplitude ranging from -1.0 to 1.0, they will output a single sine wave of a single higher harmonic frequency. The following patch computes the first six Chebyshev harmonics with weights, and also produces a normalized output by dividing by the sum of the magnitudes of all weights.

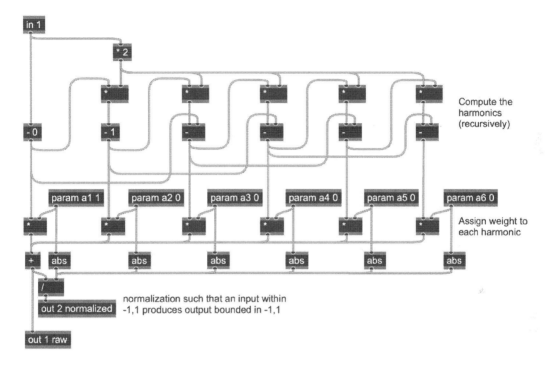

The ***bipolar_waveshaping_chebyshev.maxpat*** patch shows a few examples of computing the weights, including using exponential scaling for bandlimited impulse generation, and random walks for evolving additive drones.

Sigmoids

Sigmoids are an extremely useful class of functions that can smoothly convert a potentially infinite-ranged input into a limited range output. Here is a classic sigmoid function, the hyperbolic tangent (in gen~, this is simply the **tanh** operator):

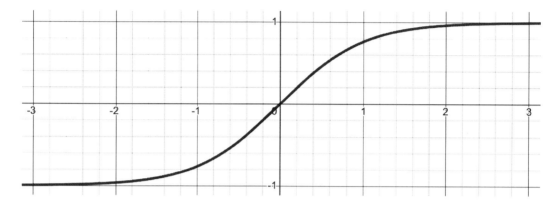

When the input is near zero, the output is near zero too, and the slope is exactly 1.0. That means, when the input is very quiet, the output signal is almost unchanged. As the input amplitude increases, whether positively or negatively, the output slope gradually tapers off, such that it curves toward but never quite reaches the limits of +1.0 or -1.0. That means that the louder the input, the more pronounced the effect of the shaping.

This makes sigmoids useful in many scenarios.[8] For example, they can be an excellent way to gain control over potentially unruly signals (not just audio!), such as might be produced by unpredictable feedback circuits. Unlike a hard limiting operation such as a **clip -1 1** operator, there is no sudden point at which the waveform is cut off; instead, the limiting is softly and gradually introduced. And as it does so, it can gradually add pleasant harmonic distortion and higher harmonics.

This harmonic distortion can be quite desirable and can be intensified simply by pre-amplifying a signal before it enters the waveshaper. For example, here is a simple **tanh** sigmoid shaper applied to a regular sine wave, with pre-amplification settings of 1x, 2x, and 8x respectively.

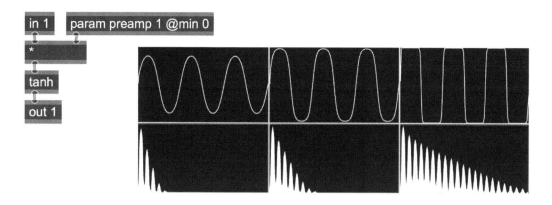

Looking at the waveforms (above), you can see how increasing the pre-amplification drives the sine shape toward the limits, where it approaches a square wave. The spectra underneath also show how overdriving the input increases the intensity of the higher harmonics. You can push the amplification as high as you want, and the output will never go beyond the -1.0 to +1.0 range; but it may run the risk of creating aliasing high frequencies.

The **tanh** operator isn't the only sigmoid shape. Here are a few classic sigmoid shapes and their implementations, normalized to produce signals within a bipolar -1.0 to +1.0 range:

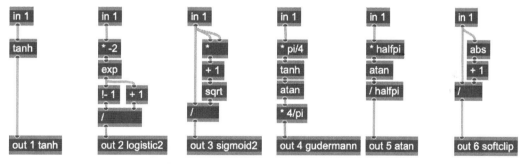

bipolar_waveshaping_sigmoids.maxpat

Each of these is also included in the book software as the **go.sigmoid.tanh, go.sigmoid.logistic, go.sigmoid2, go.sigmoid.guderman, go.sigmoid.atan,** and **go.sigmoid.softclip** abstractions.

The response shapes are very similar to each other, with the main differences being the relative distribution of energy over partials, as you can see in the spectra below.

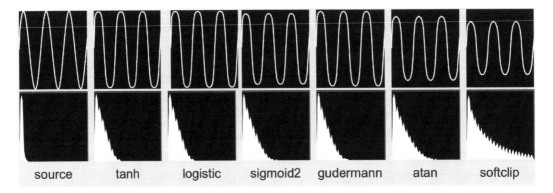

| source | tanh | logistic | sigmoid2 | gudermann | atan | softclip |

As we noted earlier in this section, waveshapers respond very naturally to enveloped sounds: as the envelope rises, not only does the sound get louder but also brighter; and as it decays, the sound also becomes duller.

The **bipolar_waveshaping_sigmoids_enveloped.maxpat** patch demonstrates this effect, and how the different sigmoid choices vary in spectral color to each other:

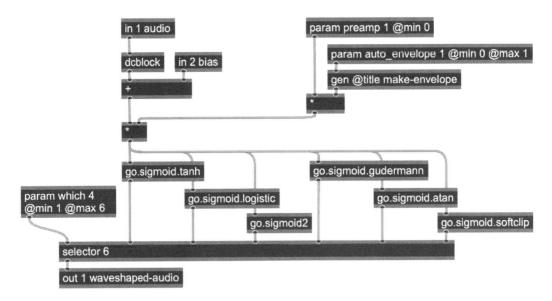

This patch also demonstrates how adding a bias offset to the Input can change the spectral response. A bias offset just means adding a constant (or very low frequency signal) that takes the average midpoint of the audio signal above or below zero. The more it moves away from the zero line, the more the waveshaping effect is different for its positive and negative halves. It may be desirable therefore to run audio through a highpass filter (such as the **dcblock** operator) to remove any unwanted bias, and then adding a separate input for more deliberate independent control over the bias effect, as we did in the patcher above.

Normalized sigmoids as unit shapers

Perhaps we don't always want the timbral shaping to be tied to the pre-amplification. Wouldn't it be nice if we could modulate the curvature effect from no effect through soft shaping to extreme clipping, without making the signal quieter or louder at the same time? Then the sigmoids could also work as unit shapers.

We can easily do this by precomputing what the shaper does to the amplification factor itself, and simply dividing by that result to normalize the output. For example, if the amplification factor is ×2, then a signal of amplitude 1.0 will be transformed into a signal of amplitude `tanh(2)`, or about 0.964. Now, if we divide our shaped signal by 0.964, we ensure that the result will be a signal that once again has an amplitude of 1.0. The following patch does this, with a couple of refinements to manage the inputs.

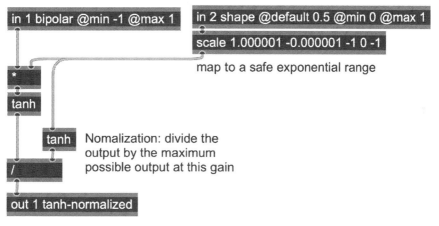

go.unit.tanh.gendsp

First, this method assumes that our input signal's amplitude will never be greater than one, or else the division could blow up. We ensure this by clipping the input **in 1** operator with **@min -1 @max 1** arguments; you could insert another sigmoid shaper before this instead for less aggressive clipping.

Second, most of our unit shapers use a shape input that ranges from 0.0 to 1.0 for convenience, as it easy to swap out one unit shaper with another. To be able to generate a vast range of possible amplification factors, we take the unipolar **in 2 shape** input, and map it through an exponentially configured **scale** operator. A shape input of 0.0 produces an amplification factor of x0.000001; a shape input of 0.5 produces an amplification factor of exactly 1.0, and a shape input of 1.0 produces an amplification factor of about x1000000!

Then, to apply the normalization, we pass both the amplified signal and the amplification factor through two copies of the shaping function; and divide the results. Now when the **in 2 shape** is 0.0, the input signal passes through practically unchanged. And when the in 2 shape increases toward 1.0, the input signal is increasingly transformed into a maximized waveform.

The book's software also includes unit shaper conversions of classic sigmoid shapers: the **go.unit.tanh, go.unit.logistic, go.unit.sigmoid2, go.unit.gudermann, go.unit.atan**, and **go.unit.softclip** abstractions.

Here are the results of shaping a sine wave with the **go.unit.tanh** abstraction at shape settings of 0.0, 0.8, and 1.0 respectively:

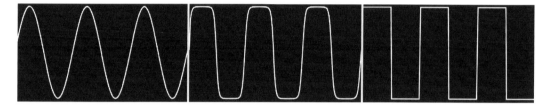

Feeding anything more complex than a sine wave can create some surprisingly complex output. Let's look at a perceptually interesting example of this, using a source signal that is slowly cross-fading between two different triangle waves, sent into a **go.unit.softclip**.

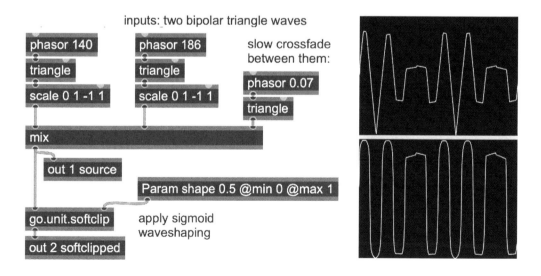

bipolar_waveshaping_intermodulaton.maxpat

The more that this input is overdriven (by increasing the **param shape**), the less it sounds like a crossfade and the more it sounds like a continuous pitch glide between the two tones! This kind of harmonic intermodulation between tones and amplitudes is what makes waveshaping so fascinating and rewarding for exploration.

We will return to see more kinds of waveshaping in Chapter 8 (p. 249), where we will see that *phase modulation* is just another kind of waveshaping, in which the carrier provides a periodic waveshaping function for the modulator.

Chapter 4: Noise, Uncertainty, and Unpredictability

Throughout this book, we talk about ways that you can add variety to simple patches to achieve interesting results—moving beyond simple counting-based processes to generate and organize variety—with ideas that you can apply just about anywhere. In this chapter, we're going to focus on the use of stochastic and unpredictable processes of noise, chance, and chaos.

The idea that the application of unpredictable processes can result in musical outcomes has been with us for a long time.[1] The list is long and interesting and includes examples as diverse as Guido D'Arezzo's 11th-century algorithms that mapped the vowels in a text to notes on a staff, the use of isorhythms in 13th-century motets, 15th-century Netherlandic canons, Mozart's dice games for writing minuets, Gottfried Michael Koenig's PROJECT 1, John Cage's use of the **I Ching** to generate his *Music of Changes*, and Iannis Xenakis' stochastic processes.

Feel the noise

The **noise** operator is the primary starting point for unpredictable variety in gen~. With each passing sample frame of time, it produces a new random value in the range of -1.0 to 1.0, in which each possible value in this range is just as likely as any other, and overall the values are distributed evenly over different time scales, which means that there is no periodic pattern.

(Note that we use the term "random" here for legibility, but we should point out that, as with most computational systems, these aren't *truly* random numbers, but are an algorithmically generated sequence of values that are evenly distributed, which means any value is roughly as likely to appear as any other. The sequence is so complex as to have no discernible pattern, making it practically quite unpredictable.)[2]

An audio-rate sequence of evenly distributed values with no discernible pattern sounds like a bright and rather harsh stream of noise. If it did have a discernible pattern, it would start to sound like a periodic tone or loop instead. Here is a challenge to try: how long does a loop of pre-recorded noise have to be before you can't hear it looping anymore?

You can try this out by opening the ***random_when_does_noise_get_forgotten.maxpat*** from the book's example patches. It might surprise you.

Audio-rate noise is sometimes described in terms of colors. Just as white light contains all colors and can be filtered to produce specific hues, white noise, such as the **noise** operator generates, has equal energy at all frequencies but can be filtered to produce different colors of noise. (We'll look at some filters you can use in Chapter 6.) For the most part, "color" here refers to the *spectral profile* of the noise, which means how much energy is distributed between lower and higher frequencies. This is perhaps a slightly odd descriptor, given that random noise is not periodic by definition! At best, perhaps we can say the noise is more or less similar to a periodic signal with high or low energy at certain frequencies.

Noise isn't just for audible timbres, but can also be the basis of random signals to control other processes. That is, the simplicity of the **noise** operator has a complex idea at its heart - the connection between noise (in the acoustic and psychoacoustic senses) and randomness (in more mathematical or musical senses). We'll see this used extensively in subsequent chapters, including using random (or stochastic) output sampled at different time scales to generate melodies, spawn microsonic grains, and so on, but in this chapter, we'll look at some more fundamental ways to use the **noise** operator and other algorithms to generate a variety of unpredictable signals.

Random ranges

The **noise** operator's range is normalized bipolar, which simply means that the numbers are between -1.0 and 1.0. This is appropriate when we want an audio-rate white noise signal, as it covers the normal range of audio values. But if we want to use noise to drive some other random processes, we often want to scale the numbers to a different range. We can map a raw **noise** operator's -1.0 to 1.0 output to *any* desired range between A and B using a **scale -1 1 A B** operator.

For example, we often want to map the **noise** operator's output to a normalized unipolar range (0.0 to 1.0), as used widely throughout this book, and we could use a **scale -1 1 0 1** operator for this. An even quicker way to get a unipolar output is to pass the **noise** operator through an **abs** operator. This will fold all the negative values around zero into the positive range (also known as full wave rectification).

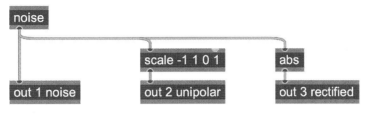

random_range.maxpat

Rate control / stepped random

The **noise** operator generates a new random value for every passing sample frame moment. For audio-rate noise, this is probably what we want, but for doing more algorithmic processes, we often want to control *when* a new random value is used. Perhaps we want a new random value on every beat, on every cycle of an oscillator, or on every note event. In this case, we can use a **latch** operator to "sample" **noise** according to a trigger (just like a traditional hardware Sample & Hold module).

In the following patch, we drive the **latch** by a **phasor** whose rate we can set by frequency using a **param** operator. The **go.ramp2trig** abstraction we built in Chapter 2 (p. 43) will generate triggers whenever the **phasor** ramp cycles.

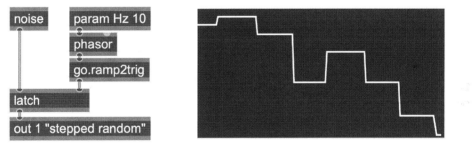

random_steps.maxpat

Once you understand this oft-used circuit, there are a number of simple variations of it that can be really useful.

Smooth stepped random

Sometimes we want a random source but without the hard edges of a raw stepped or latched random generator. We could achieve this by applying an appropriate lowpass filter or by using a slew limiter (as we explore in Chapter 6). but here we are going to adapt the "smooth-stepped" method we saw in the last chapter (p. 70). In that section. rather than immediately jumping to a new random point, we used the **mix** operator to create a linear ramp to that point (or some other more curved, shaped interpolation between a series of random points). This time, instead of using a mix operator we're going to do it using the **interp** operator.

In its default mode, the **interp** operator behaves effectively the same as the **mix** operator, except that the inlets are in a different order (the control inlet is first rather than last). What makes the **interp** operator more interesting for us is that it can use other interpolation functions, including multi-point interpolations, just by changing the **@mode** attribute. These include: **@mode linear** (the same as the **mix** operator), **@mode cosine** (a sinusoidal curve), **@mode cubic** (4-point interpolation), **@mode spline** (a 4-point Bézier spline), and **@mode spline6** (a 6-point Bézier spline).[3]

The first inlet sets the interpolation factor, sometimes called alpha. This alpha inlet expects a value in the range of 0.0 to 1.0, which sets the amount of blending between one data point and another. Each additional inlet sets the individual data points to be interpolated between. Linear and cosine interpolations require two points; cubic and spline need four points, and spline6 needs six.

Let's start with linear. For the interpolation factor alpha, we can simply use the phasor that is driving the **go.ramp2trig**. For the two points, we need both the most recently **latch**ed random value and the one previous to it. That is because the line needs to rise from the previous latched value (when alpha = 0.0) up to the new latched value (when alpha = 1.0). We can store the previous **latch**ed value by adding another **latch** and a **history** between them, like this:

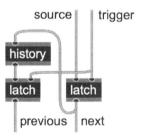

This circuit is called a (two-stage) *shift register*. Rather like a bucket brigade, the incoming value is passed from one storage (the latch) to the next whenever a new trigger comes in. We'll see shift registers in more detail with generative sequencers in Chapter 5 (p. 127).

Putting this all together:

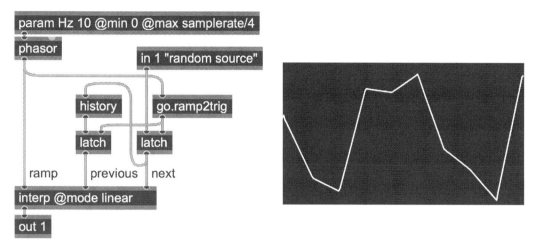

random_smoothed.maxpat

Compare this with using **interp @mode spline6**, which needs six input points, and therefore a six-stage shift register.

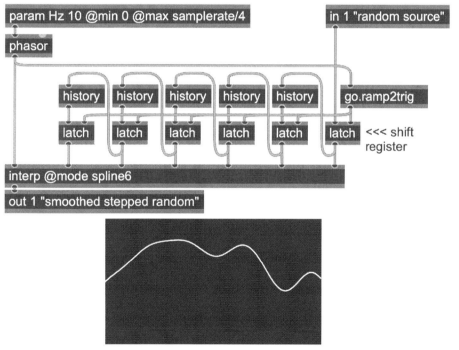

random_smoothed.maxpat (and see also go.shift.spline6.gendsp)

This technique adapts perfectly to changes in the driving phasor frequency (so long as the frequency is not negative). Each Interpolator implies a different kind of smoothing, and at audio rates this becomes a kind of sonic filtering. The **random_smoothed.maxpat** also shows a sinc interpolated implementation, based on an algorithm we will encounter in Chapter 9 (p. 283).

This general method of interpolation over a shift register works for any periodically sampled signal, not just noise. A binary chance signal, a quantized random signal, or any source—from LFOs to pitch sequences—can be smoothed in this way.

Chance and conditions of probability

Sometimes you want things to happen *some* of the time, but not *all* the time. You can create a patch that lets you create probabilistic logic signals of either 1.0 (meaning true/high/on) or 0.0 (meaning false/low/off) from unipolar noise with the addition of a less-than (<) operator.

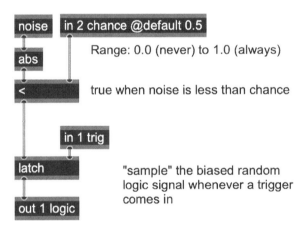

This is one of those endlessly reusable circuits which we have added to the book collection as "**go.chance.gendsp**". In this case, the **chance** input sets the probability that the next output will be a 1.0 (true). For example, if the **chance** input is set to a value of 0.25, it will output 1.0 just 25% of the time and a value of 0.0 the remaining 75% of the time. Do you want to flip a coin?

Set the **chance** parameter to 0.5. As before, we can use the phasor-driven **latch** operator to control how often this decision is made.

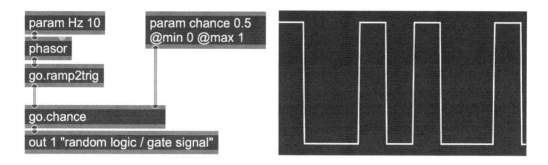

random_chance.maxpat

So now you can create a *biased* random decision at any moment you might need it. What you do with this is up to you—we use it in many parts of this book, and we will see it again later in this chapter.

If the chance operation is run at full audio rate, and the probability ratio is set quite low (try 0.001, for example), the result is a kind of randomized sequence of clicks or pops. Try multiplying this by another **noise** operator to generate dust and scratches!

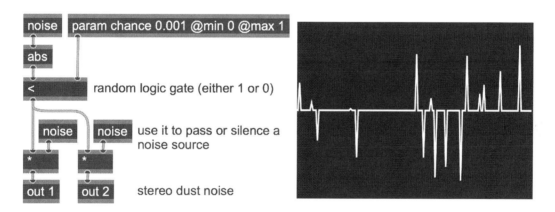

random_chance.maxpat

Bernoulli gate

A Bernoulli gate takes a trigger input and, whenever that trigger goes high, routes it to either one or another of two outputs according to some probability parameter. It can be used to skip events selectively in a series, route trigger events to two different sound sources (such as an open or closed high hat), or more generally, route event control to different sections of a patch.

Here we simply take our "**go.chance**" circuit from above and use the output to select between one of two outputs through a **gate 2** operator. The signal input that the gate routes is the same trigger **in** that was used to **latch** the chance circuit.

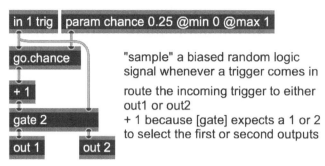

"sample" a biased random logic signal whenever a trigger comes in

route the incoming trigger to either out1 or out2

+ 1 because [gate] expects a 1 or 2 to select the first or second outputs

Random_bernoulli-gate.maxpat (and also go.bern.gendsp)

Random periods

Another way to generate sporadic events from a phasor-driven latch is to feed back the random sampling into the **phasor**'s own frequency. Every time the **phasor** operator ramp completes, a new frequency is sampled and held for the duration of the next **phasor** ramp.

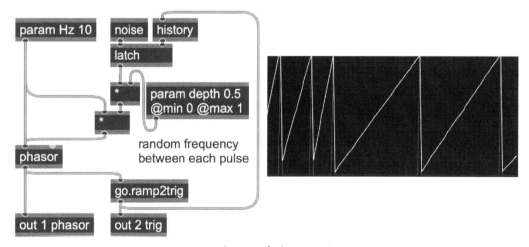

random_periods.maxpat

Here we use a **latch** operator to sample a bipolar **noise** (-1.0 to 1.0) output whenever the phasor wraps. We scale this range down by a **param depth**, then scale it up to the range of the **param Hz** to get our randomized frequency deviation. Both this computed deviation and the original **param Hz** signal are patched into the **phasor** operator's frequency input, which effectively adds them together. So, if the **param depth** is zero, this will output a steady phasor at 10Hz; if the depth is 0.1, it might vary between 9Hz and 11Hz; if the depth is 1.0, it could vary between 0Hz and 20Hz.

A classic application of random periods in modular synthesis is a "Krell patch", which at its core is a sequence of enveloped sounds, where at the start of each envelope the patch selects not only a random duration, but also a random pitch and other parameters of the next sound. To do this we could take our random ramps and shape them into envelopes using unit shapers, and synchronize other latched random processes to the same **go.ramp2trig**.

Random distributions

The distribution of a random source describes how likely each particular possible outcome is relative to another. For the **noise** operator's white noise output, all values are equally likely, so the distribution is called *flat* or *even*. We can make this distribution uneven or biased by applying different functions or curvatures to the output of the **noise** operator.

For example, if we feed the **noise** through an **abs** operator to make it unipolar, we can then feed that through any of our **go.unit** shapers from the last chapter to create a new distribution. Or more simply, if we multiply the **noise** by itself, which is to say, raise it to a power of 2, it will bias the distribution toward numbers closer to zero. (For example, 0.5 * 0.5 = 0.25, and 0.1 * 0.1 = 0.01; which is to say, the tendency of a power-of-two distribution on values between 0.0 and 1.0 is to make them smaller.)

One of the most important distributions in probability and statistics is (perhaps confusingly) called the "normal" distribution, and also the "Gaussian" or "Gauss-Laplace" distribution. It is one of the most widely measured distributions observed in the sciences, including for example quantum harmonic oscillators, the scales of living tissues, educational testing scores, and so on.

The simplest method of approximating a Gaussian distribution is to take an average of several random samples, but this isn't very accurate. A much better approximation for likely similar CPU cost can be achieved using a variant of a spatial method called Box-Muller. This method generates random points in a polar 2D space with a log radial distance and returns the Cartesian X *and* Y coordinates as the outputs (so it actually generates a random pair of values). Both X and Y have very good normal distributions.

Here are the mathematical formulae we need:

```
R = sqrt(-1/4 * log(abs(noise())))
A = pi * noise()
X = R * sin(A)
Y = R * cos(A)
```

The last two lines of this are actually a regular polar-to-Cartesian conversion, which is available in gen~ as the **poltocar** operator, and we can patch up the rest using simple math operators. Since this is a really reusable circuit, we saved it in the book collection as the abstraction ***go.noise.normal.gendsp***.

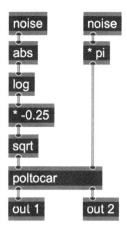

go.noise.normal.gendsp

You might have been tempted to think that changing a random distribution would also change the timbral spectrum or color of a noise algorithm. A good way to test this, and understand different distributions, is to plot them as a histogram. A histogram is simply a graph that shows how frequent (or likely) each possible output value is. The next patch shows histograms of even, exponential, and normal distributions we have encountered so far, along with a custom distribution through a **go.unit.arc** unit shaper.

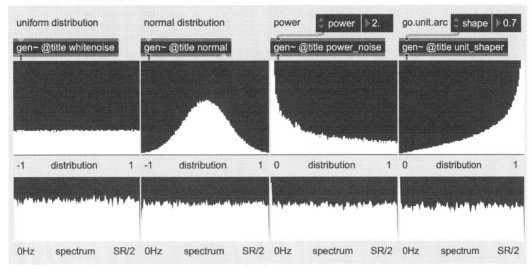

random_distributions.maxpat

As you can see in these graphs, although their distributions are all very different, their frequency spectra are all almost the same. That is, <u>the distribution (variations in amplitude) and the color (similarities over time) of noise can be quite independent of each other.</u>

Random walks in nature

Random walks are one of the most tried and tested methods of territory exploration found in natural systems (and they also occur in simpler physical systems such as Brownian motion). The method is simply put: at each step, turn a small randomly determined amount right or left, then move forward. Each forward movement is an *accumulation* or *integration of position*: take the current position, add the random deviation, and let that be the new position.

This is similar to the **drunk** object in Max or RNBO. The random walk (or drunkard's walk, as it is sometimes called) provides an interesting way to generate random outputs whose range is constrained with respect to the previous random value. That is, at each step, the output moves up or down a small, randomized amount. It is a form of counting (or *integration*) in which we *count by random steps.*

We can build a similar circuit in gen~, again using a **latch** to slow the process down to a desired step rate. Here the output of the **latch** is fed back through a **history** to **add** a new random value to it as the accumulator.

The random value is bipolar (so you can go up or down) but scaled down to some smaller *range* so that each step taken is relatively smaller.

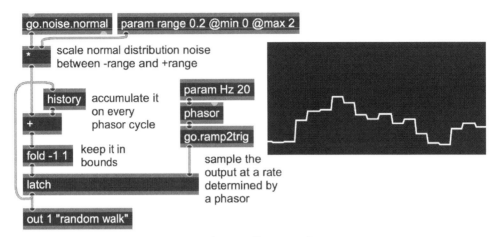

random_walks.maxpat

In the patch above, we also inserted a **fold -1 1** operator into this feedback loop to stop the accumulated value from getting too small or large.[4] We also used a normal distribution of noise rather than the raw **noise** operator, which provides a slightly more natural random walk as it is biased toward making more smaller steps and fewer larger steps.

This patch can also run at very high frequency rates. Try running it at 10,000Hz and listen to the output while playing with the range parameter. It sounds similar to a lowpass filter: the smaller the range parameter gets, the more filtered the noise output. As we explore in Chapter 7 (p. 159), there is a close relationship between the sizes of waveform steps (or steepness of their slopes) and the effects of lowpass filtering. A random walk circuit pairs well with interpolated smoothing for a very natural-sounding modulation source.

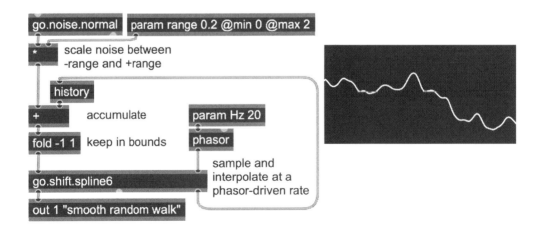

Random integers / quantized random

The **noise** operator generates values that can be any decimal value between -1.0 and 1.0. The **go.chance** circuit above quantized these values into either one or zero. We can also perform other kinds of quantization to limit the output to specific values.

For example, if you only want random whole numbers of 0, 1, 2, or 3, you can **scale** the raw noise to a 0.0 through 4.0 range (by sending through an **abs** and then a *** 4** operator) and then apply a **floor** operator to round down to the nearest whole number. Or, if you only want values of 0, ¼, ½, or ¾, you can then **div**ide the **floor**ed integer by four again. More generally, you can quantize unipolar noise to *any* choice of *N* subdivisions using a trio of operators to handle the quantization: *** N** > **floor** > **/ N**.

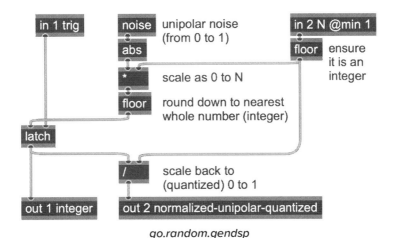

go.random.gendsp

We saw this multiply, floor, divide trio in Chapter 2 (p. 39) building the **go.ramp2steps** abstraction, and we'll see it again in Chapter 5 (p. 151) for pitch quantization purposes. Here is an example using **go.random** to generate dice rolls ten times per second:

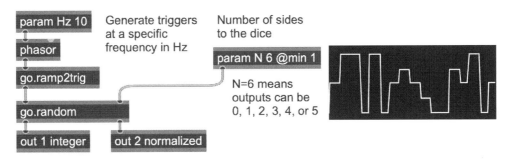

random_integer.maxpat

The urn model: pick a card, any card...

Let's continue with random integers by diving into a slightly more complicated algorithm that builds upon a few of the techniques we have found so far.

An interesting way to select random outputs from a finite set of possibilities uses what probability theorists call the Pólya urn model[5], where each iteration of the algorithm chooses a value that cannot be selected again until *all* options have been used once (at which point the process begins again). For our purposes, the "urned" output could be used for any kind of table lookup, pitch computation, rhythm subdivision, sample slice selection, etc.

Why is the urn model interesting? Well, for one thing, it ensures that every item is picked the same number of times, enforcing a fully even distribution even over short periods (whereas a random number generator with statistically even distribution in the long term might not be so even over short durations). As a musical reference, this was at least part of the inspiration for the twelve-tone technique of serialist composers a century ago: if all twelve notes of the chromatic scale are sounded as often as one another, they will prevent the emphasis of any one note, key, or other harmonic bias in particular, thus liberating composers from existing tonal traditions.

It is also one of the core methods of distributing events in many board and card games: "shuffle the pack." Let's imagine a deck of twelve cards, numbered 0 through 11, as a way to select pitches. The method is then a loop: The note we play is determined by the top card, which then goes on the discard pile. Once we have gone through all the cards, the discard pile becomes the new deck. The same pattern of numbers will repeat every time, creating a twelve-card (twelve-note) loop.

The *urn* method makes just one simple change: instead of always picking the top card on the deck, we randomly pick a card (any card) from somewhere in the deck. Everything else remains the same. Still, we play the note for that card and put it on the discard pile as before, and once the deck runs out, we simply turn over the discard pile as the new deck. The result is that, instead of repeating the same sequence every time, the sequence now has a random order each time, but each card still only comes up once.[6]

To construct this in gen~, we'll need to store the state of the deck (and discard pile), for which we can use a **data** operator. For a deck of twelve cards, we can use **data deck 12**. Each one of the twelve slots in this **data deck** operator should hold one card value: 0, 1, 2, 3, 4, 5, 6, 7, 8, 9, 10, or 11.

In the midst of a game, it could be laid out something like this:

	Discard pile				→		(top)	Remaining deck				(bottom)
Data index:	0	1	2	3		4	5	6	7	8	9	10	11
Initial:	0	1	2	3		4	5	6	7	8	9	10	11
Shuffled:	10	4	9	6		2	11	7	1	0	8	5	3

We need this deck to be set up when the patch loads, and we're going to use a **codebox** operator in this case since we'll need to do some procedural coding involving an **if** condition and a **for** loop.

```
                                              CodeBox
1 if (elapsed == 0) {
2     for (i=0; i<dim(deck); i+=1) {
3         poke(deck, i, i);
4     }
5 }

                                           data deck 8
```

initialize a deck with sorted card values of 0, 1, 2, 3, etc.

First, we want this to happen only once when the patch loads. Here we use a trick using the `elapsed` global variable, which always carries the number of sample frames of time that have elapsed since a patch loads. At the very first moment a patch is loaded, this value is zero. Then, on the next sample frame, it is one, and so on. Therefore, when using `if (elapsed == 0) { ... }`, any code between the { and the } will only run *once* when a patch is loaded. (Incidentally, like all global variables, `elapsed` is also available outside of a codebox as an **elapsed** operator.)

When this happens, we want to update each slot of the **data deck immediately**. Here we use a **for** loop to iterate over each slot in turn and run the same piece of code for each one of them. The **for** loop has a *loop counter variable* called `i`, which starts at 0 (`i=0`), continues while it is less than the deck length (`i<dim(deck)`), and increases by 1 for each iteration (`i+=1`).

On each iteration of this loop, `i` steps from 0, 1, 2, 3, and so on to the last iteration, where `i` equals 7. Each time, we use the **poke** operator to write a new value into the deck. In this case, we write the value `i` into the slot at position `i`, using **poke**(deck, i, i). And with that, our deck is initialized!

Note also that we used **dim**(deck) rather than simply "hard-coding" 8 here. That way, if we decide to change the size of the data deck at a later point, we don't need to rewrite this code.

Next, we want to step through this deck card by card. Drawing a new card would depend on receiving some kind of trigger. Here we can use a **go.zerox** abstraction to turn any rising-edge input signal into a single-sample impulse trigger.[7] If we feed this into a **counter**, where the counter's limit is set by the size of the deck, we will get an output step signal cycling through 0, 1, 2, etc., up to 7 and then looping back to 0 with each incoming impulse. This might be a useful signal outside of the current patch, so we route it to an **out 2**.

To quickly test whether everything we have done so far is working (a good habit to have!), we could hook up a **peek deck** operator to the step value and verify that it outputs the sequence 0, 1, 2, etc.

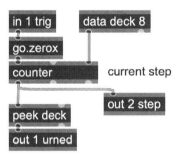

The current step value tells us how many cards we have gone through in the deck, which is the same as how many cards are on the discard pile (and is the position of the black column in the diagram a couple of pages ago). But we also want to know how many still remain in the deck, which is just the current step (discard pile size) **sub**tracted from the total number of cards.

We can now choose a random integer with the range of what remains using the same **noise**, **abs**, multiply (*), and **floor** method we saw earlier and adding (+) this to the current step to get a random index within the remaining deck.

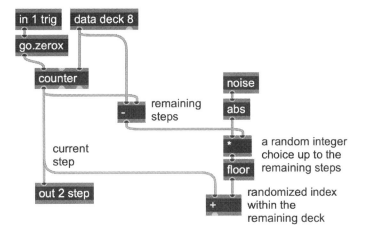

Now we have two indices into the **data**: the index of the current step (the current card) and the index to swap it with (a randomly chosen card in the remaining deck).

The swap should only happen when the clock ticks, not on every sample frame of passing time. That is, when a trigger is received, we draw a new card from the random location of the deck and hold that value until the next trigger. With visual patching here, we'd probably reach for a **latch** here, but since the swap will involve several operations, using a simple **latch** isn't ideal. Instead, we will turn to a **codebox** again to use an **if** block to control when a series of operations can take place (in this case, selecting and swapping a new card). We would like this card value to be remembered and continually output between each trigger, and anything remembered needs to be written into a **history**.

Let's start with the framework of code we'll need for this and look through each part in turn:

```
History held;

trig, step, swap = in1, in2, in3;

if (trig) {
        // things here happen only when in1 is nonzero
        // if in1 is a trig impulse signal, this is
        // only when it "fires"
        // here something will assign a new value to the "held" history
}

out1 = held;
```

First, in a codebox, **history** operators need to be declared <u>at the top of the code before</u> <u>any other instructions</u> since they are visible to all code and therefore must exist before any code can run. Such declarations are required to be capitalized as `History` (which has the benefit of making them more visible). These requirements are also true when we use `Param,` `Data`, and `Delay`.

Next, we declare the inputs to the codebox. In general, to connect a codebox with the surrounding patch, we need to use some inputs (using `in1, in2, in3`, etc.) and assign some outputs (using **out1** = 0; etc.). Simply mentioning `in3` in the code will give us a codebox with three inlets, and assigning to **out2** would give us two outlets. (Note that there is no text space between "`in`" and "`1`" here; "`in1`" is one word.) It's a good habit to plan to declare these in the codebox before writing other code, just as it is a good habit in patching to create the **in** and **out** (and **param** etc.) operators before patching up an algorithm. In our case, we need the trigger input, and we also need to feed both the current step and swap indices into the codebox. We also need one output at the end for the currently held card.

Between the inputs and outputs, we have our `if` block. An `if` block needs a logical condition to test to determine whether its block will run (if the condition is nonzero) or not (if the condition is zero). In this case, we use the incoming trigger as the condition so that the block of code it contains only runs per each incoming trigger tick.

So now all we need to do is fill out the body of this `if` block. The task here is to swap the cards at the step and swap indices. That means we need to read the data (using **peek**) to find out what each card value is and then write these values back to the data (using **poke**) with the indices swapped. Notice here that using a codebox operator also ensures that our reads and writes happen in the order we need them to:

```
// read both positions:
a = peek(deck, swap);
b = peek(deck, step);
// write them back, swapped:
poke(deck, a, step);
poke(deck, b, swap);
```

And finally, it's the card "a" at the random index that we actually chose, which the urn algorithm should output:

```
held = a;
```

Put all together:

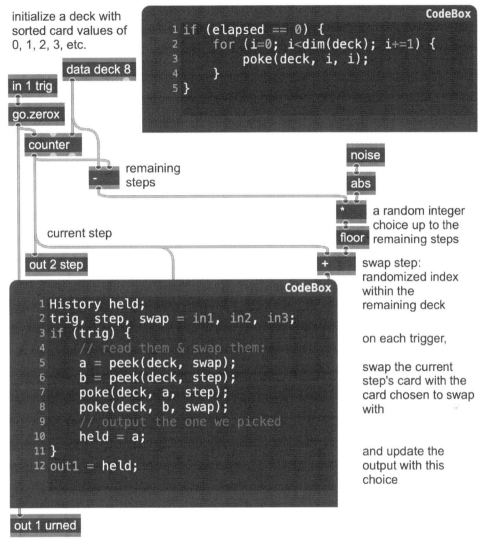

random_urn.maxpat

Here is an example trace of the output with the step signal (gray) against the current urn output (white) which plays every card exactly once:

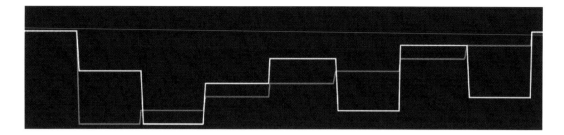

A more flexible urn

We can extend this patch a little further to get some very useful features.

For example, we can add a second trigger input to "reset" the **counter** back to zero (using the **counter's** 2nd inlet) so that we can synchronize the pattern with another clock.

We could also make the size of the deck be configurable as a **param**eter (up to some limit of the size of the **data** operator). That just means adding the **param** operator and using the parameter value instead of the **data** length. In that case, we probably also want to re-sort the deck when this parameter changes—which we easily can do by substituting our `elapsed() == 0` condition for a `change(len)` condition).

More interestingly, we could choose whether to perform the urn swap or simply continue looping an existing pattern according to a **param loop** control. If looping is enabled, we do not need to randomize the swap position or perform the swap. We can either bypass the swap code, in this case, using another **if** block, or we can simply set swap to equal step to achieve the same result with simpler patching.[8] This creates a quite performable tool: disable looping for a while until you find a pattern you like, then flip looping on to keep that pattern running for a while until you feel like you want it to change again.

We could even make this choice probabilistic using our earlier **go.chance** circuit; we can have the algorithm loop for, say, 90% of the time and swap cards 10% of the time for a more structured but still random variety. By setting the looping probability high, the loop will evolve very slowly. If you want to scramble the pattern, set the probability to zero. We'll encounter this kind of probabilistic evolution of a pattern again when we look at using shift registers as a way of creating sequences in Chapter 5 (p. 129).

Here are all of those changes made to our ***random_urn.maxpat*** patch:

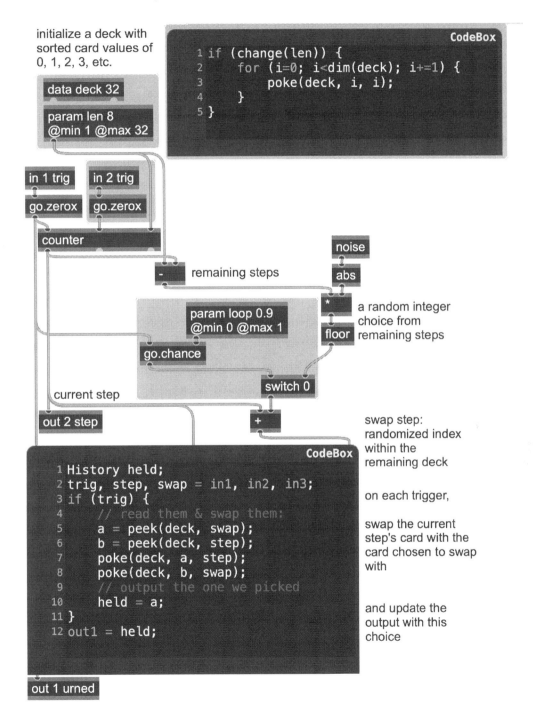

initialize a deck with sorted card values of 0, 1, 2, 3, etc.

```
CodeBox
1 if (change(len)) {
2     for (i=0; i<dim(deck); i+=1) {
3         poke(deck, i, i);
4     }
5 }
```

data deck 32

param len 8 @min 1 @max 32

in 1 trig   in 2 trig

go.zerox   go.zerox

counter

noise

-    remaining steps

abs

param loop 0.9 @min 0 @max 1

*   a random integer choice from

go.chance

floor   remaining steps

switch 0

current step

out 2 step

+

swap step: randomized index within the remaining deck

```
CodeBox
1 History held;
2 trig, step, swap = in1, in2, in3;
3 if (trig) {
4     // read them & swap them:
5     a = peek(deck, swap);
6     b = peek(deck, step);
7     poke(deck, a, step);
8     poke(deck, b, swap);
9     // output the one we picked
10    held = a;
11 }
12 out1 = held;
```

on each trigger,

swap the current step's card with the card chosen to swap with

and update the output with this choice

out 1 urned

Chaos (and why we like it)

Alongside stochastic sources, there's another category of functions that are of great use as an alternative for controlled unpredictability: *chaotic* equations.

The equations we're talking about when we use terms like *chaos* or *chaotic attractors* are not actually random at all. They are really a class of mathematical equations whose output over time is also quite deterministic but nevertheless unpredictable in a way that is different from the deterministic unpredictability of **noise**. A chaotic system's behavior can be very sensitive to its initial conditions, falling between one set of characteristic behaviors (one "attractor" or another). It might hold steady for a while in one such regime before suddenly switching to another. Or, more simply, it might seem to oscillate in a characteristic way but which nevertheless, unlike a typical periodic LFO, does not exactly ever repeat. It's all about sensitivity and variation.

When you think of music, it's easy to characterize it as starting with a simple unit - a motif or a timbre - that's transformed or distorted over time and perhaps then followed by some kind of return to the material it started with. Chaotic equations are a useful category of compositional or improvisational tools for creating such A-B-A* transitions in your work. The possibilities extend over a broad range of scales, from generating timbres at a very low level, up to phrases and on to larger formal kinds of organization. Chaos is one of the ways to ride that line between tedious repetition and incoherent randomness, which happens to be a line where the complexity, and the *useful* information content, increases.

A Lorenz attractor

Let's create a patch that enacts the Lorenz attractor[9] — a system of three equations used to develop a simplified model of atmospheric convection (this same set of equations also shows up in models of forward osmosis, brushless DC motors, and some chemical reactions).

Each of the three equations defines the changes of a single dimension, called the X, Y, and Z variables. Since these are equations of change, they are defined as the deltas (using the Greek letter "∂") of each dimension. On each step of passing time, this change (delta) is accumulated (integrated) onto the dimension's value. (So, again, this is a kind of counting!) The change is scaled by a ∂t ("delta-T") amount to indicate the rate of passing time. The resulting changes are added to the X, Y, and Z values and then stored to be used when the next cycle of the system is calculated.

So, in a way, each of these equations models a kind of motion, much like our random walks, ramps, and other accumulation-based algorithms throughout the book. What makes this system nonlinear is that each of these changes is dependent on the previous X, Y, and

Z outputs in a feedback loop, and what makes it chaotic emerges from the specific ways these feedback interdependencies cause unpredictable trends over time.

Our patch is composed of three basic sections:

1. The patching necessary to represent the calculation of the individual X, Y, and Z values.

2. The patching that stores and recalls the last iteration of the system and outputs the current X, Y, and Z results.

3. The patching that provides the representation of time used to increment the result of the current calculation.

Let's start with the three equations in the system. Here is the Lorenz equation in its basic form. It includes three parameters (a, b, and c, set to values of 10, 28, and 2.6667, respectively).

```
∂x/∂t = a * (y - x)

∂y/∂t = (x * (b - z)) - y

∂z/∂t = (x * y) - (c * z)
```

Since these dimensions of X, Y, and Z need to persist over time, we can declare them in a patch as **history** operators. The initial values for each of them are set to 1.0, so we declare them as **history x 1**, **history y 1**, and **history z 1**.

Although the Lorenz equations are defined as continuous differentials (∂x/∂t etc.), our patches are operating in a discrete sampled time in which each step is a finite difference of one sample-frame's duration. On each step, we compute the finite difference and scale it by some very small "dt" value. This small amount is then added and fed back to update the stored history value. As code, it could be written something like this:

```
x = x + dt * (a * (y - x))
y = y + dt * ((x * (b - z)) - y)
z = z + dt * ((x * y) - (c * z))
```

As a patch, it looks like this:

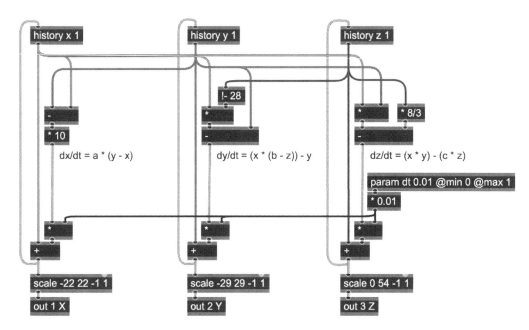

chaos_Lorenz.maxpat

The small dt we use as our time unit should be the same for all three calculations. Choosing a very small value for dt will output the results at a smooth and controllable rate, while increasing the dt value will bring the attractor code up to audible output rates, too. (But don't expect the resulting outputs at audio rate to be "in tune" with anything but themselves!) The **param dt 0.01 @min 0 @max 1** and *** 0.01** operator pair sets a reasonable range for the dt values.

We start at the top with the trio **history** operators, whose arguments set the initial X, Y, and Z values. (Using the **history** operator also gives us a way to restart the calculation by sending the message reset to the **gen~** object or override specific states by sending x, y, and z messages.) Those **history** operator values are used to calculate a single iteration of the equation. Each of these previous X, Y, and Z values then feeds into the equations for each dimension's *rate of change.* These delta values are then multiplied by the **dt** parameter to produce smaller and more controllable increments. These dt-scaled increments are then added to the previously stored X, Y, and Z values to compute the new X, Y, and Z values, which are output from the patch and also routed back to store into the **history** operators for the next iteration.

The ***chaos_Lorenz.maxpat*** patch shows the attractor in action, plotting each of the three dimensions over time and visualizing each pair of dimensions as a 2D Lissajous plot (which reveals the characteristic butterfly loop shapes).

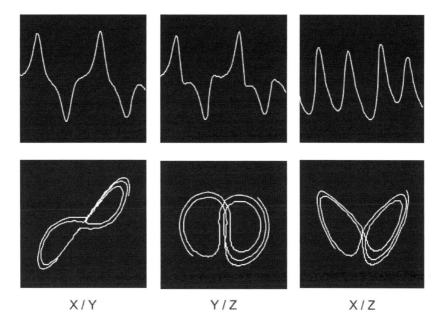

X / Y   Y / Z   X / Z

Over time, you can see some almost periodic motions (one cyclic attractor) punctuated by sudden swoops and dives into different periodic motions (another attractor). In the 2D plots, it is clearer how each cycle is slightly different to the previous one, even within a single attractor.

If you route one or more of the outputs to an audio output and increase the dt up to around 0.1, you might start to hear a low rumble. Keep going up, and you can hear a somewhat noisy, intermittent tone, or perhaps a complex of two noisy tones with sub-rhythms. (The scope view might look quite jagged, but this is just a limitation of the scope resolution.)

Finding the limits

One other little catch that we didn't mention yet: most chaotic equations operate over quite limited ranges of values and usually will need to be rescaled (using a **scale** operator, for example) for most useful applications. With the Lorenz equations, the X value ranges between around -22 to +22, the Y value between around -29 and +29, and the z value between around 0 and +54. So, in our patch, you may have noticed that we scaled our outputs to a normalized bipolar range (-1 to +1) using a **scale -22 22 -1 1**, **scale -29 29 -1 1**, and a **scale 0 54 -1 1**, respectively.

These ranges are often not published alongside the equations themselves, but we can find them out easily enough by keeping track of the attractor's minimum and maximum outputs over time. Here is a bit of patching to track the lowest and highest values of any incoming signal by looping **min** and **max** operators through **history** operators. We use a **switch** operator to initialize (and have the option to later reset) these minima and maxima with extreme cases, rather than zero, in order to catch signals that never swing positive or never swing negative at all.

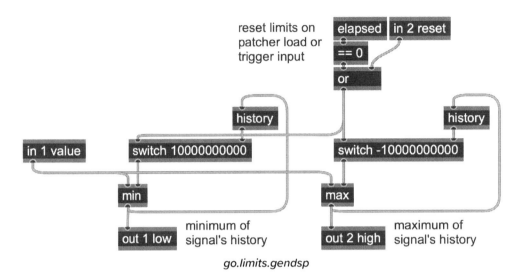

go.limits.gendsp

We can use this **go.limits** abstraction to find the highest and lowest values of each output of any signal's history. Better still, we can use these values with a **scale** operator to keep our output within a desired range (here specified to be bipolar by **param lo** and **param hi**).

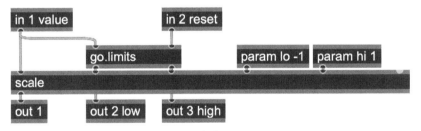

go.autolimit.gendsp

We can use this **go.autolimit** abstraction on each of the outputs from our Lorenz attractor equation to keep them in a normalized range.

For any specific chaotic equation, you could probably run the **go.limits** abstraction for a while and read off the reported low and high peak values from **number~** boxes in a Max or RNBO patch, and then write those values as constants into **scale** objects in your patch, just as we did for our Lorenz attractor earlier.

There's one other limit to watch out for. As you work with these chaotic attractor equations or port your own, you may notice that setting the dt parameter to larger values can sometimes make the attractor "blow up." That can halecause increasing the dt parameter is effectively decreasing the sampling resolution of the chaotic equation itself. This can cause bigger jumps along the function between each calculation that can lead to too much overshooting or undershooting of the curved function, as it is approximated by linear segments until it shoots off to infinity. That's the reason that nearly all the chaotic attractor code out there explicitly mentions what the dt parameter should be and the reason that we limit the dt param from going beyond a maximum value.

go.chaos

This book comes with a collection of patches modeling other chaotic attractor equations besides the Lorenz system, which you can use in your patching. You'll find many patches in the **examples** folder and also many **go.chaos** abstractions in the **patches** folder.

For example, here's the Liu Chen attractor from **go.chaos.liu_chen** with **go.autolimits** to keep it in bounds and an extra averaged output for a bonus signal:

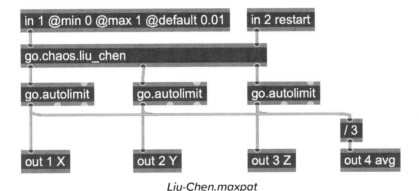

Liu-Chen.maxpat

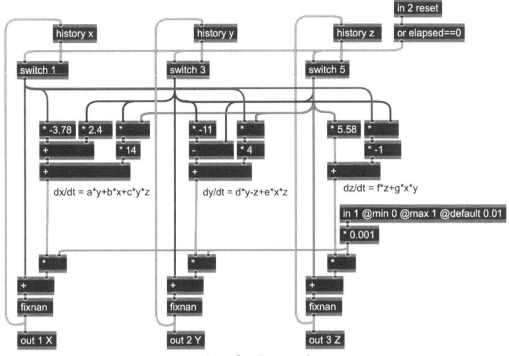

go.chaos.liu_chen.gendsp

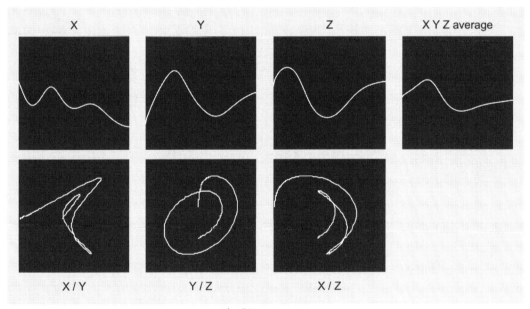

Liu-Chen.maxpat

Balancing order and unpredictability

Working with sources of noise, randomness and chaos is always a balancing act between unpredictability and control.

Unpredictable signals can sometimes seem too boisterous and take over the character of a sound, but there are many ways we can tame and gain control over them. We've seen how we can control the ranges, skews (distributions) and quantizations of random levels; as well as how sporadic sampling over time can reduce noise to timed chances and choices, which we can synchronize as desired. We have also seen how filtering, smoothing, and integration can soften noise and stepped into continuously wandering fluctuations (and shape the audio spectrum).

Conversely, we can use unpredictability to counteract the overabundance of control and stale repetition that digital processing offers by default. Adding a small amount of random walk, smoothed noise, or chaos to almost any parameter is a simple way bring an algorithm to life. Doing this to two copies of an algorithm can create compelling stereo space. Even mixing barely perceptible noise into audio can create a sense of natural air. Or at a slower rate, we can find evolution through occasional deviation such as the near-looping patterns of the urn model (and of the shift registers we'll see next chapter).

But before moving on, let's look at a couple more examples of balancing order and chaos.

Example: adding natural looseness to a tempo clock

Digital clock tempo sources are highly accurate, but sometimes this accuracy can come across as overly robotic or non-human. Aside from warping a ramp-based clock for swing as we saw in Chapter 3 (p. 58), we can also add micro-modulations to the ramp to reduce the robotic qualities of a rhythm through slight indeterminacies. Such deviations will also carry through to any other ramps derived from it.

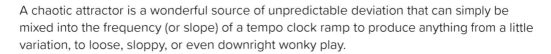

A chaotic attractor is a wonderful source of unpredictable deviation that can simply be mixed into the frequency (or slope) of a tempo clock ramp to produce anything from a little variation, to loose, sloppy, or even downright wonky play.

Here we used a Coullet attractor system, autolimited and scaled by a **param humanize** control, to disturb the slope of a ramp-based clock:

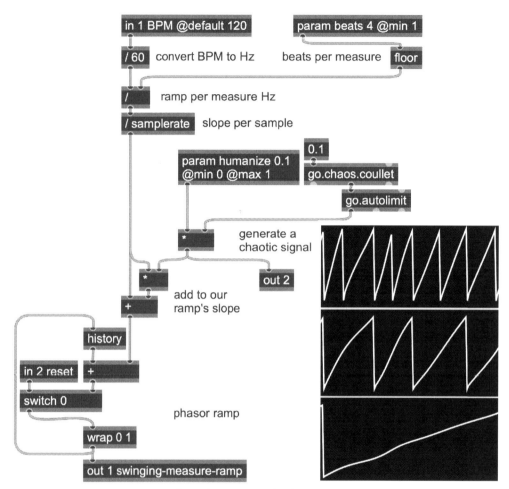

chaos.tempo.nonrobotic.maxpat

Example: injecting audio into chaos

After translating mathematical equations into patches, we can of course start to modify them to gain more control over them. For example, in this patcher, we added in operators to allow us to insert audio signals directly into the recirculating feedback loops, in order to sometimes drive the system away from its attractors.

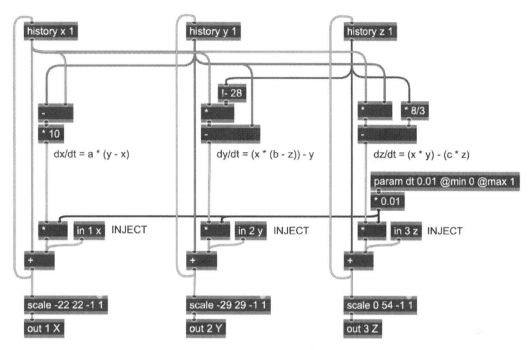

chaos_Lorenz_audioinjection.maxpat

Try mixing a sine or triangle wave into the **in 2 Y** input and vary the **param dt** to hear something like filter with noisy instabilities! The louder the input signal, the more it takes control.

Why not explore inserting other signal processes from elsewhere in this book into these feedback loops: perhaps a sigmoid waveshaper to control those blowups, or a smoothed bitcrusher to steer the attractors, perhaps a filter for extra ripple, perhaps a delay for strange harmonics. This kind of exploratory flexibility is part of what makes gen~ so valuable!

Chapter 5:
Stepping in Time and Space

In this chapter, we will look at stepped signals and how they can be used for sequences of pitches and rhythms. This isn't a chapter about how to play deliberately entered melodies, but rather an exploration of interesting methods to *generate* these kinds of patterns. Many well-loved sequencer circuits in the modular synthesis world can produce interesting rhythm and pitch sequences without ever having to enter a single note or step manually. Taking inspiration from these, we will look at ways to generate and transform interesting stepped patterns and how they can be used for pitches and other modulations of a sound.

Stepped pitches and logic gates

The way we think of sequencing is affected by our experience with music and the tools we use to make it. The realm of MIDI notes uses a paradigm inspired by pianos and Western music notation, in which variations of *pitch* and *dynamics* are synchronized together into a single message: much like a piano, a new pitch happens only when a new note begins. In the realm of modular synthesis, pitch and dynamics are typically represented as two independent signals, one for pitch and one for dynamics. Separating signals of pitch and dynamics allows their patterns to be defined independently, which, as we'll see, opens up some interesting possibilities for generating musical complexity.

For example, if we were to graph the pitches of a monophonic melody we're likely to get a stepped signal, where pitch values hold relatively steady for some duration and then jump to a new value for the next note, and so on (more or less).[1]

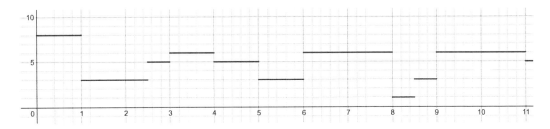

Most melodies don't sound continuously; there can be rests or silences between notes. Graphing out whether a note is sounding or not also results in a "logic" or "gate" signal, where the value may indicate a note playing (being "on") or a rest, where no note is playing (being "off").

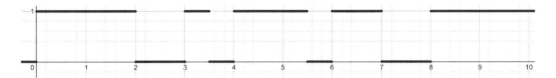

This kind of on/off logic signal is just about the simplest possible form of dynamics, but there's still quite a lot we can do with it.

Creating step patterns by mixing logic signals

One of the simplest tricks to generate melodies in the modular synthesis world is to feed a few different logic signals into a mixer. That means, building a stepped sequence pattern by adding a series of related logic gate patterns at different levels. In a sense, it is a bit like melodic transposition—temporarily shifting a pitch from one basis to another—but in this case, we build the entire melody out of multiple overlapping transpositions at once.

This simple method can produce quite complex melodic patterns, particularly when the gate patterns loop with different durations (when they are polyrhythmic or polymetric). Here is an example of three gate patterns at different levels on the left and the combined complex pattern on the right:

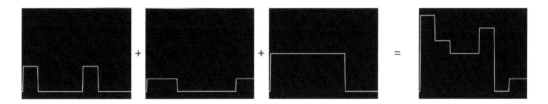

We saw in Chapter 2 (p. 46) how we can build related rhythms from a single ramp source (such as a **phasor** operator) with the **go.ramp.div** abstraction.

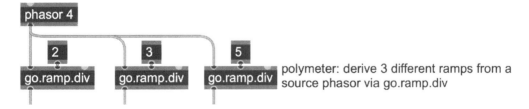

polymeter: derive 3 different ramps from a source phasor via go.ramp.div

The patch fragment above is an example driving 2nd, 3rd, and 5th divided ramps from a common **phasor** ramp clock. To turn these ramps into logic gate signals, we can use a comparator operator. For example, we can use a < (less than) operator to send a gate high for the first portion of a ramp:

derive gates from the ramps using a simple comparison. E.g., with "< 1/4" the gate will be on for the first quarter of the ramp

Each of the gate signals should then be multiplied (attenuated or amplified) by a specific parameter level, and the sequencer outputs the total sum of these scaled gate patterns as an evolving "melody". Here is all that put together:

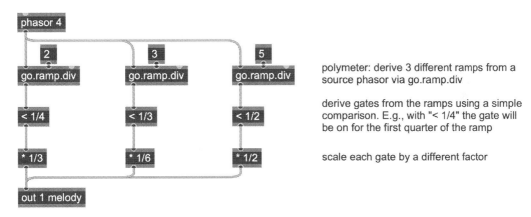

polymeter: derive 3 different ramps from a source phasor via go.ramp.div

derive gates from the ramps using a simple comparison. E.g., with "< 1/4" the gate will be on for the first quarter of the ramp

scale each gate by a different factor

mixer-sequencer.maxpat

In the ***mixer-sequencer.maxpat*** patch, we map the output as a pitch value to set the frequency of a sine oscillator, but—of course—it could be mapped to pretty much anything you like.

Sample and hold patterns

Another common technique for generating a stepped signal sequence is to route the output of an LFO, envelope generator, or noise source (or any other signal) through a *sample and hold* module clocked by some rhythm or meter. Despite the simplicity of this technique, the results are a great starting point for modulation and experimentation.

We can use the **latch** operator to sample and hold any signal value. The **latch** operator's left input is the signal to sample. The right input is a logic switch control which either allows the left input through to the output or *holds* the previous output constant. Any nonzero (true) value here will let the input signal through, while a zero (false) input value makes the **latch** continue to output the same value as it did on the previous sample frame. If the right control input is a trigger signal (i.e., mostly zero values with sparse single-sample spikes), then the **latch** operator acts just like a classic sample and hold module.

So, all we need to start constructing all kinds of interesting step sequencers is:

- A source to sample: some arbitrary curve, such as an LFO we created in Chapter 2 (p. 37).
- A rhythmic trigger sequence, such as we generated from ramps using **go.ramp2trig** in Chapter 2 (p. 43).
- A **latch** operator.

The ***latched-sequencer.maxpat*** patch shows a simple example: A phasor-driven LFO on the left producing a sine wave is latched by a different phasor-driven clock on the right.

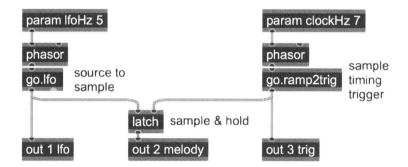

The output is shown in the following graph. The dashed line is the source (the **go.lfo** sine wave), the dotted line is the rhythmic trigger (the **go.ramp2trig** output), and the solid lines are the output values of the sample & hold **latch** operator.

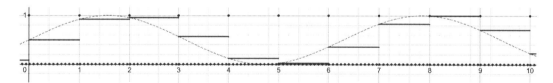

Try setting the LFO rate to some multiple of the clock rate. If the LFO rate divided by the clock rate is a simple ratio, it will produce a static repeating sequence.

In fact, the length of the resulting sequence will be equal to the denominator of the smallest whole number equivalent to the original ratio. For example: If the LFO rate is 42 Hz and the clock rate is 4 Hz, then the ratio is 42:4, which can be reduced to the ratio of 21:2. The denominator of this ratio is 2, and—as expected—the sequence repeats every two ticks of the clock. If you change the LFO rate to 43 Hz, the resulting ratio of 43:4 can't be reduced any further, so the sequence loop length is four steps.[2]

However, if the two rates do not easily reduce to a simple integer ratio, then their proportions are *inharmonic*, and the sequence will evolve over a very long time. It might have short repetitive fragments, but these fragments will seem to shift gradually in a way somewhat analogous to beat frequencies and musical phasing. These results can provide a rather interesting source of variety.

Note that the output of this sequencer can be any numeric value that the LFO (or another source) produces; you might want to quantize this into a set of specific pitches. We'll come back to pitch quantization toward the end of this chapter.

A shift register canon

We can expand this patch to create the signal equivalent of a musical round, or canon, by chaining two or more **latch** operators in series using history operators.

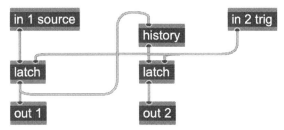

go.shiftregister2.gendsp

We saw some patching like this in Chapter 4 (p. 93), where we used a **latch**/**history** series to generate random signals that smoothly interpolate from older to newer values, and we called it a "shift register." That's just a technical name for a kind of sequence of stages, each of which stores a value passed down from the previous stage. Here is an 8-stage shift register:

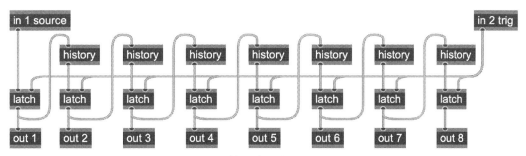

go.shiftregister8.gendsp

The layout of these stages resembles a "bucket brigade": at each step of a clock, the values are shuffled down one stage in the brigade, and a new value is inserted at the front. That is, on every trigger (nonzero value) received at **in 1**, the left-most **latch** (the one above **out 1**) will sample a new value from the input source at **in 2**. However, its previous value, which was cached by the next **history** operator, will be passed along to the second **latch** (the one above **out 2**). Similarly, the previous contents of *that* **latch** operator will be passed along to the latch above **out 3**, and so on, cascading down to the rightmost **latch**. As a result, an input trigger causes the values of *all* the **latch**es to shuffle one step to the right.

This is a general form of a shift register is also known as a FIFO—First In, First Out sequence—and thus is also a very simple kind of delay. The value sent from **out 8** will be the same as the value sent from **out 1**, but delayed by the amount of time it took for seven more triggers to be received at **in 1**.

That delay also makes this bit of patching a generally useful tool for any situation where we want to work with any prior values at a given clock rate. We can also use this algorithm as a general kind of stepped delay in situations where we want to duplicate delayed copies of a stepped sequence that we can route to different purposes. For example, we might route delayed pitch sequences to different oscillators to create musical canons or route modulation sequences to different filter cutoffs, amplitudes, and so on.

For the following patch, we feed a **go.shiftregister8** abstraction with a simple triangle wave LFO. The first stage of the shift register creates a pitch sequence by sampling and holding that input whenever the **go.ramp2trig** trigger fires. Each subsequent stage of the shift register creates a delayed copy of this pitch sequence.

To demonstrate the effect, the first and last stages are fed to oscillators (sounding like a canon or pseudo-delay effect) and visualized in scopes.

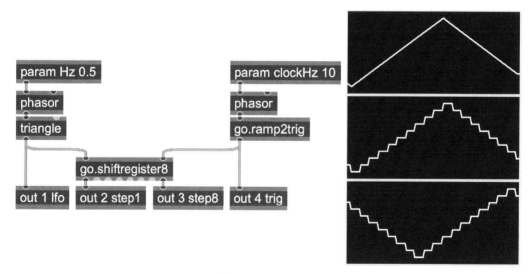

shift-register.maxpat

In the image above, the top scope shows the LFO waveform (the triangle wave at 0.5Hz) that is being fed into the **go.shiftregister8** abstraction. The middle scope shows the *first* stage of the shift register (the first **latch** operator), as it is clocked at a rate of 20Hz. (So far, this is much the same as we did for the sample and hold sequencer at the start of this chapter.) The bottom scope shows the output of the *final* stage of the shift register (the eighth **latch** operator), which is a copy of the first stage delayed by seven clock triggers.

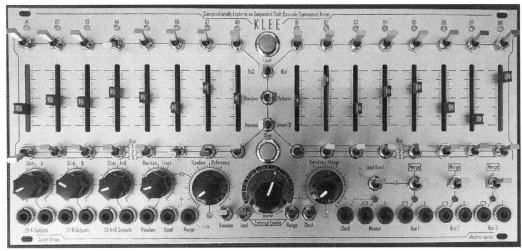

The Klee Sequencer; photo courtesy of Wiley Abt

Sequencing algorithms with binary shift registers

Shift registers also turn out to be at the heart of a number of popular and revered sequencing modules in the modular synthesis world — Scott Stite's Klee sequencer (pictured above), Ken Stone's Gated Comparator and Infinite Melody, Rob Hordijk's Rungler & Benjolin, Tom Whitwell's Turing Machine, and Mutable Instruments' Marbles, to name a few.[3] All these modules build their complexity out of shift registers.

In hardware, the equivalent of a **latch/history** operator chain circuit is sometimes called an *analog* shift register, since it can store and pass down any voltage value. A digital (or binary) shift register is even simpler since the values stored in each stage are only a single binary bit: either zero (false) or 1 (true). Most of the hardware shift-register sequencers we mentioned above are in fact digital shift registers.

All this means for our purposes here is that the input signal on the left should be a logic gate signal of either 0 or 1, such as is produced by any comparator operator. We could, for example, compare a **phasor** ramp against a threshold of 0.5 using a **< 0.5** operator for an alternating 0, 1, 0, etc. series.

That also means that the output of the latch stages are logical signals, either zero or one, which we can combine to produce interesting stepped signals. Just like the mixer-sequencer patch we saw in the first section of this chapter, we can multiply each of these logical signals by an arbitrary "weight" or voltage that is assigned to it, and the final output is produced by summing all of the weighted logic patterns together. In the ***shift-register-weighted.maxpat*** patch, we used an 8-channel **buffer** operator's channels to retrieve a unique weight for each stage:

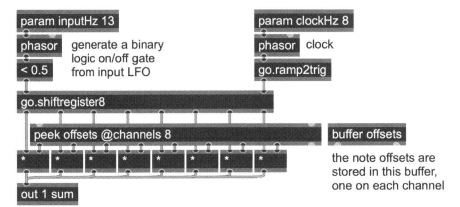

shift-register-weighted.maxpat

This technique can produce really complex sequences even if only a few steps have nonzero weights. Assigning negative weight values can make it even more interesting. As with the sample & hold sequencer, choosing a phasor frequency that is a simple multiple of the clock frequency will produce repeating cycles, but choosing a phasor frequency that is inharmonic to the clock rate will produce an evolving melody built out of common pitch offset fragments and motifs.[4] sAs an alternative, we could drive the shift register with a *probabilistic* gate input. For example, we could compare a **noise** source against a threshold **param**eter, just as we did with the **go.chance** abstraction in Chapter 4 (p. 96):

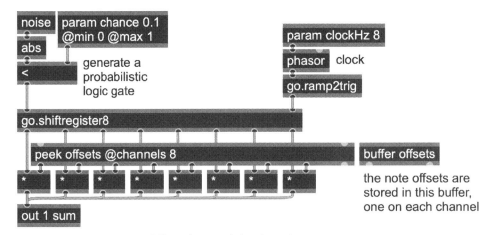

shift-register-weighted-random.maxpat

With a **param chance** probability of 0.0, you will hear a steady output at zero, as no data is flowing into the shift register. Raising **param chance** to 0.1, you will begin to hear a copy of the motif pattern stored in the buffer play through from time to time, and sometimes you will hear several of those motifs overlapping each other as a more complex phrase. Turning **param chance** up to 1.0 also produces a stable state, but this is because every single step is now overlaying the full motif. The most unpredictable patterns occur when **param chance** is at 0.5, with many random overlaps.

Looping

What if we heard a fragment of this random sequence that we like–can we modify the patch to keep a pattern looping, rather like we did for the Urn patch in the previous chapter (p. 104)? To keep any shift register looping forever, all we'd need to do is take the output of the final stage and feed it back to the input of the first stage. But then we'd lose the use of the original input, which we needed to get a pattern going in the first place!

One way we could solve this is to add some kind of switch to determine whether the shift register should use the live input or the looping feedback. We could even use a param chance operator and a random choice whether to loop or feed back.

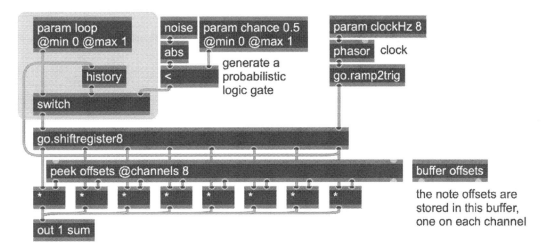

shift-register-weighted-random.maxpat

Evolving loops

If we did feed the last stage back, rather than just looping directly, we could feed it through some other logic operation to make the loop more complex. For example, if we use a **not** operator, the binary pattern will be inverted each time it passes through the loop, so we'll alternately play the pattern and then play back its logical inverse (effectively doubling the loop length).

Tom Whitwell's Turing Machine and Mutable Instruments' Marbles modules have a single parameter (called "déjà vu" on Marbles) that cleverly combines control over looping, inverting, and probabilistic choice. There's a quite neat trick we can do to our patch to achieve the same thing—and all it takes is adding an **xor** (exclusive or) operator!

What is an exclusive or? It is one of the most fundamental logic relations, along with **and** and **or**:

- The **and** operator returns true (1.0) only if <u>both</u> of its inputs are true (nonzero).
- The **or** operator returns true (1.0) if <u>either</u> of its inputs is true (nonzero).
- The **xor** operator returns true (1.0) if <u>only one</u> of its inputs is true (nonzero) and the other is false (zero).

Let's think about what happens if we feed our pattern back through the **xor** operator under different inputs, like this:

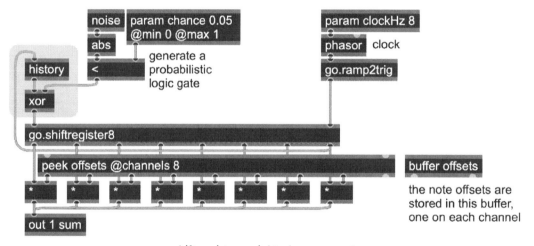

shift-register-weighted-xor.maxpat

Imagine we already have a pattern going, and we set our **param chance** to zero, meaning the input signal is also always zero (false). Wherever there is a 1.0 in the feedback signal, the **xor** will output 1.0; wherever there is a zero in the feedback signal, the **xor** will output 0.0. That is, with **param chance** set to zero, the **xor** output <u>copies</u> the feedback signal, and our pattern will repeat in a loop.

If we set our **param chance** to 1.0, then the input signal will always be 1.0 (true). Now, wherever there is a 1.0 in the feedback signal, the **xor** will output 0.0, and vice versa: the **xor** operator <u>inverts</u> the feedback signal! In this case the pattern plays a normal copy and then an inverted copy, for a total loop twice as long.

For any value of **param chance** between, we will have some probabilistic chance of either copying or inverting the pattern. Essentially, the param chance sets the probability of the next step inverting. If the **param chance** is exactly 0.5, where any step is equally likely to copy or invert, we will get an entirely random sequence.

So, with just one **xor** operator and a probability input, we've replicated the full set of random pattern looping capabilities. To summarize:

param chance	comparator output	**xor** output	**resulting pattern**
0.0	All 0s	Copy of feedback	The pattern loops
0.0 to 0.5	More 0s than 1s		Loop with chance of changing
0.5	Even mix of 0s and 1s	Even mix of 0.0's and 1.0s	Random gates
0.5 to 1.0	More 1s than 0s		Mostly inverting loop
1.0	All 1s	Inverted copy of feedback	Double-length loop

Using xor for pseudo-random sequences

Some interesting longer loops can also happen if we replace the probabilistic gate by feeding back another stage of the shift register to the **xor** operator instead. These kinds of circuits are called "linear feedback shift registers" (LFSRs).

For example, here's an example takomg the **xor** of the 3rd and 8th stages of our **go.shiftregister8**, which ends up creating a sequence that repeats every 217 steps! All it needs is one bit pushed in at the start to get it going, which we do in this patch using an **elapsed** and **== 0** pair of operators:

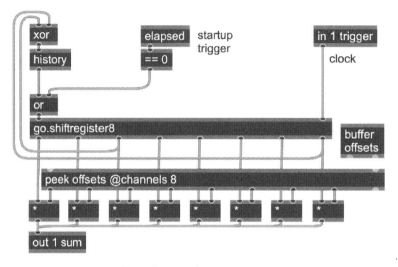

shift-register-weighted-xor.maxpat

Not every pair of outputs will give the same sequence length. For example, the **xor** of the 4th and 8th outputs has a sequence length of only 12 steps. Some combinations can give even longer outputs; for example, combining the 3rd, 5th, 6th and 8th outputs through **xor** operators (in any order) will give a sequence length of 255 steps; the longest possible sequence an 8-bit shift register can produce. Such "maximal length" sequences have a very even statistical distribution, and this makes them attractive as pseudo-random number generators. (In fact, the **noise** operator is based on a far more complex example of the same basic principle.[5])

The Buchla 266 Source of Uncertainty synthesizer module from the mid 1970's used a 6-stage digital shift register to produce pseudo-random signal sequences, including both a gaussian distribution by summing all the stages, as well as an even distribution through binary decoding, as described in the next section.

Binary decoding

Many of the hardware shift-register sequencers mentioned earlier don't even have control knobs for the mixer weights: instead, the weights of each stage are fed into a "digital-to-analog converter," or DAC, which produces a binary-encoded integer at the output. All this means is that we take each individual stage's value—which is either "on" (1) or "off" (0)—and multiply it by a corresponding power of 2 (2^0, 2^1, 2^2, 2^3, 2^4, etc.). So the weights start at

1 for the first stage, then 2 for the second stage, 4 for the third stage, then 8, 16, etc., and all of these results are added up for the output value. That is, a DAC is really nothing more than a special case of a mixer in which the mixer levels are a series of powers of two, and the mixer inputs are binary gates. Another name for that is a *binary decoder*.

Here is what our random looping shift register from the last section looks if we convert it to feed an 8-stage (or 8-bit) binary decoder:

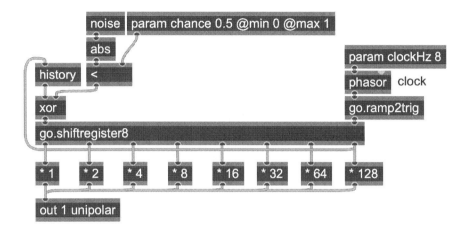

Since the shift register is being fed by a completely random input, you might expect that the output patterns are completely random too, but that's not quite the case. Interestingly, the nature of shifting the bits tends to produce a lot of ascending or descending series, as well as other recognizable motifs:

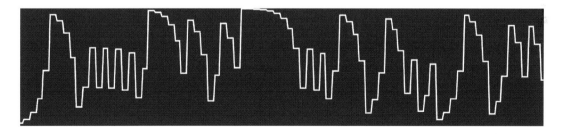

An 8-bit decoder can produce an integer output from 0 when all gates are zero, to 255, when all gates are 1. (That limit of 255 is in math terms, 2^8-1, or in code terms, $\exp2(8) - 1$.)

What can we do with this integer value? We could scale it down to a useful range by dividing the result by 255, which would give us a unipolar normalized signal in the range of 0.0 to 1.0. Or we could scale it to some other useful range using a **scale** operator, and quantize that to select from a set of pitches, for example.

Integers as patterns

This brings us to an important feature of binary encoding: every different possible sequence of bits (the pattern of gates) encodes a *unique* integer, and vice versa: every integer encodes a *unique* gate pattern. Put another way; both the binary gate pattern and integers are two representations of the same thing. That means that <u>the entire pattern can be represented as a single integer</u> at any time.

This suggests the idea that the same results could be produced just by a few operations on integer signals rather than shuffling gates through a series of shift registers. Rather than using a chain of **latch** and **history** operators, we could simply apply numeric operations on a single integer at each clock trigger. But which numeric operations?

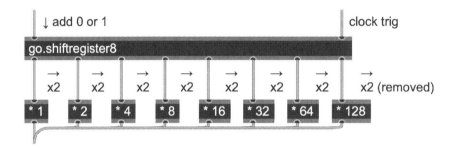

If you look at the 8-bit binary decoder patch again, you can see that every clock step shifts each gate one step to the right, which effectively doubles its contribution to the output. That's equivalent to multiplying the whole integer by two. The first step input then adds a new gate—either 0 or 1—to the sum. Finally, if the last step was 1, contributing 128, then its doubled contribution would be 256. But 256 is outside the range of 8 bits (0 to 255), so we can remove it simply by shifting our number back into the 0 to 255 range with a modulo remainder operation.

In this way, we can precisely replicate our shift register binary decoder with just five operators.

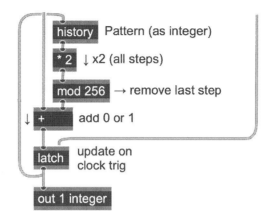

Here is what that means: For each clock trigger, we double the currently stored integer (equivalent to shifting the entire binary pattern right by 1 step); then add the new input (which is either zero or one), and then remove any surplus bits beyond stage 8 by using a **mod** operator to bring the integer value back into the 0 to 255 range.

Here is that circuit with an input source and clock added:

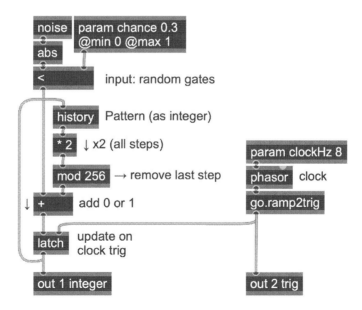

This isn't merely simpler to patch — it's more efficient, uses less memory, and is more flexible. For example, you can change the length of the loop simply by setting the value the **mod** operator uses to a different power of 2. To calculate what power of 2 you need for a specific pattern length (number of bits), you can use the **exp2** operator.

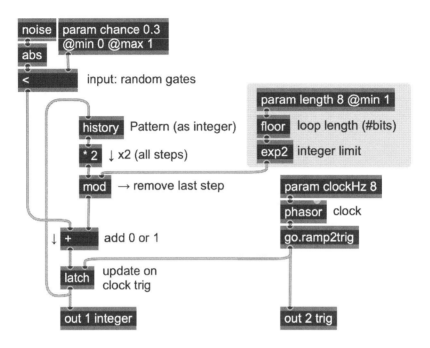

If the number of bits changes, this will also change how large the integer output can be. We could, however, normalize the output to a 0.0 to 1.0 range simply by dividing it by the limit value that the **exp2** operator computed for us.

We can also get the value of the last step just by testing whether the result of the * **2** operator is greater than or equal to this limit value and use this "overflow bit" to feed the looping **xor** operator circuit like before.

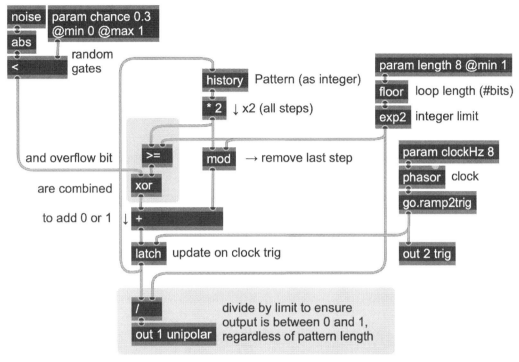

shift-register-integer.maxpat

Working with the bits of an integer

Shifting the bits one step to the right is far from the only thing we can do. Let's look at a few different operations we can apply to the integer and what they may be useful for.

Extracting the first bit: If you want to read off the first bit from any integer, all you have to do is get the modulo remainder by 2, using a **mod 2** operator. (Incidentally, this is also how we detect whether an integer is odd.)

Extracting all the bits: Perhaps we want all the individual stages to route into a mixer or to drive rhythmic elements. To pull out the 2nd bit, we can first shift the integer left one bit and then read off the first bit. We already saw that shifting right is like multiplying by two; shifting left is just the opposite, dividing by two. However, this can result in something that isn't an integer (e.g., 3/2 = 1.5). We can fix that back into an integer by passing the result through a **floor** operator to remove the fractional part, resulting in 1.

So, to break apart an integer into eight bits, then one way to do it is to shift left by one bit progressively (dividing by two and throwing away the fraction via the **floor** operator) and using a **mod 2** operator to extract the first bit of each.

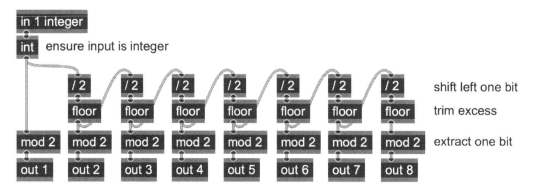

go.bit.unpack8.gendsp

Shifting N steps left or right: If you just want to right or left shift an integer by several steps, you can do it simply by multiplying by the corresponding power of 2. The effect of shifting N bits to the right is like multiplying by 2^N, and shifting N bits to the left is like multiplying by 2^{-N}, which is to say, dividing by 2^N. Again, we add a **floor** operator to ensure the result is still an integer.

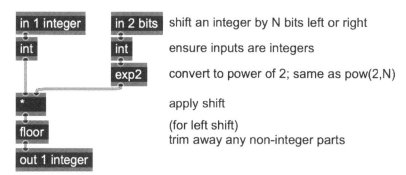

go.bit.shift.gendsp

A left shift can be used to reduce the *bit depth* of a sequence, as the left edge is trimmed away by the **floor** operator.

Limiting the total bits: We can also limit the bit depth of any integer just by trimming off the right end by removing any value greater than a certain limit using a **wrap** operator. For example, if we trim our number to 3 bits, then the limit is $\exp2(3) = 2^3 = 8$. That means we can represent any integer from 0 to 7 with only 3 bits, so a **wrap** operator with the upper bound of 8 does the job perfectly.

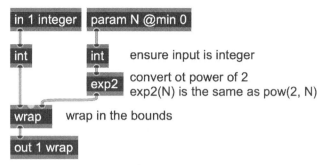

go.bit.wrap.gendsp

Extracting a subset of bits: We can combine these two operations to extract any subsequence of bits from an integer.

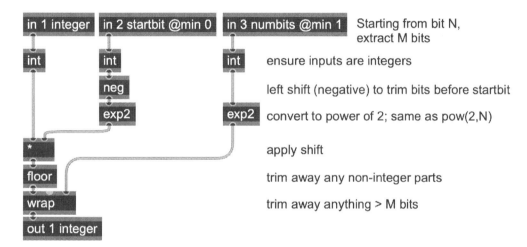

go.bit.extract.gendsp

If we are looking for a semitone pitch sequence, an 8-bit range of 0-255 is far too wide, but we could certainly work with smaller ranges simply by deriving our note values from a subsequence of fewer bits. Many of the hardware modules we mentioned earlier derive signals from just three bits in the register, which reduces the range to 8 distinct values since $2^3 = 8$. For example, that might work well to select from 8 values of a pre-defined pitch scale or to choose between 8 sub-slices of an audio file. Using the **go.bit.extract** abstraction, we could even pick out several different 3-bit subsequences from the same integer.

Rotating a bit sequence: Bit *rotation* is similar to shifting but without losing any information. Any bits shifted off the left end appear at the right, and vice versa. That is, bitwise rotation is another kind of modular arithmetic: shifting the bits around is a movement in a cyclic space. You just need to define our bit depth in order to know where the right-side end is. If you look carefully, you can see this is just another combination of a left shift and a bit depth wrap.

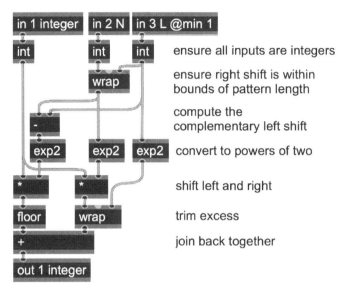

go.bit.rotate.gendsp

Understanding this operation opens up some amazing possibilities. You don't have to limit yourself to always stepping the sequence one stage to the right in each clock trigger; you can have the sequence run backward or shift in larger steps just by choosing the appropriate bit rotation and then replacing the very first bit with the new input to your sequence.

Inverting a bit sequence: We can also flip all the bits of an integer at once—so all the 1's become 0's and vice versa. If the integer has N bits, then the maximum value would be 2^N-1, and we can subtract from that maximum to get our inverted output.

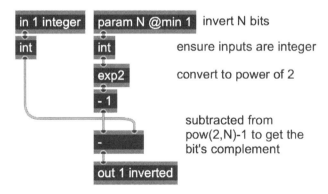

Taking this further: Combining a few of these bit operations, we can derive a wide range of related patterns. If you're familiar with serial composition and musical forms such as fugue, those techniques may spark some ideas for you. Additionally, since the entire state of the shift register we've been looking at is expressed as a single integer, we can easily store many different patterns and recall them again later using a **data** or **buffer** operator. We can also generate entire new patterns at once with a **go.random** abstraction. That means we can undo changes to a sequence we don't like, and we could explore mutations and crossovers for evolution between different stored sequences, for example.

Throughout this section, we have used a clock signal at a steady tempo to drive the shift register. However, this clock signal could also be replaced by a more patterned rhythm or something even more irregular. Let's have a look at patterned rhythms next!

Euclidean rhythms (digitized ratios)

In Chapter 2 (p. 29), we looked at metric musical time as a cyclic phenomenon, which we represented as unipolar ramps, and we explored ways of producing more interesting rhythms using modular arithmetic. Another example of modular arithmetic at work in rhythm is Euclid's algorithm for computing the greatest common divisor (GCD) of two whole numbers.

In 2004, Godfried Toussaint discovered that this method also happens to correspond to traditional rhythmic patterns of many musical cultures across the globe. In this rhythmic application, Euclid's algorithm effectively spaces a number of events as evenly as possible over a given duration of a fixed meter.

All of these rhythms can be specified by just three integers:

- **N** = pattern duration, in beats (the dividend)
- **K** = number of events (the divisor)
- **S** = offset where the first event starts (rotation)

Euclid's algorithm is a recursive procedure that requires a varying number of steps to be taken to compute the final pattern. This computation is also "outside of time" in the sense that it must generate the whole pattern at once rather than computing each step as needed. These factors make the algorithm itself less attractive for an "in-time" progressive computational context such as gen~.

We *could* write the Euclidean GCD algorithm using a **codebox** `for()` loop to implement the recursive operations, but there's a much simpler way of getting the same results. It's known as Bresenham's line algorithm, which has been widely used in computer graphics for calculating the rasterization of a line onto a grid of pixels. This also happens to result in the most balanced way of spacing transitions over a fixed distance. Not only is this computable without recursion, it's also "random-access"–you don't need to compute the entire pattern all at once just to get the value at a single point.

Here is an example that spaces 7 events across 16 spaces:

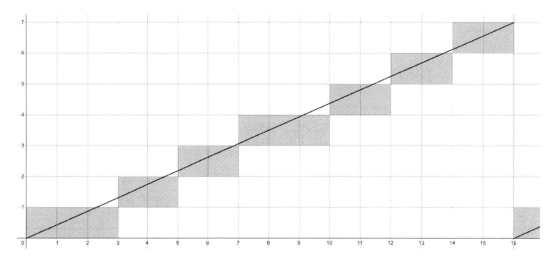

If we imagine a point walking from the start of the line to the end at a constant horizontal speed, we can make a few observations:

- Every column it passes represents one beat of the tempo. When it gets to the end of the line, it starts again at the beginning. So the number of columns (and the number of shaded pixels) is the loop length **N**=16, in beats.
- A cell is shaded if the line crosses the starting boundary of that cell. If we round the time down to the nearest integer column and round the height down to the nearest integer row, it will give us the shaded cell index.
- Every time the shaded cell moves up from one pixel row to another, we will trigger a sound event. So, the height of the line represents the number of sound events **K**=7.
- These two values determine the slope of the line as height/width or **K/N** taken together, which gives us the average rate of events.

To implement this we'll start with a step function aligned to the beat that counts from 0 to N. We can take a looping phasor, such as the ramp-per-measure produced by a **go.ramp.frombpm** abstraction, and simply multiply it by **N** (shown as a dotted line in the following graph), and then apply a **floor** operation to get the position of this line at the start of each beat (shown as a solid line in the following graph).

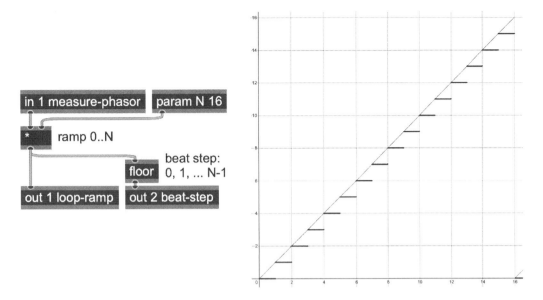

Next, we can apply the required slope K/N to this step signal simply by multiplying by K/N (shown as a dashed line in the following graph) and round that down using the **floor** operator to get the step signal that identifies the shaded pixels (shown as a solid line in the following graph).

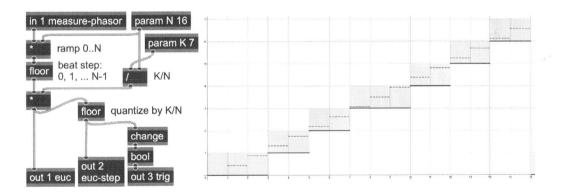

Euclidean Ramps

We can get Euclidean rhythm triggers from this step function by tracking when it changes using the **change** operator and getting positive-only triggers from that via the **bool** operator. But since we already saw in Chapter 2 how useful ramp-based rhythms can be, we'd like to make our Euclidean rhythm generator also produce ramps for each of the events. Then we could use it to drive any of the LFOs we created in Chapter 3 for Euclidean LFOs!

The first question is this: what do we need to do to our existing ramp to make it restart from zero at every new event? If we knew what beat the event starts on, it would be simple: just subtract that from the ramp! As it turns out, we can compute the start point of our quantized events simply by applying reverse transformations.

First, we must re-scale our event step pattern, which runs from 0 to K-1, back to the loop beat pattern, which runs from 0 to N-1. We can do that by dividing by K/N (dashed line in the following graph), but—as you can see—we may end up with some non-integer results. To fix that, we can apply a **ceil** operator to round to the nearest whole beat (shown as a solid line in the following graph). That gives us the start point of every event in beats, which we can subtract from the loop ramp to get a ramp per event (shown as a dotted line in the following graph).

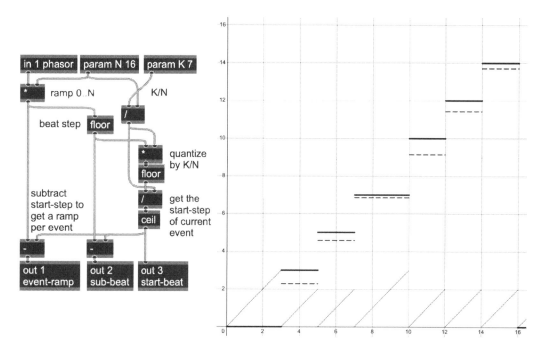

As you can see, these ramps are now aligned to the beats as we wanted, but unfortunately they are not normalized from 0.0 to 1.0 and thus may cause unwanted results with further ramp-based rhythm processing.

We could fix this if we knew not only when an event starts but also *how long it will last* (shown as a dotted line in the following graph), since dividing the ramp by this length would normalize the ramps (shown as a solid line below):

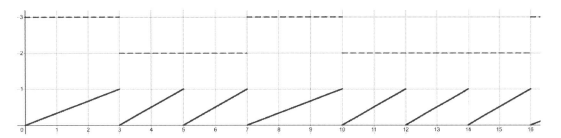

We can get the length of each event if we know when the subsequent event will happen, and computing their difference. To get the subsequent event, we can simply add one to our current position and apply the same division and **ceil** operations to compute the end point in beats. Then we can subtract the start and end points to get the length and divide by this to normalize the ramp:

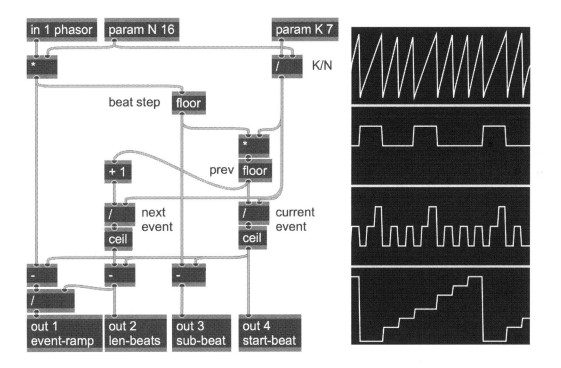

We are still missing the parameter **S** for setting the offset of the Euclidean pattern. This is easy to add: first subtract the offset **S** from the incoming ramp, then **wrap** back into the desired range of 0 to N. While we are refining this patch, let's also add some parameter handling, including using **latch** operators to sync our parameters to the beat and inserting **floor** operators to ensure the K, N, and S parameters are integers.

We might also want to work with polymetric loop lengths while still keeping our events on a constant tempo, which we could do in the same way as we did with the ***ramp.modulo.rhythm.maxpat*** patch in Chapter 2 (p. 50): by first multiplying by a beat division **param beats**, and then wrapping by our pattern length **N**.

Here's what all these additions look like:

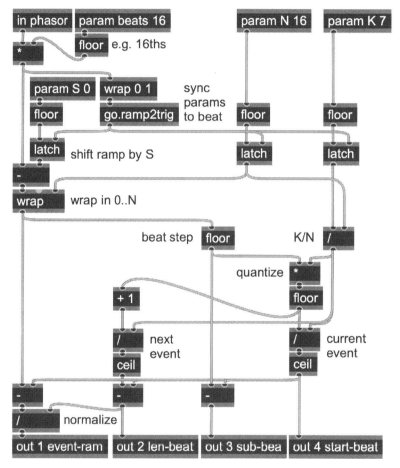

euclidean_rhythms.maxpat

Refinements

This is already a very useful Euclidean pattern generator, but we could think about extending some of the parameter handling further to make this patch more expressive. For example, we could extend the algorithm to handle negative values of K or N to run a pattern in reverse. This is actually quite simple:

- We use the **sign** operator to detect if K/N is negative and multiply our ramp by this sign accordingly.
- We use an **abs** operator after K/N for all other uses of it in the patch.

The *euclidean_rhythms.maxpat* patch shows an example of this.

Additionally, since the basic idea is to distribute a number of events (K) over a number of steps (N), then you would ordinarily expect K to be equal to or less than N. But that means that a "K" knob will have a certain range of travel (when K is greater than N) in which it doesn't do anything useful. Wouldn't it be more interesting to give the case where K > N a more meaningful or useful behavior? Here are some ideas:

- We could swap the values for K and N. So, for example, if N=4 and K=5, it would swap to K=4 and N=5, which is to say, we let $N=\max(K,N)$ and $K=\min(K, N)$. This is what the **go.ramp.euclidean** abstraction does.
- We could apply a **wrap** or **fold** operation to K by N. So, if N=4 and K=5, then K would be changed to 1 (via **wrap 0 N**) or to 3 (via **fold 0 N**).
- We could normalize our number of events in the range 0.0 to 1.0 as a "density" parameter and multiply this by N, and then **round** to the nearest integer to get the integer K value.
- We could ratchet (double-up) our steps. So, if N=4 and K=5, then every step would have an event, but one of those steps would have two events. First, we need to compute the required ratchet level R as the **ceil** of K/N, and then we use that number of steps to look ahead for our "next event" to compare with for the event length. Second, we determine the ratchet depth as $\exp2(R-1)$ so that we get double hits, then quadruple hits, etc., as R is 2, 3, and so on. The *euclidean_ratchets.maxpat* patch shows an example of this.

Once you get the hang of seeing the Euclidean rhythm generator as the rasterization of a straight line, another next step seems obvious: What if the line wasn't straight? As we saw in Chapter 3 (p. 58), we can warp a timing ramp to produce all kinds of different shuffles and swings. Warps and changes like these will also propagate through our Euclidean ramp generator perfectly—but so will more extreme shapings of ramps.

You could even run one Euclidean generator into another. For an example, see the *euclidean_LFO.maxpat* patch.

Pitch spaces

Modular arithmetic shows up in music in other places besides metric rhythms. In most musical traditions, pitch is also cyclic: a particular set of intervals (such as the pitch classes of A, B, C, etc. of a Western classical scale), is a kind of step pattern that repeats over each octave. So, we might expect to be able to apply similar kinds of step and ramp processing to pitch signals too. But before we dive into that, we should look at how we can represent pitch as a signal.

An octave is the interval between the first and second harmonic of an overtone series, which means the interval over which a frequency is multiplied by two. That means the frequency difference between octaves is larger at higher frequencies and smaller at lower frequencies. However, that's not usually how it seems to us as we hear it. As an instrument runs up through octaves, the distance between each subsequent octave sounds about the same. That is to say, we tend to hear octaves and other pitch intervals as steps of addition, not multiplication.

So, an octave is *exponential* in terms of frequency but can be seen as *linear* in terms of pitch.[6] Although most of our oscillators, filters, and so on are naturally parameterized by the exponential space of frequencies, there are a lot of musical advantages to working in a linear space of pitch. For example, pitch transpositions, chord inversions, and so on are all just simple additions and subtractions of numbers, no matter whether at low or high frequencies. And, as we shall see, working in linear scales of pitch can make quantization to scales very simple. For these reasons, we're going to look at working in a pitch space rather than frequency space.

There are several conventions for pitch space in use in software and hardware synthesizers. For example, the MIDI protocol borrows from the piano's Western 12-tone equal temperament (12-TET) system system in which the distance between any octave as an addition of 12 equally sized pitch steps, called semitones. Adding one to a MIDI note number means going up by one semitone; adding 12 means going up by one octave. We can convert between frequencies and semitones in gen~ easily thanks to the **mtof** and **ftom** operators, which convert from MIDI note numbers to frequency (Hz) representations, and vice versa. Note that the **mtof** and **ftom** operators work with any numeric value, not just whole numbers, so they will handle continuous glides and microtonal pitches if you want.

Another convention, more common to hardware modular synthesizers, works with the octave as the primary unit. In the "volt-per-octave" (or v/oct for short) convention, adding 1 volt to a signal means raising the pitch by 1 octave. This has the advantage that the integer part of a signal carries the octave register, while the fractional part of a signal carries the position within an octave, and it is less bound to a Western tradition. We are not dealing with electrical signal voltages in gen~, so we will simply refer to this representation as "octave" signals. The software with this book includes abstractions to convert between octave-based signals and MIDI or Hz representations: **go.octave2midi**, **go.midi2octave**, **go.octave2hz**, and **go.hz2octave**.

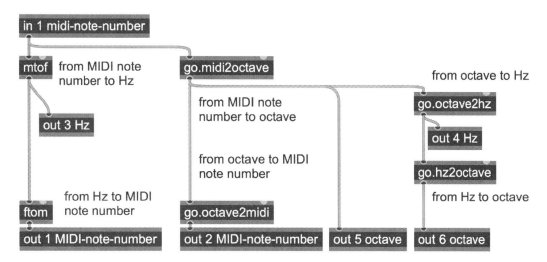

pitch.maxpat

(As an aside, we should note frequency can mean far more than pitch. For example, in Chapter 2 we saw how to express rhythmic frequencies in terms of beats per minute BPM (p. 28 and p. 37). We encounter the notion of a normalized frequency or "slope" (equal to a phasor's increment per sample) throughout this book, especially when creating oscillators.[7] We can also think about frequency in terms of its period, or the duration of one repetition, which is simply the reciprocal (**!/ 1**) of the frequency.[8] And for probabilistic processes frequency can mean a "chance per sample", where a frequency of 0.1 (e.g. as a parameter for a **go.chance** abstraction, see p. 96) means there is a 1 in 10 chance of an event firing on each sample, leading to an average density of 10%.)

Quantization

To quantize a MIDI note signal to the nearest 12-TET semitone, we can just round to the nearest whole number using a **floor**, **ceil**, or **round** operator. (Remember, the **floor** operator rounds down, the **ceil** operator rounds up, and the **round** operator rounds to the nearest whole number.) For an octave pitch signal, we can do the same, but we need to first project into a semitone space by multiplying by 12, where we can apply the rounding and then divide by 12 to return to our original octave-based pitch space.

If we wanted to apply a transposition or key change, we could simply add an integer bias while working in N-space.

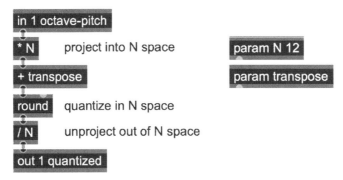

pitch-quantized.maxpat

This technique will work for *any* equal temperament base N, not just 12-tone equal temperament.

Euclidean patterns of length 12 produce common scales

Here is where things get interesting: if you quantize to one domain first (we'll call it K), and then to another finer domain (which we'll call N, where N is greater than K), you achieve exactly the same result as if you'd rasterized to the grid of KxN. Just as with the Euclidean rhythms, this quantization will align exactly to a grid of length N and will distribute K points as evenly as it can across it.

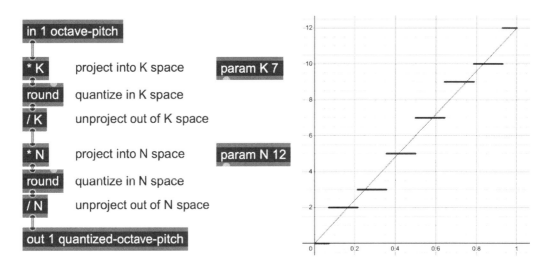

Remarkably, the same Euclidean rasterization algorithm we used before for rhythms can also be used to produce a variety of pitch scales common to many Western musical traditions. All you do is to set the number of divisions **N** to be equal to 12. In the Euclidean rhythms patch that corresponded to 12 beats per loop; in pitch space, it corresponds to the number of semitone pitches in an equal tempered octave. Here are a few of the distributions for different K values when N=12:

K	Scales produced
1	Octaves only
2	Octaves and tritone
4	Major 3rds
5	Classical pentatonic modes
6	Whole tone scale
7	Major and natural minor diatonic scales
8	Octatonic / Diminished scale

Moreover, where we can add an offset S to "rotate" the rhythm for Euclidean rhythms, here you can insert an addition in "N-space" here for key transpositions and in "K-space" for scale/chord inversions.

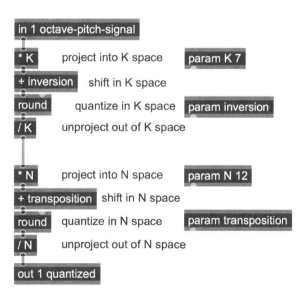

And if you can feed this patch with a ramp function or a triangle, you'll get an arpeggiator.

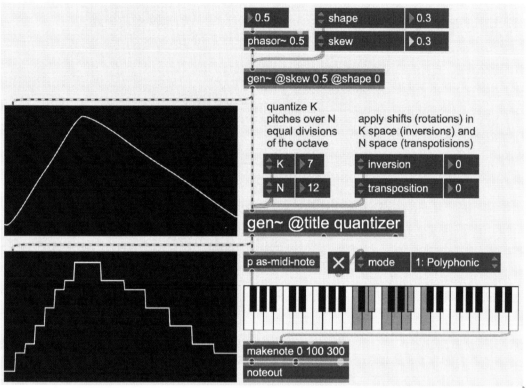

quantizing-pitch.maxpat

The space between notes

Some quantizers have useful trigger outputs to mark whenever the quantized pitch changes. We could do this by looking for a **change** in the output of the **round** operator, but—as usual—we think it is more interesting to output a unipolar ramp signal to tell you where you are between one note and the next, like this:

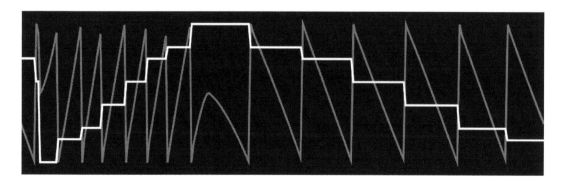

To do this, we can simply look at the difference (by subtraction) between the input and output of the **round** operator. That will begin at -0.5 as we enter a new note from below, and will rise to +0.5 just as we are about to leave the note from above. If we just add 0.5 to this difference, we will get a unipolar ramp running from 0.0 to 1.0 between each note as we rise (or from 1.0 to 0.0 as we fall).

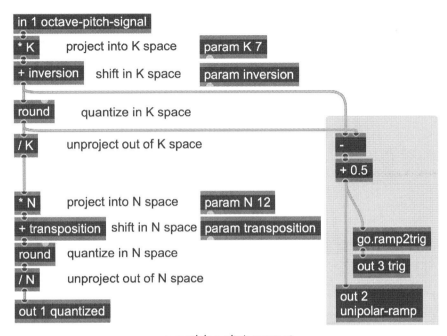

quantizing-pitch.maxpat

We can derive triggers from this, as usual, using a **go.ramp2trig** abstraction, or apply any other kinds of ramp shaping we like.

Smooth-stepped quantization

A really useful variant of this is to soften the edges between each quantization step to create subtle glides rather than sudden leaps between notes. A neat way to do this is to crossfade between the quantized and unquantized versions of the input signal using a **mix** operator.

All we need to do to make the smooth glides is set the amount of crossfade applied according to how similar the quantized and unquantized pitches are. So, when they are similar, it snaps more to the quantized value; but when they are not as close, it blends more toward the original source pitch.[9]

The **absdiff** operator gives us a very simple measure of similarity (it subtracts the two inputs to get the difference, then tells you only the absolute magnitude, so the output is always positive). That difference will be 0.5 at most when the original signal is halfway between two quantized points, so we can multiply by 2 to get a range of 0.0 to 1.0 needed to drive the **mix** operator.

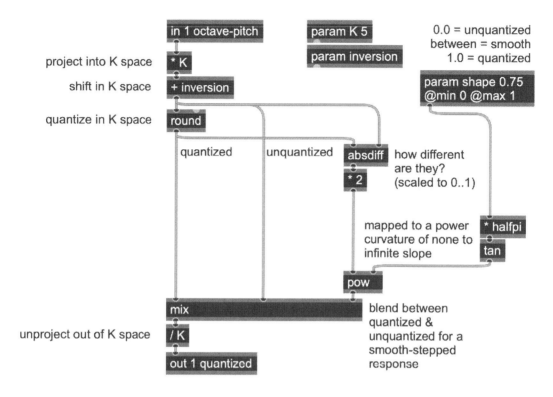

This effectively turns the sharp divisions between quantized levels into smoother glides. You might want to compare this to the pitch glides we encountered in Chapter 3 (p. 76).

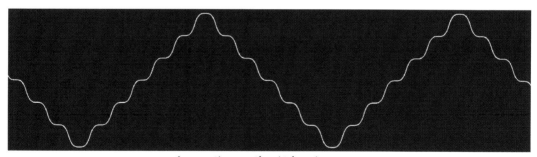

A smooth-quantized triangle wave.

Here is that patch adapted for scale-based quantization with K and N:

```
in 1 octave-pitch    param K 5       param inversion
  |                  param N 12       param transposition
* K
  |
+ inversion                                         param shape 0.75
  |                                                 @min 0 @max 1
round    quantized    unquantized
  |                                  difference
                                     between
/ K              / K          absdiff quantized and
  |               |            |      unquantized,
                              * 2     as 0.0 to 1.0
                                                    * halfpi
* N              * N           mapped to a power
  |               |            curvature of none   tan
+ transposition  + transposition  to infinite slope
  |               |
round                         pow
  |
mix
  |
/ N          blend between quantized & unquantized
  |          for a smooth-stepped response
out 1 quantized
```

quantizing-pitch-smoothed.maxpat

Quantization as a timbral shaper

The sequence of operations of *multiplying by N, rounding, and dividing by N* is useful for any kind of quantization purposes, not just pitch! It is another example of the old trick of converting a problem into a more conducive domain where applying our desired changes is easier, and then converting back to our original domain. In fact, we already used this technique earlier in this book to convert tempo ramps to steps (p. 39) and generate random integers (p. 103), for example.

It can also usefully process audio signals too. Quantizing audio produces a so-called "bitcrusher" effect, which transforms all curves into stepped waves. What's interesting is that you aren't limited to only quantizing to integer values; you can quantize to fractional steps, too (i.e., N can be a fractional number). This is important as it allows you to continuously vary N over time, which smoothly changes the depth of the bitcrushing effect to produce sounds that might remind you of pulse-width modulation (PWM), wave folding, or hard sync. Also, comparably to waveshaping, the results are very sensitive to signal levels: however with quantized bitcrushing, quieter sounds will be more intensely affected than louder ones.

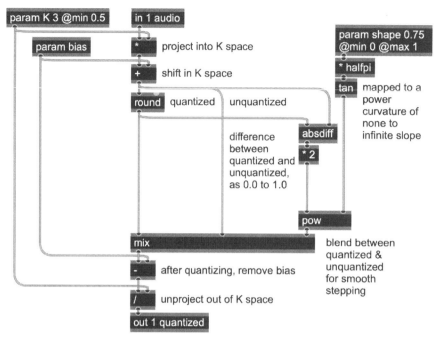

quantizing-audio-bitcrush.maxpat

In this patch, we incorporated the option of smoothing between the level changes, just as we did for the smoothed pitch quantizer. On audio, this acts as a crude lowpass filter and softens the harsher edges of the effect. You could try other unit shapers here too.

We also added the bias offset (just as we did for inversion/transposition in the pitch quantizer), but we are careful to reverse this bias after quantization to keep the audio centered around zero. The effect is more subtle at higher *N*, but with lower *N* adds another timbral aspect (reminiscent of wave folding asymmetry). Modulation recommended!

In fact, slight low frequency modulation of all parameters can be quite rewarding. Since this algorithm is very cheap, try mixing and panning a few together with slightly different parameters for a rich spatialized drone (for an example, see the ***quantizing-audio-bitcrush-drone.maxpat*** patch).

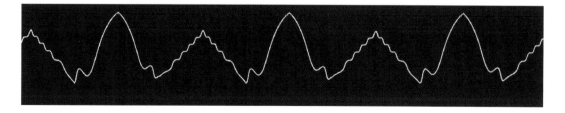

Chapter 6: Filters, Diagrams, and the Balance of Time

You can use gen~ to implement many varieties of audio filters. While there are a lot of examples of audio filters that are specified using mathematical formulae, audio filters are also often depicted using "block diagrams" in textbooks and research literature. In this section, we'll look at how to use those block diagrams to guide your patching and recreate them using standard gen~ operators. We'll also use these to dig a little deeper into understanding what's really going on with digital filters in the time domain.

One-pole lowpass filter

Let's start with a simple one-pole lowpass filter. Here is a typical block diagram for it:

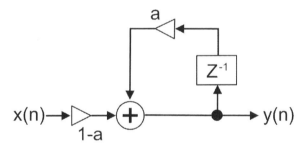

The block diagram is a kind of map of the flow of audio data through the filter from start to finish. The flow of data is from the left (starting at **x(n)**) to the right (ending with **y(n)**), with arrows also demonstrating the order in which calculations are done.

From blocks to operators

Implementing the filter from the block diagram is a matter of substituting the various graphic blocks with corresponding gen~ operators.

Here is what each one represents:

The "x(n)" represents the input signal sample value, which we can implement using the **in** operator.

The "y(n)" represents the output signal sample value, which we can implement using the **out** operator.

A circle with a plus sign (+) in it represents a point at which signals are summed together. Sometimes this is written with the Greek letter Sigma (Σ), but it means the same thing. In gen~, we can implement this with an add (+) operator or simply by routing two or more signals into any operator's inlet.

A Z^{-1} box is a convention used to represent single sample values. If Z^0 represents the signal's current sample value, then Z^{-1} is the previous sample value. In gen~, we can implement the "signal's previous sample" Z^{-1} operation using a **history** operator. (If the diagram uses Z^{-N}, this simply means the signal's value N sample frames ago, lh is a delay effect, and we can implement this using a **delay** operator.)

A triangle object represents an operation to multiply (amplify or attenuate) the input. It could be labeled with a numeric value, or the name of a parameter, or perhaps some mathematical expression of parameters. The block diagram at the start of this chapter contains two of them; one has a multiplier of "a," and the other has a multiplier of "1-a". In gen~, the operation of amplification/attenuation is a simple multiply (*) operator. The parameter can be replaced by a signal to its right inlet, for example, routed from a **param** object.

Turning Heads

Now we know what operators we'll use to patch our filter, how are they hooked together? In a 2014 SEAMUS workshop on physical modeling using gen~, Jon Christopher Nelson introduced a simple and elegant way to help translate a filter diagram to a gen~ patch, simply by rotating the block diagram 90 degrees clockwise. That simple transformation re-orients the diagram so that the information flows from top to bottom in a way that more closely resembles the flow of gen~ patching, making it more obvious how to wire them up. We'll do the same.

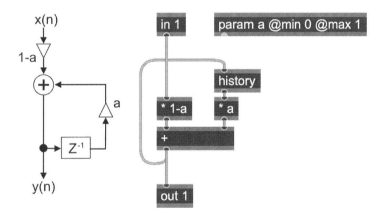

Note that since the two multply operators refer to the same "a" parameter, we just added one **param a** operator and then used its name in both of the multiply operators.

The one pole low pass filter is one of the simplest filters you can build, and we'll see in the next section how we can patch it even more simply, however we'll also see how it hides within it several fascinating implications. But first, what is it useful for?

You can use it to smooth out control parameters, add slide and glide to pitch changes, and so on, and it also works as a simple audio filter, though it is not particularly exciting: it has a very gentle -6db/octave slope — the gain drops by half (-6db) as the frequency is doubled (one octave higher). If you want a steeper slope, you could chain a few of these one pole filters in series (each processing the output of the last), but—as we shall see later in this chapter—other filter architectures can be more effective for this. The humble one-pole filter does have a particular advantage, however: it will never overshoot the target or wobble (it does not "ring").

When is a filter more than a filter?

Before we go further, we'd like to point out several intriguing ideas lurking in this simple patch. We're mentioning this here because we think it's useful to develop the habit of seeing how circuits can be understood in more than one way. In this case, our one-pole filter can also be understood as an *integrator*, an *averager*, and a *translator*; you'll see all three of these perspectives used throughout this book.

Integration: Let's start by considering this patch as an integrator — that is, something that adds up everything it receives. You can see this in the feedback path that goes from the output through the history operator and adds back to the input — it's similar to the integration that an **accum** operator does, as we saw in Chapter 2 (p. 319). The difference here is that this integrator is "leaky": the multiplier of "a" (which is less than one) means that each time the signal goes through the feedback loop, a little bit of its energy is lost (and the multiplier of "1-a", which is also less than one, means that a little bit of energy from the new input is also lost). That's why this is called a "leaky integrator." The smaller the value of "a" is, the more the integrator leaks.

Averaging: How does this patch represent averaging? The key lies in asking what you get when you average two signals, X and Y. You get a mix or crossfade that is halfway in between them. Normally we think of the average as $(X+Y)/2$, but there are a couple of other ways of expressing that expression:

$$X + 0.5*(Y - X) \qquad\qquad (0.5*X) + (0.5*Y)$$

Each of these three expressions works because both *X* and *Y* are given an equal weight of 0.5 each, and since 0.5 + 0.5 = 1.0, the total remains balanced. But these weights don't necessarily have to be the same. A "weighted average" changes the weight values, but it keeps them balanced so that the sum of both weights is still equal to 1.0. For example, if we used $0.8*X + 0.2*Y$, we have an average that is balanced (since 0.8 + 0.2 = 1.0) but weighted more toward *X* than toward *Y*. For a more general weighted average, we can express it in terms of a common factor, a. Here are two equivalent ways to write this mathematically:

$$X + a*(Y - X) \qquad\qquad (1-a)*X + (a)*Y$$

(as a line equation)   (as a weighted average)

The format on the left shows how this is a *linear* expression. if you imagine a straight line traveling from X to Y, then the "a" tells you how far you have traveled along that line. So, what this expression does is also called *linear* interpolation.

The format on the right is like a crossfader, where the variable *a* sets the crossfade amount. As we have seen earlier in the book, you can do this using the **mix** operator, whose inputs correspond to the values of X, Y, and a respectively.[1]

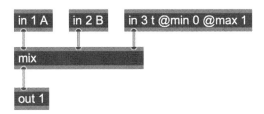

If you look at our one-pole filter patch again, you might notice that, at its heart, it has precisely the same weighted average expression as the **mix** operator, $(1-a)*X + (a)*Y$.

So, we can simply drop a **mix** operator in as a replacement, and the results of these patches will be exactly the same:

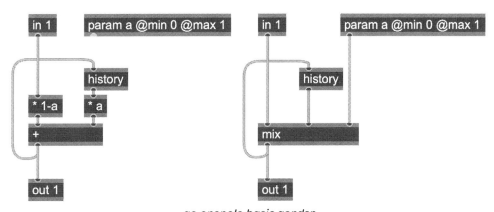

go.onepole.basic.gendsp

Seen in this way, what a one-pole lowpass filter is really doing is taking a weighted average between a signal and its own history, or equivalently, tracing a straight line from its history to its input!

Translation: Our final observation is that this circuit is also a *translator*. This is perhaps the least obvious aspect of the patch, but we can demonstrate it a little more clearly by rearranging our patch. Again, both versions are exactly equivalent:

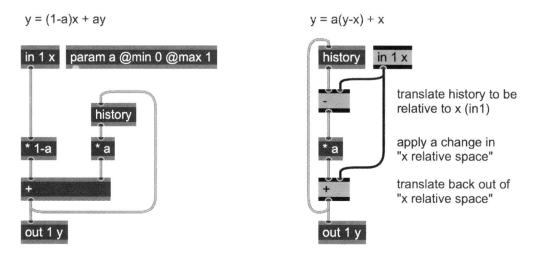

$y = (1-a)x + ay$

$y = a(y-x) + x$

in 1 x   param a @min 0 @max 1

history

history   in 1 x

* 1-a   * a

translate history to be relative to x (in1)

* a

apply a change in "x relative space"

+

translate back out of "x relative space"

out 1 y

out 1 y

With the re-arranged version on the right, we can see that the recirculating feedback from the **history** operator is first translated to be relative to the input (by subtracting the **in 1**), then transformed in this relative state (by multiplication with **param a**), and then "un-translated" back to a non-relativized state (by adding the **in 1** back again).

This technique of translating (or "projecting") a problem into a new space, applying a change more easily in this space, and then reversing the translation to return to the original space is a very general design pattern for solving problems, and we use it often in this book.[2] It is analogous to shifting a problem to a temporarily more convenient perspective; in the case of the one-pole filter above, we shift into a perspective that is relative to the input in order to make our **history** operator's feedback loop gradually minimize its difference from the input, and thus trend smoothly toward it. From this point of view, the signal at the **history** operator "wants" to get as close as it can to the signal at **in 1** but can only do so sluggishly.

Setting the frequency

Let's feed our one-pole filter with a slow pulse wave to see how it responds. The balance parameter needs to be just slightly less than 1.0 for the effect to be visible.

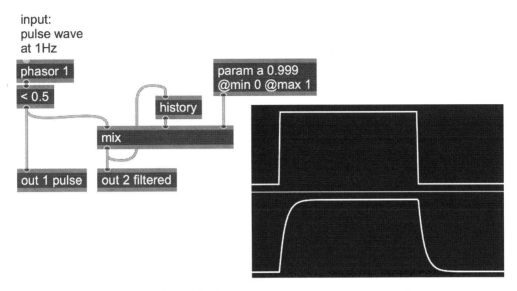

input:
pulse wave
at 1Hz

phasor 1

< 0.5

param a 0.999
@min 0 @max 1

history

mix

out 1 pulse

out 2 filtered

The top scope trace shows the original pulse wave, and the bottom scope trace shows the result of the mix operator with its own history.

So, over time, it smoothes the sharp edges, exponentially getting closer to the input signal. The filter coefficient (the 3rd input to the **mix** operator) determines how slowly or quickly it can do so. It's a kind of *adaptive average* of a signal, which tries to ignore any skittish divergences of the input and instead lazily focuses on following the signal's central trends. That's why we often use this kind of patch to smooth out noisy controls, such as removing clicks from sudden parameter changes and so on.

You might notice that the **param a** operator's setting is very sensitive: most of the interesting response is when the value is very close to 1.0. As it approaches 1.0, the curvature gets smoother and longer, and the sound output gets duller and darker. If **param a** is exactly 1.0, then we make no changes to our **history**, and the output holds constant forever. If **param a** is slightly below 1.0, then changes in the input will have only a tiny influence to pull the **history** this way and that; and only sustained changes (low frequencies) in the input will be able to significantly influence the **history** and the output. That is, in a lowpass filter the output is always trying to reach the input, and the **param** determines how slowly or quickly it can do so.

Thus **param a** determines what frequencies are slow enough to be followed by the **history** and thus pass through the filter mostly unchanged, versus what frequencies are too fast to be followed and thus lose power when passed through the filter. Typically, we express the balance point between these two regimes as the "cutoff frequency", which usually means the frequency which would lose half of its power (a loss of -3dB) when sent through the filter.

If you want to compute what the **mix** balance should be for a specific frequency cutoff frequency in Hz, you can use this calculation (first in math, then in code):

$$\text{balance} = e^{-2\pi\,|hz|\,/\,\text{samplerate}}$$

```
balance = exp(-twopi * abs(hz)/samplerate)
```

Here is how this looks as a patch (left), along with the resulting spectrum when filtering a white noise source (right):

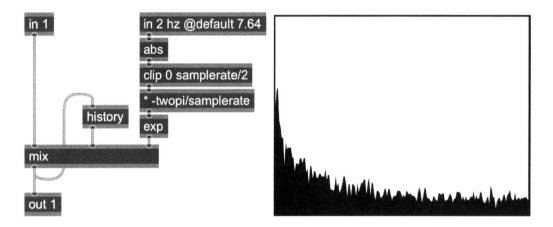

What's going on there? First, we take the absolute value of the cutoff value using the **abs** operator because negative frequencies should behave the same as positive frequencies (and otherwise, the **exp** operator's output will blow up). Then we added a **clip 0 samplerate/2** operator to keep the frequency within a range that the filter can reproduce. Then we divide the frequency by the **samplerate** to get a normalized frequency (between 0.0 and 1.0), and multiply by **twopi**, to get a normalized frequency in radians per sample frame (between 0.0 and **twopi**). That is, if this were a sinusoidal oscillator, this number is its angular rotation in radians per sample frame of real-time. Finally, this is made negative and passed through an exponential **exp** operator to balance the fact that a feedback loop will have an exponential decay: the longer the decay, the closer this exponent gets to 1.0.

Did you notice in that last example that we used an **in** operator rather than a **param** operator to set the frequency? While a **param** operator is a convenient way to explore a patch, it has a slight drawback when it comes to modulating a filter — changes to a **param** operator come from outside of gen~ and are updated at best only once per signal vector (i.e., the number of samples that Max or RNBO processes per object as its scheduler runs), rather than at the single sample rate that gen~ operators use. That difference may result in stepping, popping, or other filter glitching if you try to modulate it quickly. In most cases, filters behave better if their control parameters modulate smoothly. To be able to modulate with continuous audio rate signals, we replaced the **param** operator with an **in 2** operator, which responds at full sample rate. (Alternatively, you could add a smoothing filter to the parameter itself. That will smoothen the parameter but will also limit how quickly our filter can be modulated.)

Half-lives: setting a filter decay in seconds

There's another way we can set the response of the one-pole filter that is particularly useful when using the filter to smooth out low-frequency modulations and parameter controls: by setting the "response time" in seconds.

The one-pole lowpass filter has an exponential response: given a step input, it will output a curve that gets flatter and flatter as it approaches the target. This is called an exponential decay. These are reminiscent of many natural phenomena, including the typical responses of physical instruments. This stems from the unique nature of the mathematical function $y=e^x$ (represented in gen~ by the **exp** operator), defined as the function whose slope (i.e., its rate of change) is equal to y. That is, the slope of e^x is equal to the output of e^x. For example:

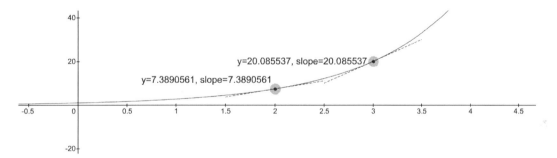

Any function whose growth rate is proportional to its size, as seen in population growth, compounded interest, etc., can be written as an exponential function of time multiplied by a growth constant. The growth constant identifies how sharply the exponential curve rises.

The same holds for systems showing exponential decay, except that the growth constant there is negative and identifies how sharply it falls. Here, for example, is e^{-x}:

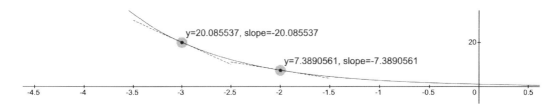

This sharpness of exponential decay is a kind of "characteristic time". Radioactive elements have a characteristic half-life, which is the amount of time by which 50% of a clump of that element will probably have decayed. Similarly, in audio, we can talk about the characteristic decay time of a reverberator, delay, or other resonator. A widely used measure for this is the T60 time, which is the time for an input signal to decay by -60db. Since every -6db halves the amplitude, -60db simply means a fall in amplitude of 2^{-10}, which is very nearly 0.001. Why this level? Because it is a convenient number that is close to a threshold of auditory perception.[3]

If you play a calculator game, starting with a value of 1.0, how many times can you multiply it by 0.5 until you get below 0.001? How many times if you multiply by 0.9? How many times if you multiply by 0.999? These decay multipliers (0.5, 0.9, 0.999) each specify a different T60 time in terms of the number of multiplications needed to reach 0.001. If we apply this multiplication once per sample frame (as we do in the one-pole filter), the number of multiplications equals the T60 time in sample frames.

In gen~, the **t60time** operator will tell you exactly how many of these multiplications (how many sample frames) a given decay multiplier will need to decay by -60db. The **t60** operator does the opposite: it will tell you what multiplier you need to decay by -60db over a given number of multiplications.[4] With this, we can create very natural decays with precisely specified durations.

And, it turns out, we can feed this directly into our mix & history one-pole filter.

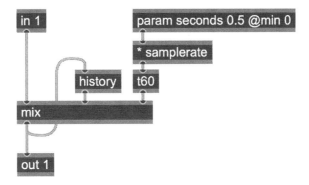

The one pole filter's exponential response can also create quite natural sounding envelopes. You might want to use different response times for rise and fall, depending on whether the envelope is rising or falling.

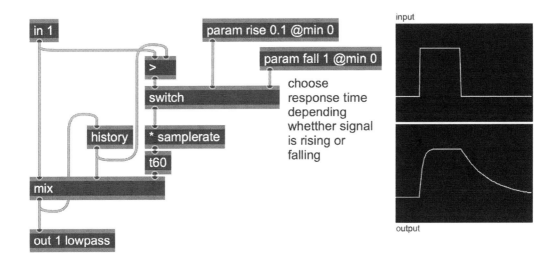

A lowpass gate (LPG)

Let's build on that last example to create a lowpass gate (LPG).[5] A lowpass gate is a particular kind of analog synthesizer circuit originating with the Buchla 200 modular synthesizer series that came to be highly regarded (and remains popular today) for its natural enveloping qualities.

Here, the envelope is not simply applied by amplifying and attenuating an audio input signal, but by opening and closing a lowpass filter according to a control signal:

- When the control signal is zero, the cutoff frequency of the filter is well below the audible frequency range, so no audio passes through the filter.
- As the control signal is increased above zero, the cutoff frequency rises into the audible range so that more of the audio at the input now passes through the filter.

Additionally, the Buchla design used a vactrol[6] to process the control signal input, which adds a characteristically gradual response: even using a sharp-edged logic gate signal to drive the lowpass gate will result in a smooth opening and a more gentle closing of the filter envelope. That smooth and nonlinear behavior makes a lowpass gate a good source for imitating the timbral changes of natural percussion sounds.

Our lowpass gate patch thus requires two basic components — the lowpass filter itself and some patching to emulate the behavior of a vactrol. Let's start with the vactrol emulation.

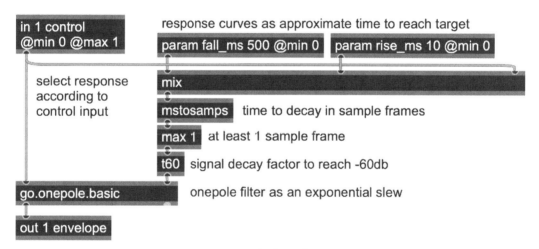

go.vactrol.gendsp

Two **param** operators set the response times in milliseconds for the extremes of the control input. The control value from the **in 1** operator is used with a **mix** operator to blend between these two response times; when the control is 1.0, we use the **param rise_ms** time, and when the control is 0.0, we use the **param fall_ms** time. For any intermediate control value, we use an intermediate response time. This is then converted to samples using an **mstosamps** operator and then processed through the **t60** operator we've just examined to set the signal decay coefficient (the time to reach -60dB) for a **go.onepole.basic** abstraction, whose job is to smoothen out the control signal for the vactrol output.

Here is the result of feeding some randomized gates (top scope) into the **go.vactrol** abstraction and the emulated vactrol's output (bottom scope):

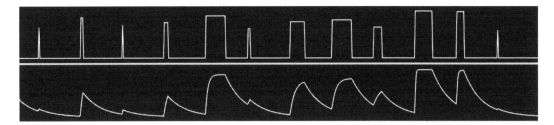

We can then use this vactrol output as an envelope to open and close a lowpass filter to complete the lowpass gate. For example, in the following patch, we use it to drive three onepole filters arranged in series so that the rather gentle -6db slope of a one-pole filter becomes a steeper -18db slope. We also used a **scale** operator to map the envelope shape to a more expressive frequency range.

The scope in the following image shows the effect of this lowpass gate on a square wave oscillator:

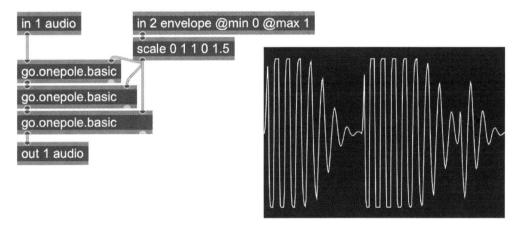

lowpass-gate.maxpat

There's no need to limit yourself to a simple lowpass gate emulation like this, of course. For a more interesting filter-based envelope, we can use a more interesting filter and more configurable control over the envelope response.

In the following patch, we used both lowpass and peak bandpass outputs of the **go.svf** trapezoidal state variable filter (which we will build later in this chapter) and added some additional parameters to control its response. (The **go.equalpower** abstraction is included to perform an energetically balanced mix between the two filtered signals, resulting in a more exaggerated response.)

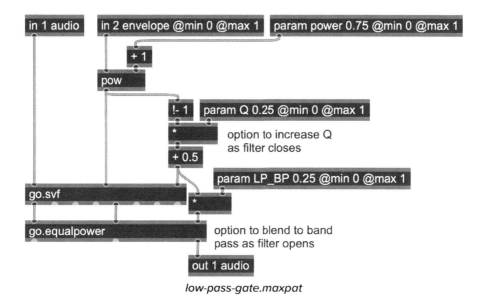

low-pass-gate.maxpat

A lowpass gives you a free highpass

Here is another trick: subtract the one pole's output from the original signal, and you get a complimentary highpass filter. If you think about it, by taking away a smoothed version from an input signal, the residual you are left with is all of the "non-smooth" differences; that is, the deviations away from its average.

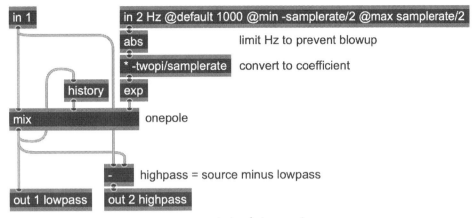

go.onepole.basic.hz.gendsp

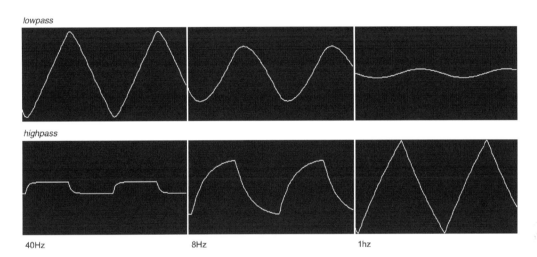

The images above show the effects of filtering an 8Hz triangle wave with the cutoff frequency at 40Hz (left), 8Hz (center), and 1Hz (right). The lowpass filter (top row) softens the signal, rounding its corners, while the highpass filter (bottom row) captures what was lost in that lowpass. Notice how in the 40Hz case (left), the highpass seems to represent the *slopes* of the original signal more than the signal itself. In the 8Hz case (center), both filtered signals are closer to representing the original waveform but notice how they are also shifted in time relative to the original signal.

In the 1Hz case (right), now the highpass most closely represents the original, with the lowpass capturing what was taken away. It makes sense: changing the filter frequency is changing the **mix** parameter, and that is changing the balance between the original signal and its changes in a **history** operator. (As we noted earlier, a lowpass filter approximates an integrator, and now we can see the highpass approximates a differentiator, where the filter coefficient sets up the balance between a signal and its changes.)[7]

A common use of this one-pole highpass filter is to recenter a signal around the zero line. Imagine you have a signal that has a continuous value of 0.5. The running average (lowpass filtered version) of this signal is, of course, 0.5, while the deviations from the average (highpass filtered version) of this signal are zero.

Whatever the input, a lowpass will try to recenter itself on the signal's average, whereas a highpass will try to recenter around zero. They will recenter gradually if the cutoff frequency is low or very quickly if the cutoff frequency is high. (This is also known as a DC blocking filter, where "DC" is short for "direct current," an analog electronics concept of any constant or extremely slowly changing offset that takes the signal average away from zero volts.)

It's especially important to apply DC-blocking highpass filtering in a feedback delay line or reverb algorithm. Otherwise, the delay can build up any low frequency or constant components until it saturates well beyond acceptable signal amplitudes! We'll see this again as we build physical models in Chapter 7 (p. 218) and frequency modulation in Chapter 8 (p. 254). This routine is so useful that there's a built-in operator specifically for this purpose: **dcblock**. The **dcblock** operator is a highpass filter below 3Hz.

Allpass filters

Our next block diagram example is an allpass filter. Allpass filters pass all frequencies evenly, which means that they don't shape the frequency spectrum of a sound at all: by itself, the output will sound essentially the same as the input. So how is an allpass filter useful?

What an allpass filter does is to *delay* different parts of the frequency spectrum by different amounts, which can create differences in *phase*. Normally, we can't directly hear phase changes, but we can when they are mixed with other versions of the original signal. For example, we'll see that if you mix the result of a chain of allpass filters back with the raw input, you get a classic whooshing "phaser" effect. Or, you can use an allpass filter to counteract unwanted phase shifts that another filter might have created. Or, if you mix several allpass-filtered signals together, you can create a sense of spaciousness as the signal phases are decorrelated from each other. For this reason, allpass filters are often found within reverb algorithms.

Let's start by noting something that you're likely to encounter as you start looking for filter block diagrams. You may discover that - just as there's more than one way to represent a mathematical equation or more than one way to represent an algorithm as a patch - there's also more than one way to represent a given filter as a block diagram. For example, you might find allpass filters described using any of the three following diagrams:

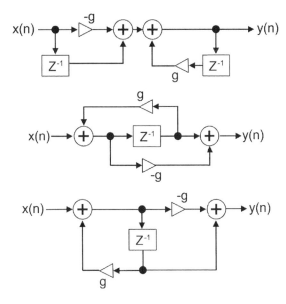

Although these three block diagrams look quite different on the surface, when you work through the underlying operations, you will find that remarkably they produce the same results. You could take any one of them as a starting point for translating into gen~. We're going to pick the one at the bottom, and as before, start by rotating the diagram 90 degrees clockwise so that the flow of data is top to bottom.

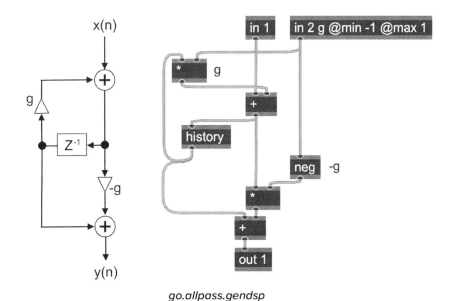

go.allpass.gendsp

After the rotation, we replace portions of our block diagram with the corresponding gen~ operators. We needed two * (multiply) operators — one for each of the feedback (**g**) and feedforward (**-g**) parameters, and two + (add) operators for summing. We added a single **in** operator for the g/-g values as well. Note that we also added **@min -1 @max 1** arguments to our **in 2** operator to constrain the range of the coefficient within safe limits.

Phaser

We can create a simple four-stage phaser effect by processing an input sound through a series of four allpass filters and mixing the result back with the original input.

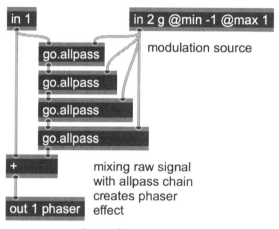

phaser-4stage.maxpat

On the next page we extended that patch to eight stages, with a **selector** to choose how many stages to use, and a feedback path to create a more resonant phasor.

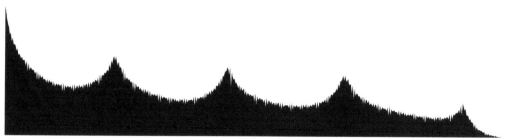

The resulting spectrum on a low frequency pulse wave, with the phaser-8stage-resonant.maxpat using all 8 stages set to a coefficient g=0.5 and feedback level fb=0.85.

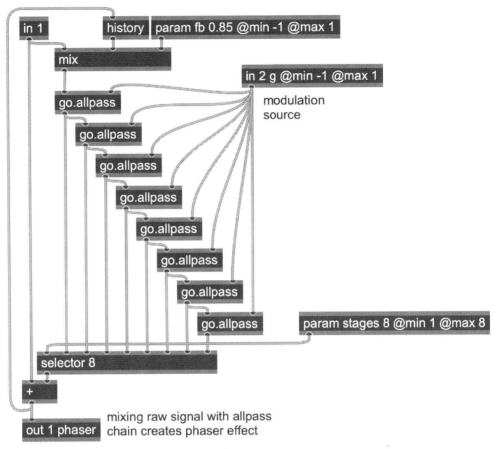

phaser-8stage-res.maxpat

Computing the allpass coefficient from a frequency

To compute the coefficient **g** from a desired frequency, we start by computing the angular radians per sample, which represents the rate of rotation of a sampled sinusoid at the desired frequency. We can compute this from a frequency in Hz using `abs(frequency) * twopi/samplerate`, the same conversion we saw with the one pole lowpass filter. From this angular radians per sample **w** we can derive the required coefficient **g** as `(sin(w)-1)/cos(w)`.

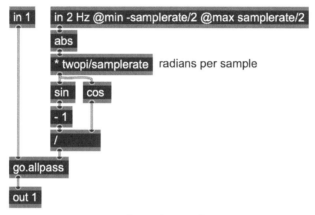

go.allpass.hz.gendsp

Biquad filters

Let's take an in-depth look at one of the most widely used digital audio filters: the biquadratic (or biquad) filter. This incredibly versatile general-purpose filter can be set up for many configurations–lowpass, highpass, bandpass, notch, highshelf, lowshelf, allpass, etc.–by doing nothing more than adjusting the parameters (also known as coefficients) of the filter. Here is a typical block diagram of a biquad filter:

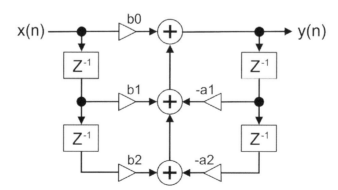

The biquad filter architecture has a direct path from input to output (via **b0**), as well as two feedforward sample delay paths (via **b1** and **b2**) and two feedback sample delay paths (via **a1** and a2), but otherwise doesn't introduce any new concepts. (You can compare this with the allpass filter in the previous section, which has one feedforward and one feedback path.)

As we've done before, we rotate the block diagram 90 degrees clockwise, drop in gen~ operator substitutes, and wire them up.

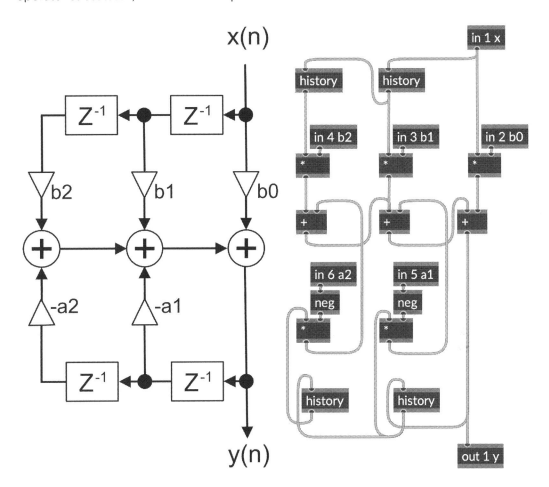

As a patch, this looks pretty tangled. We can clean it up by moving things around a little, and we can also make a few modifications to simplify the patch.

The a1 and a2 coefficients in the block diagram are labeled as negative values (-a1 and -a2). We can simplify this patch slightly by removing the **neg** operators and instead replacing + (plus) operators with a - (minus) operators. That's because subtracting the result of the multiplication with a coefficient is equivalent to adding a multiplication with the negative of that coefficient.

We can also simplify some of the patching, removing the need for + (plus) operators by connecting multiple patch cords to the next operator's inlet. This is because gen~ operator inlets always handle multiple incoming connections by summing multiple signals together.

The result looks a lot simpler:

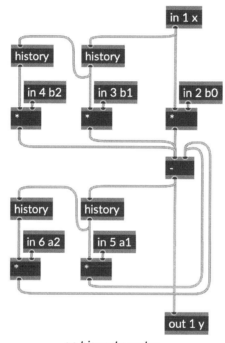

go.biquad.gendsp

Depending on how you're using the biquad, you might also want to add some limiting after the output to protect our ears and hardware; it could be one of the sigmoid bipolar waveshapers from Chapter 3 (p. 84) or simply a hard limiting **clip -1 1** operator. This is because it is quite possible to set the input coefficients for the biquad filter in such a way that the filter feedback "blows up."

The one-pole filter we built earlier in this chapter took care of that by simply setting bounds for the filter coefficient, but due to the complexity of the biquad circuit, we cannot ensure this by clipping the coefficients, so instead we may need to limit the signals somewhere in our patch before it reaches our ears.

Biquad Filter Coefficients

Now we have a biquad filter; how do we use it? The digital signal processing literature has many examples of algorithms we can use to compute the coefficients for different filter types (lowpass, highpass, bandpass, etc.) and for different cutoff frequencies, resonance/Q, and gain factors.[8]

While a detailed description of how these values are derived is beyond the scope of this book, we can certainly implement them in gen~. In fact, we have done exactly that, with the **go.biquad.lp** (low pass), **go.biquad.hp** (high pass), **go.biquad.bp** (band pass), **go.biquad.res** (resonant band pass), **go.biquad.np** (notch pass), **go.biquad.ap** (all pass), **go.biquad.ls** (low shelf), and **go.biquad.hs** (high-shelf) abstractions, which you can drop into your patches as you need.

However, if you look closer at the equations of many of these common filter types, you might notice that many share a lot of the same underlying computations.[9] In fact, we can conveniently build a coefficient calculator for all of these filter types, optimized to make use of the many calculations they share:

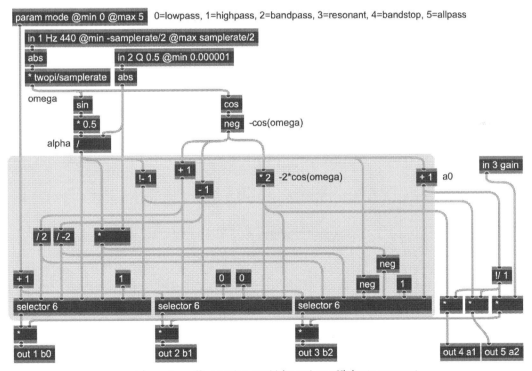

go.biquad.coeffs.gendsp and biquad-coefficients.maxpat

In this **go.biquad.coeffs** abstraction the highlighted part of the patch is the *only* part that differs between each filter type.[10] Using the selector operators here to route the different *b0*, *b1*, and *b2* calculations is more efficient than switching between six completely different biquads. Looking for opportunities of shared computation like this is a good patching habit!

Cascades

Apart from the flexibility of creating many filter types just by changing coefficients, the biquad filter is also useful in how it can be cascaded in series to create more complex filters. Our humble one-pole filter achieved a 6dB per octave slope due to it having one feedback path. The biquad, with two feedback paths, achieves a steeper 12dB per octave falloff. So, if you wanted an even more "aggressive" filter with a steeper falloff, you might imagine adding more feedback paths. Unfortunately, such circuits can get increasingly susceptible to numerical instability and more easily blow up. Fortunately, we can achieve the same result through a "cascade" of biquad filters in series, all using the same coefficients.

The following block diagram arranges two biquads in series to achieve a 24dB per octave falloff.

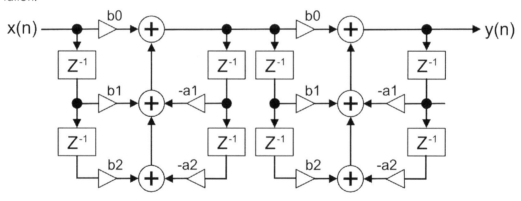

The next patch goes even further: four **go.biquad** abstractions are serially connected with a single **go.biquad.coeffs** abstraction converting filter cutoff, Q, and gain values to supply the same coefficients to all four abstractions. You can see the difference in filter roll-off in the visual displays. The fourth output, as a series of four biquads, has an extremely sharp falloff of 48dB per octave!

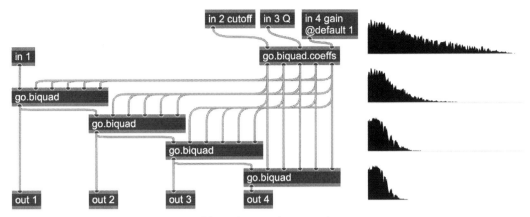

biquad-cascade.maxpat

The software with this book includes a **go.biquad4** abstraction that chains four biquads in series (using the same coefficients), and there are also variants of each of the common filter such as **go.biquad4.lp**, **go.biquad4.hp**, and so on.

Another approach to cascaded filters involves configuring several biquad filters for different modes and controlling each filter individually. This can be particularly interesting when the filter parameters are modulated. The following example uses four biquads: one as a lowpass filter, two as resonant filters, and one as a highpass filter, each of which allows for the specification for the filter cutoff ranges individually:

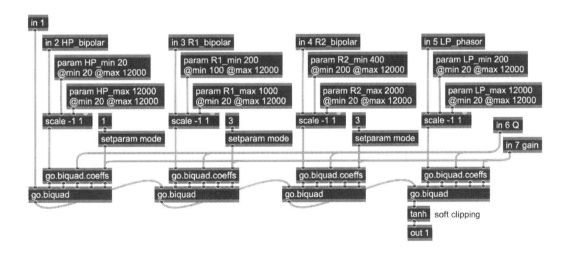

We can then use LFOs running at different rates to modulate the filter cutoff frequencies of each of these filter sections continuously, and the ***morphing_biquad_cascade.maxpat*** patch lets you experiment with various filter ranges for each.

Trapezoidal filters

We saw earlier in this chapter that a one-pole lowpass filter is effectively a weighted average between the filter's input and its output. A more subtle point is that the timing is thus slightly skewed: it is a mixture of the *current sample frame's* input with the *previous sample frame's* output. This means that the phase response (the frequency-dependent delay) will also be skewed. Lower frequencies that are passed through the filter mostly unchanged will have almost no delay; higher frequencies that are attenuated by the filter are more significantly influenced by the previous output and thus have a greater delay. When combined with other filtering processes or when filtering under high-frequency modulations, these frequency-dependent delays and phase responses can make a real difference. But there's an alternative topology we can use, sometimes called the trapezoidal or bilinear transform, which can better balance this temporal skew.

To understand how this works, we can first look at integrators since we have already seen that integrators are at the heart of all filters. Here are two simple integrators:

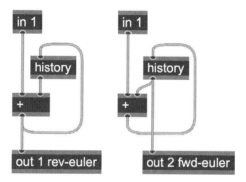

The one on the left is like the **accum** operator: it outputs the signal plus the integrator's previous value. It is also known as reverse Euler integration. With an input signal of 1.0, it will count from one with a series of 1.0, 2.0, 3.0, etc.

The one on the right taps the output at the **history** operator instead, so we get the current count plus the previous input; this is called forward Euler integration. This is effectively the same as the patch on the left but delayed by one sample, such that the new count appears on the next sample frame. With an input signal of 1.0, it will count from zero with a series of 0.0, 1.0, 2.0, etc.

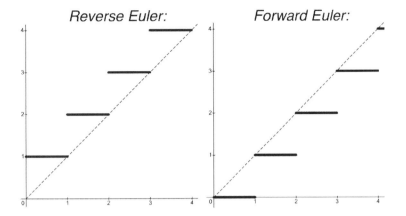

Where the circuit on the left is biased toward the signal at the *end* of a sample frame, the one on the right is biased toward the value at the *start* of a sample frame. But wouldn't it be better to avoid bias to either end and approximate the signal in the middle of the sample frame instead? This is what the *trapezoidal* architecture does, producing an *average* between forward and reverse integration. There are two ways to do this.

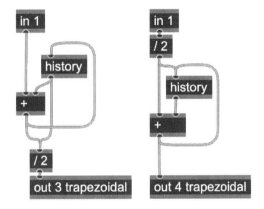

Look at the patch on the left: it takes both of the outputs that the reverse and forward integration used and averages them (using the **/ 2** operator). So, with an input signal of 1.0, the output will be 0.5, 1.5, 2.5, etc.—exactly the midpoint. (It is a counter with a delay of one-half of a sample frame.) On the right, we achieve exactly the same result simply by splitting the input into halves instead of averaging the output.

This is the format that the integrator is usually presented in block diagrams.

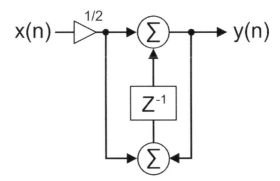

By balancing the forward and reverse integration step functions, this architecture produces an interpolation that better approximates the real signal.

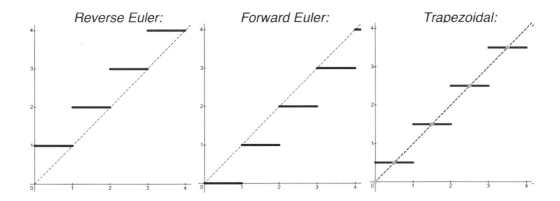

A one-pole filter

To turn this integrator core into a one-pole filter, we simply need to make the integrator leaky, just like we did for the simple one-pole filter at the start of this chapter. We can do this by subtracting the integrator output from the input and scaling it by an appropriate coefficient.

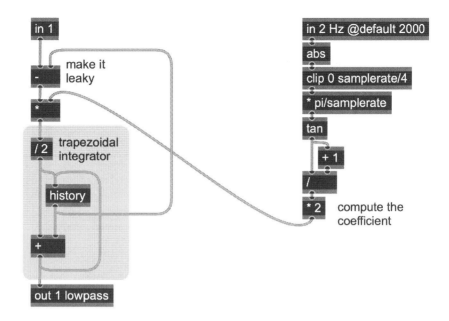

You might notice that this bilinear transform version requires a slightly different formula to convert the desired cutoff frequency in Hz to the multiplier coefficient compared to the one pole filter we saw at the start of this chapter. The reason why is mathematically beyond the scope of this book, but has to do with counteracting a certain warping of the frequency range that the bilinear transform implies.[11] This change also means tht we can only use cutoff frequencies up to one-quarter of the sample rate (a 12kHz limit at a samplerate of 48kHz), here ensured using a **clip** operator. We can also simplify this patch slightly by rearranging and noting that the *** 2** and **/ 2** operators cancel each other out.

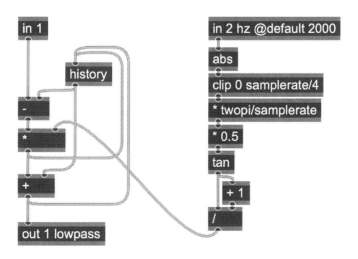

The trapezoidal architecture allows block diagram designs that more closely resemble analog circuit designs. That is, the trapezoidal form of the one-pole filter here is much closer to the ideal form of a blend between the raw and filtered signal (which is otherwise impossible due to there being ideally no delay), with better phase response, and thus a better approximation of what an actual analog resistor-capacitor circuit should produce. Another advantage is that the implementation is very stable and handles quite extreme frequency modulations up to audio rates very well.

As with the naïve one-pole filter, we get a free highpass filter by subtracting the lowpass from the input (and, with another subtraction, an allpass filter).

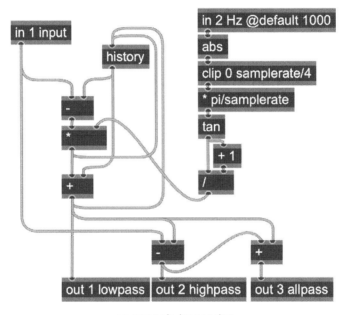

go.onepole.hz.gendsp

State Variable Filter

From this trapezoidal filter core, we can also build up many other filter structures fairly easily and at less computational cost than direct form biquads. For example, by nesting just one additional trapezoidal core, we can construct a "state variable filter" (SVF: a filter that produces many different spectral shapes at once) simply by tapping the circuit at different points.

Here is the block diagram together with our gen~ operator translation of it:

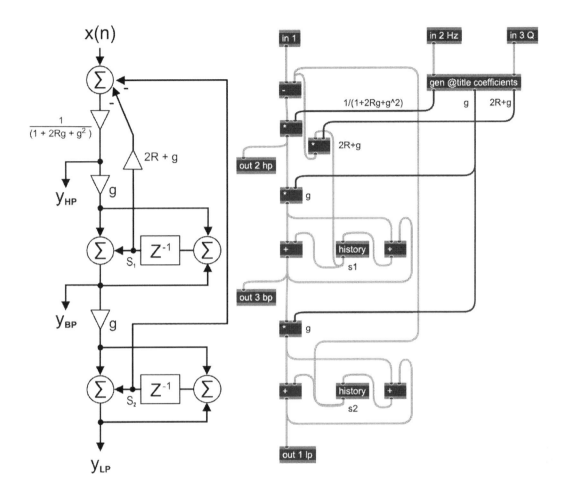

Here is the "coefficients" subpatch:

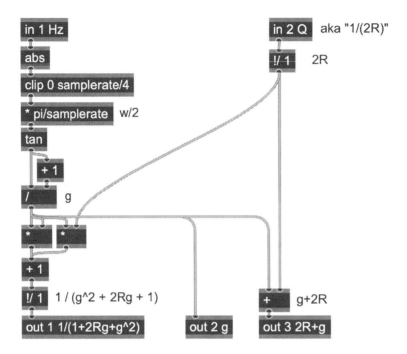

Note that, unlike the biquad, we don't need to compute new coefficients for each of the filter shapes–they are all produced simultaneously. Moreover, we can also derive several other filter shapes from this patch, including a peak, two different bandpass filters, a notch, and another allpass filter. These additional shapes come at almost no computational cost, using fewer components than a biquad, and without needing to compute *any* new coefficients.

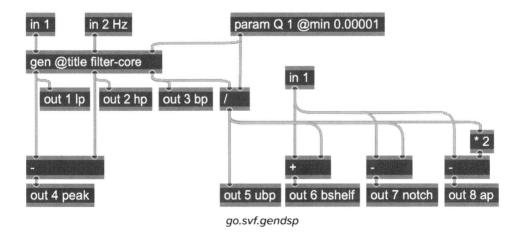

go.svf.gendsp

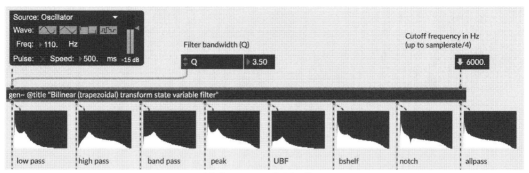

trapezoidal-state-variable-filter.maxpat

Crossover filter

Sometimes we want to split a signal into different frequency ranges and then treat the two outputs separately — spatializing or compressing them differently or splitting the signal to build a simple equalizer. You might assume that splitting a signal into two ranges could be done by passing a signal through both a lowpass filter and a highpass filter, but it's not quite that simple. If you try adding the lowpass-filtered and highpass-filtered signals back together, the result sounds somehow still colored compared to the original source. The reason for this is that when we put our original signal through the two filters, each one adds different phase delays that interfere with each other when mixed back together.

We can work around this problem by inserting an allpass filter that uses the same frequency parameter as the lowpass filter, in order to compensate for the phase delay. That is, if we split a signal into two paths, feeding one path through a lowpass to shape the sound and the other path through an allpass (which doesn't shape the sound but applies the same phase delay), we can then mix the two resulting signals without any distortion. And as we saw in the last section, this also means we can get a highpass filter simply by subtracting them.

But what kind of lowpass filter would we want, and what works? We don't want a resonant filter for a clean crossover, and we know a one-pole filter doesn't resonate. Although a regular allpass doesn't have the same phase response as a single one-pole lowpass filter, it does happen to have the same phase response as two one-pole lowpass filters in series.

So, let's feed our audio input into both a chain two onepole lowpass filters, and subtract them from allpass filtered copy of our input, to create our two phase matched crossover signals:

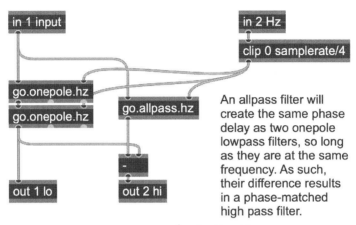

An allpass filter will create the same phase delay as two onepole lowpass filters, so long as they are at the same frequency. As such, their difference results in a phase-matched high pass filter.

crossover_simple.maxpat

This method of creating a crossover filter can be expanded further to increase the number of frequency-band channels. All you need to do is ensure to add matching allpass filters to each remaining channel in order to preserve the total phase delay. Here is an example of a three-band crossover filter.

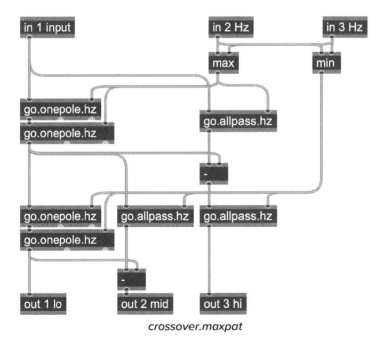

crossover.maxpat

Block diagrams: between theory and practice

As you go off in search of block diagrams that you might like to try implementing in gen~, here are a few suggestions you might want to keep in mind.

It is often not enough simply to copy a block diagram and start patching from there; you may need to spend some time reading through the source from which you copy the block diagram. For example, block diagrams are sometimes meant to provide conceptual models rather than a starting point for implementation. One obvious place you may notice this is a situation where you realize that your block diagram has a feedback loop with absolutely no delay — which is simply not possible in the digital world. It is often the case that reading further into the text will reveal how the problem is resolved.[12]

Or, you might encounter a block diagram symbol whose meaning isn't as well defined. For example, you might run across the Integral symbol ($\int$). That can be a tricky one to encounter since it might mean a simple integrator (which would be a simple substitution using the **accum** operator), but it might also mean that you need a "leaky integrator" (as we have seen with lowpass filters), or it might be a conceptual indication of an "impractical" filter. You may need to go beyond the block diagram into the text to figure out what you need.

Finally, it's also sometimes the case that the way that a block diagram describes signal flow isn't actually the way that most algorithms do the calculation. We've already made a few changes to block diagrams in the patches in this to make them easier to read, and sometimes more efficient.

Smoothing control signals with lines and slews

We mentioned earlier that a one-pole lowpass filter can also be used to smooth out noisy or steppy control signals (and that's exactly what the **slide** operator does), but it's not the only way to do this and not always the best choice. As we saw with the lowpass gate, the one-pole approaches its target *exponentially*, starting off quite quickly and getting slower as it closes the gap with each passing sample frame. This varying slope isn't always desirable, nor is the fact that an exponential approach never actually quite reaches the target. Here we'd like to introduce a couple of alternatives that maintain a constant slope and do reach their targets.

Limiting a slope (slew limiting)

One simple way is to limit how much change can happen on any sample frame, which means limiting how steep a slope can ever be. This is known as a slew limiter, and it will turn any stepped signal into one with smooth ramps between the steps. We can think of this as a kind of constrained motion. Here we'll use a **history** operator to store our current position, and we can compare this to the input target to find out what direction we need to go to meet it. If we then limit this difference to a maximum positive or negative amount using a **clip** operator, we can set the maximum movement our line can take in one sample frame. Adding that movement to our **history** position takes us a little closer to the target, and this is fed back to update the **history** for the next sample frame.

This is such a handy little circuit that we created abstractions for it, including one in which you can set the maximum rising slope independently of the maximum falling slope (very handy for creating a basic envelope from a gate signal):

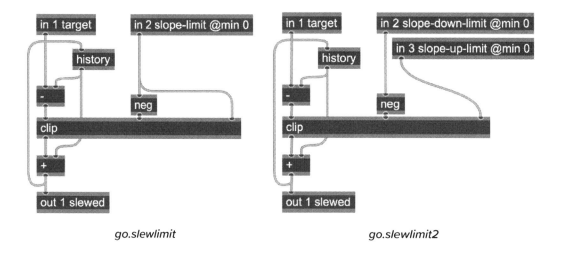

go.slewlimit   go.slewlimit2

The slope-limit inputs specify the maximum rate of change per sample frame. That might not be the most intuitive form, but it is easy to compute a unipolar ramp slope as `frequency/samplerate` or, more generally, to specify a slope in terms of a duration in milliseconds using a **!/ 1000/samplerate** operator

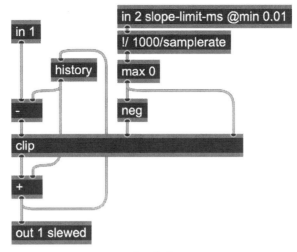

go.slewlimit.ms

Drawing a line (lag generator)

A slew limiter will take a longer time to cover a larger distance or a shorter time to cover a shorter distance, but that's not always what we want. Sometimes we simply want to be able to trigger a ramp from one point to another, somewhat like the Max or RNBO **line~** object.[13]

As we saw with the "smooth-stepped" circuits in Chapter 3 (p. 76), we can create linear glides from 0.0 to 1.0 over a fixed duration using an **accum** and a **clip 0 1** operator. The first inlet of the **accum** operator sets how quickly it will rise (the slope per sample frame), which we can compute as *1 / duration in samples*, just like any phasor ramp (or we could set using Hz or milliseconds just like we did for the slew limiter in the last section). Any non-zero trigger to the **accum** operator's second inlet will restart the ramp from zero again.

The "smooth-stepped" circuit from Chapter 3 can generalize this 0.0 to 1.0 ramp to any start and end point. We'll again start from a **history** operator that represents our current location and an input representing the goal we want to reach. We can restart our **accum** ramp whenever this target changes, using a **change** operator. At this moment, we can use a couple of **latch** operators to capture the current value of the input as well as our current location. Then we can simply use a **mix** operator to create a linear path between these two points, where the blend factor is simply our clipped accumulator. (You can also experiment with adding unit shapers to the clipped accumulator here to create nonlinear paths.)

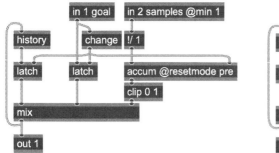

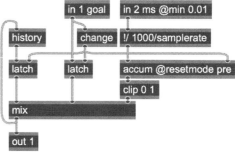

go.line.samples   *go.line.ms*

The smoothing filter we've created here is also known as a "lag generator": it will try to replicate the signal at its input, but with a certain amount of delay in catching up to it. If the goal changes mid-ramp, that's not a problem. The **change** operator will cause the first **latch** to capture the start point as wherever we currently are, and the new endpoint as the changed input, and a new ramp will start. But there's one important subtlety here: we used **accum @resetmode pre** here to ensure that even on the first sample frame in which a **change** occurs, the ramp has already set off in motion. (If we didn't do this and just used a regular **accum** operator or **accum @resetmode post**, then the ramp will be at 0.0 whenever the input changes. With a continuously changing input, the ramp would never move away from 0.0, and so neither would our output.)

Finally, here are three control signal smoothing methods compared in the *slide_slew_and_line.maxpat* patch, using the same stepped signal as input. Notice that with **go.line**, the duration of each ramp is the same, but the slope differs. With the slew limiter, the slope is nearly always the same, but the duration can differ.

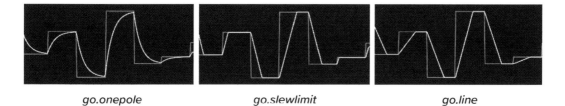

go.onepole   *go.slewlimit*   *go.line*

Chapter 7: The Effects of Delay

Repetition is the mirror of the infinite, and working with delay is like traveling through time, which can get a little mind-bending — especially when feedback is involved. It may be helpful to approach the subject in terms of analogy. Consider a tape loop:

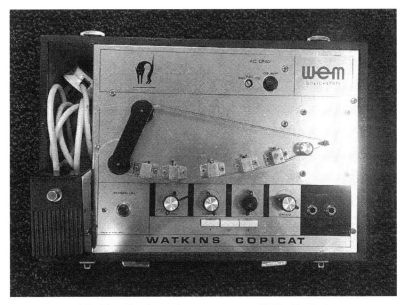

Watkins Copicat photo courtesy of Mike Podest

A basic tape loop has three kinds of "heads," which just means points where information goes in or comes out of the tape:

A write head   One or more read heads   An erase head

These heads can be positioned anywhere on the tape loop as the tape passes through them at a steady rate. The distance between the read and write head determines the length of the delay. The delay corresponds to the time between the moment a signal goes into the tape at the write head and the moment when that same bit of tape comes through the read head and the signal is read out. A larger distance between a read head and the write head results in a longer delay.

A "multitap delay" has several read heads—one for each "tap"—usually located in different positions, corresponding to different delay times. The tape stores data written in the past, and each reader picks a different distance in the past to read from.

The eraser head is usually located right before the write head so that new sounds can *replace* the sounds already on the tape. (Or, if the erase head is disengaged from the tape, then new sounds will *overdub* or mix with sounds already on the tape for layering sound on sound loops.)

A basic delay loop

A digital delay is similar to having a tape delay, but the physical tape is replaced with an array of sample slots in digital memory.

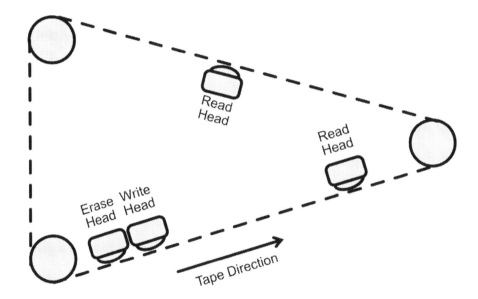

Here is what that means:

- The tape loop is always moving at a constant rate, corresponding to the current sample rate. The tape is thus "ticking" through in discrete steps at thousands of times per second.
- Every new input at the "write head" fills the next sample slot in the array of samples (the "tape").
- The delay time sets how far back in this tape the "read head" looks to fetch its next output.

In gen~, we can do this using the **delay** operator. This operator can take two arguments:

1. The first argument defines the maximum possible delay time in samples and thus the amount of memory to be allocated. In effect, it specifies the length of the "tape loop." If you don't specify this length, it will default to one second at the current sample rate.

2. The second argument sets the number of read heads (or "taps"). The default is 1 (a single tap). The number of taps specified in the argument will determine the number of inlets and outlets the **delay** operator will have.

The first inlet to the **delay** operator sends audio to the write head. Additional inlets set the positions of the other read heads (taps) in sample frames, which means their distance from the write head. The outlet(s) are what these read heads read from the tape. (The eraser head is inside the delay, sitting right before the write head).

Here's an example of the **delay** operator in use:[1]

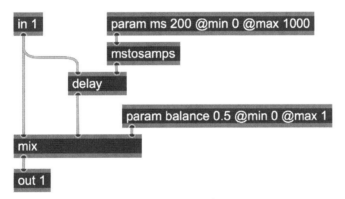

*delay_feedforward_basic.**maxpat***

We set the delay time in terms of samples since that's what the tape itself uses. We can use the **mstosamps** operator to handle conversion from milliseconds for us. In the patch above, we also added a **mix** operator to let us blend the wet (delayed) and dry (original) outputs so that we can hear a blend of both.

Feedback

The previous patch is called a "feedforward" delay because the output of the delay feeds forward to the output of the patch. But we can also create delays that "feed back" upon themselves, creating a feedback loop. So far, we've only patched feedback loops in gen~ using the **history** operator, but the **delay** operator can do this too.[2]

So, we could simply take our mixed output and feed the result back into the delay.

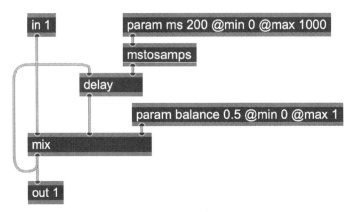

delay_feedback_basic.maxpat

You might notice that this bears a striking resemblance to the basic one-pole filter example we built using **mix** and **history** operators in Chapter 6 (p. 159), but with the **history** replaced by a **delay**. That is, the feedback delay is just a one-pole filter stretched out in time! (We'll see later in this chapter that you can also turn other filter structures into interesting delay effects by replacing **history** operators with **delay** operators).

Try playing a sound through this patch. Set the balance to 0.5 and delay time to 200 milliseconds for a classic echo sound. Now, turn the balance up to 1.0, and the sound will appear to freeze into a loop. At this point, we only hear the recirculating "tape." Set the balance to around 0.97, and the captured loop will slowly fade away again.

If you wanted to separate the control of the wet/dry balance from control over the amount of feedback, it could look like the following patch. We marked the signal feedback loop clearly in a darker color to identify it.

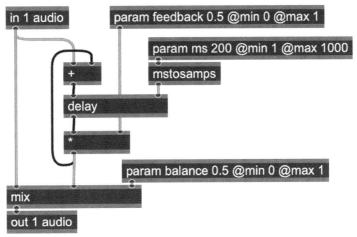

delay_feedback_basic.maxpat

Watch out, however — setting the feedback to 1.0 can start to overflow since the input is still being fed into the delay (meaning that nothing is ever lost), like trying to squash more and more stuff into a bag; we will return to the issues this can cause a little later.

Setting the feedback decay time

You might notice that a delay-based feedback loop fades away more quickly when the delay time is short and more slowly when the delay time is long. It makes sense: the shorter the loop is, the more often the feedback multiplication is applied to a given sound, so the more quickly it shrinks. How can we ensure that a delay effect will *decay* over a specific amount of time, regardless of the delay time setting? Just as we used the **t60** operator in Chapter 6 (p. 167) to determine filter response times, we can also use it here to determine a delay's decay times.

It helps to think of the **t60** value as a multiplication *per feedback loop*. In a **history** loop, the feedback is just one sample long, so there's multiplication at every sample frame of real-time. In a **delay** tape loop of 10 samples' length, the feedback multiplication applies to a specific step in the tape loop only once every 10 sample frames of real-time since it takes that long for the "tape" to loop around. That's just 1/10th as often.

So, to compute the feedback multiplier for any feedback delay, we divide the desired decay time (in samples) by the delay length (in samples) and feed that into the **t60** operator, as shown in the following patch. The echoes will now decay over the same amount of time (**param decay_ms**) regardless of how long or short the tape is.

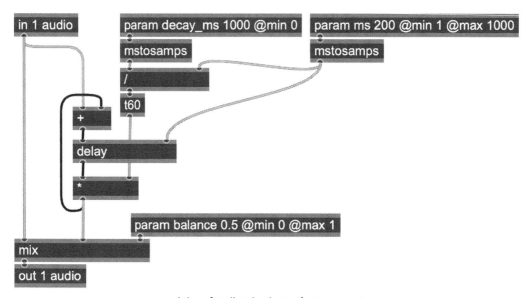

delay_feedback_decaytime.maxpat

Feedback filtering

Most physical echoes don't just get quieter over time. They also get duller as the physical objects that echoes reflect off absorb higher frequency energy with each bounce. We can easily emulate this by placing a lowpass filter into the delay feedback loop. However, we should be careful not to use a resonating filter that would increase energy at any frequency, or the sound could blow up! Here we can reuse the **go.onepole** abstraction we built in Chapter 6 as a non-resonating filter placed in the feedback loop.

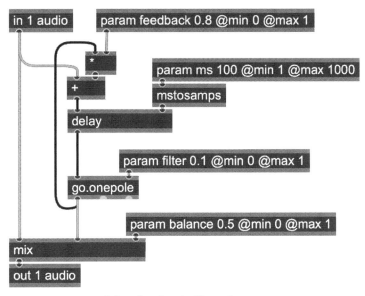

delay_feedback_filtered.maxpat

Removing DC

If you set the feedback parameter to 1.0 for infinite repeats and keep feeding a signal into the delay, you might notice that with some inputs the delay output waveform begins to drift away from the center zero line (for example, try looping the ***anton.aif*** sound file).

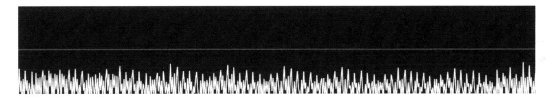

What's happening is that the average value of the input sound's average is not quite aligned to zero, and this small deviation is being added each time through the feedback loop. This recirculated drift can accumulate to the point that the signal entirely wanders beyond the acceptable bounds of -1.0 to +1.0 and begins to clip and distort. The shift away from the zero point you see here as an electronic average is known as DC (direct current) or near-zero frequency energy. We can eliminate this problem by use of a "DC-blocking trap," which is simply a highpass filter with a cutoff frequency below the audible range. This will drain away accumulated deviations from the zero line without affecting the frequencies we can hear.

For example, we can use the second (highpass) outlet of the **go.onepole.hz** abstraction that we built in Chapter 6 set to a sub-audible cutoff frequency of 3Hz. Here, we put this on the *input* to the delay so that it will also reduce DC before it even gets a chance to enter the delay loop.

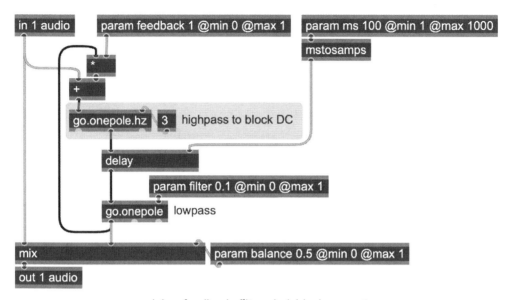

delay_feedback_filtered_dcblock.maxpat

Feedback limiting

Accumulating DC isn't the only thing that can go wrong with a feedback loop. Another is simply the accumulation of too much energy overall, especially if our feedback parameter is set high or we have a resonant filter in the loop. More generally, for any feedback system, we may end up producing positive feedback (in which the energy recirculating in the system is amplified) that can very quickly blow up into exponentially large signals.

One strategy we can take here is to apply some kind of limiting process, such as hard clipping with a **clip -1 1** operator such that positive feedback cannot go beyond the safe -1.0 and +1.0 limits; however, this sharp cut will add very harsh distortion to any signal that does.

Alternatively, we could use a soft saturator, including any of the sigmoid functions we encountered in Chapter 3 (p. 84) within the feedback loop, such as a **go.sigmoid2** abstraction. These will also ensure that no matter how much the signal gains positive feedback, the output remains between the safe -1.0 and +1.0 limits, and instead of the harsh distortion of the **clip** operator, they will impart a softer and more pleasant harmonic distortion. The ***delay_feedback_saturated.maxpat*** patch shows an example of combining a resonant bandpass filter with sigmoid waveshaping distortion, evoking a classic space echo dub delay effect.

As nice as this distortion can be, it will change the sound of *any* signal going through it, regardless of whether it is excessively loud or not. If we didn't want the saturation to influence the sound this much, we could apply a pragmatic solution: up to a certain threshold (sometimes called the "knee"), we can pass through the signal unchanged. Beyond this threshold, we can apply the nonlinear distortion, scaled such that it squishes the remainder to a more limited range.

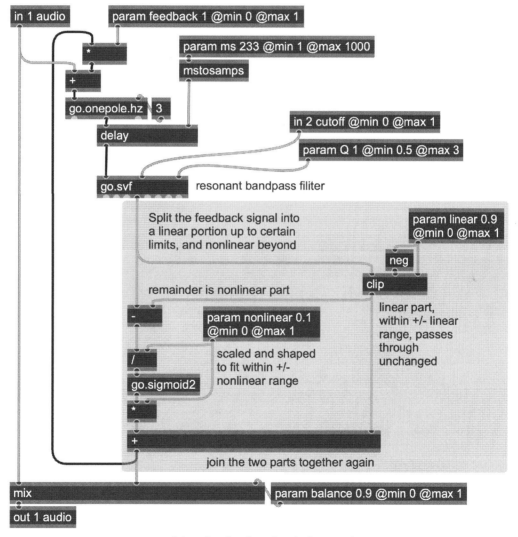

delay_feedback_saturated.maxpat

Up to the **param linear** threshold, the signal passes through unchanged, while the remainder of the signal beyond this threshold is squished to fit within the **param nonlinear** range. In this way, the final output amplitude cannot be greater than **linear** + **nonlinear**.

Here are these three approaches compared graphically, in which the horizontal axis represents the input amplitude, and the vertical axis is the output amplitude:

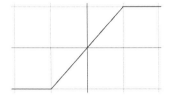 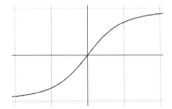 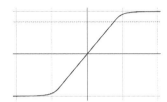

Hard limiting (**clip -1 1**) causes harsh distortion as soon as any signal breaches the -1.0 or +1.0 limits.

Soft saturation (e.g. **go.sigmoid2**), applies nonlinear distortion to every signal passing through

In the knee-based patch above, soft saturation kicks in only when the signal goes beyond the threshold marked by the dotted line (**param linear** = 0.75), and softly saturates signals beyond this (**param nonlinear** = 0.25).

Avoiding clicks

You'll probably notice that changing balance and feedback parameters can sometimes cause clicks in the output. It makes sense when you think about it. If you scroll values in a Max or RNBO number box, param attrui, or any user interface that is updated lower than audio sample rate, the value will be stepping in short jumps. Since these parameters are being used to multiply an audio signal, it is like making an instantaneous "jump" of a volume fader, which would result in a click.

This can be fixed by adding parameter smoothing—turning a sudden change into something more gradual. We could reuse the **go.line.ms** lag generator we built in Chapter 7 (p. 195), or a one pole or slew limiter, to ensure that all parameter changes are smoothed over a period of time, as shown in the following patch. The amount of ramp time we need doesn't have to be very much — a handful of milliseconds or a couple of hundred samples is usually enough to remove the clicks.

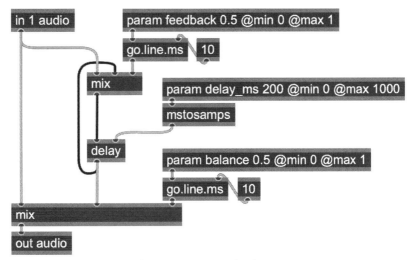

delay_param_smoothed.maxpat

When you twiddle the *delay_ms* parameter, it can also create artifacts, but this happens for a different reason. If the delay is like a tape of sample frames, then a sudden change of the delay time parameter is instantaneously like teleporting the read head from one position on the tape to an entirely different position on the tape. That's very likely to cause a click because the waveforms at two different locations are likely to be quite different, causing a sudden jump in the output. We'll look at two possible solutions for this next.

Smooth changes to delay time cause Doppler shifts

What if we were to use parameter smoothing for the delay time too? Then our read head will not be teleporting but will be moving gradually and continuously back and forth around the tape: each jump is now so small that it doesn't cause glitches.

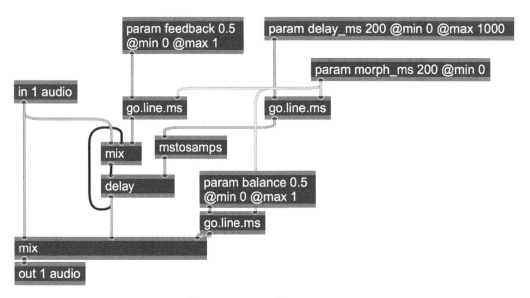

delay_morphed_times.maxpat

Instead, this gradual change of delay time ends up creating a pitch-changing effect. Here, we spread the ramp over 200ms to make the effect more visible:

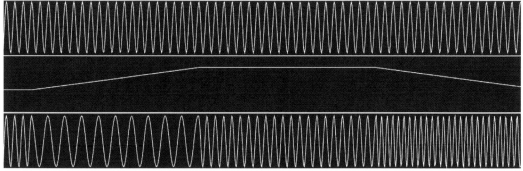

Top trace: Sine wave input at 100Hz. Middle trace: the delay time (ramping up and down between 100ms and 200ms). Bottom trace: the delayed sine wave. Notice how the sine wave is stretched out (pitched down) as delay times increase and is compressed (pitched up) while delay times decrease.

The pitch change is due to relativity. Increasing the delay time is like moving the read head away from the write head, which, relativistically speaking, is the same as if the tape were playing more slowly—from the point of view of the read head. Some digital instrument designers call this "analog-style delay" since it mimics what happens when you move heads on physical tape delays, but it is also equivalent to the Doppler shift of a fast-moving object in space. Moving a sound source and listener apart (increasing delay time) will effectively stretch the traveling wavefronts out (lowering the frequency) while moving them closer together will compress the traveling wavefronts (which raises the frequency).

Suppose you want to know precisely what the pitch change will be for any delay time modulation. In that case, you can send the delay time parameter through a **mstosamps** operator to convert it to sample frames first, then get the slope with a **delta** operator. This gives you a positive value when the delay time is increasing, negative when it is decreasing, and will be zero when the delay time is not changing. If you subtract that from 1.0 using a **!- 1** operator it will return a value of 1.0 when the delay time is not changing, a value of 2.0 when the delay time modulation causes the sound to double in frequency, a value of 0.5 when the delay modulation causes the frequency to halve, and so on.

We can turn this into an octave pitch signal by passing it through a **log2** operator for the exponential pitch space and a **go.octave2midi** abstraction if we want MIDI pitch offsets.

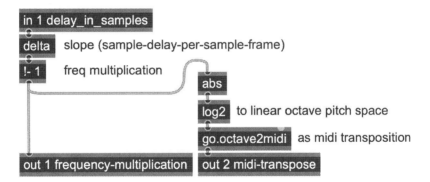

Conversely, we can reverse this calculation to modulate a delay for a desired pitch change: from an octave pitch signal, apply the **exp2** operator to get back to the linear frequency multiplier, add **+ 1** for the base multiplier, and feed that into an **accum** operator to integrate the required variable delay time in samples. Both of these transformations are demonstrated in the ***delay_morphed_times.maxpat*** patch. Now you can play a Doppler melody on any sound input!

Changing delay time without pitch shift

If we want to change delay times without causing clicks and also without causing any pitch shifting, we can resort to a little sleight of hand. We'll run two taps—let's call them tap A and tap B—and we use a **mix** crossfader so that normally only one of the taps is being heard. If the mix factor is 0.0, we only hear tap A, so we can freely change the delay time of tap B without clicks. If the mix factor is 1.0, we only hear tap B, so we can freely change tap A. (You could think of this as a bit like a DJ flipping the crossfader over to deck B in order to rewind the track on deck A, then crossfading back.) The crossfade can be just a few milliseconds long — just long enough to soften any sudden change in the waveform. In the following patch, we use a **go.line.ms** abstraction to perform the crossfade over 12 milliseconds.

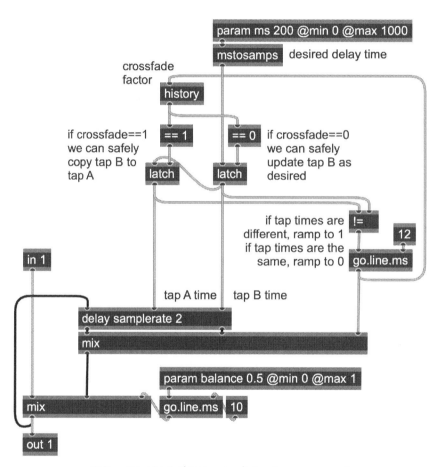

delay_morphed_times_no_pitch_change.maxpat

This crossfader value (stored in the **history** at the top right) acts as a kind of *state machine* that drives the whole patch. The states are either:

- A value of 0.0 (listening to tap A)
- A value of 1.0 (listening to tap B)
- A value in transition somewhere in between (hearing the crossfade)

That bit of patching is quite a useful little combination, and we'll use it again later, so we saved it as ***go.background.change.gendsp***.

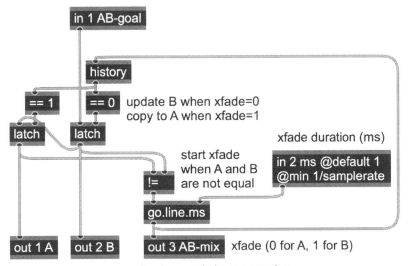

go.background.change.gendsp

A garden of earthly delays

So far, we have been looking at delays as a way to create echoes or periodically repeat input sounds with a time offset, but there is a much broader range of well-known and beloved audio effects made possible by delay operations at shorter time scales, including chorusing, flanging, voice doubling and so on. The main differences lie in the range of the delay times used and how they are modulated and mixed—many of them also employ some kind of low frequency (LFO) modulation of the delay time.[3]

In fact, we can create a single patch combining some of the ideas we've seen so far in this chapter that can be used to reproduce many different delay-based effects by simply varying its parameters.

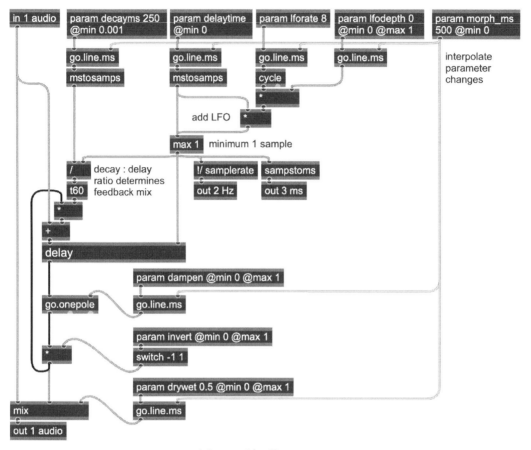

delay_multi_effect.maxpat

This patch combines a delay with a feedback loop using the **t60** operator to set the total decay time and a **go.onepole** abstraction to apply filtering to the feedback, as we have seen earlier in this chapter. In addition, the **param invert** adds the ability to multiply the signal by -1 each time through the feedback loop. But probably the most important addition is the ability to modulate the delay time with an LFO whose rate is set by the **param lforate** operator and the intensity of its effect by the param **lfodepth** operator. Most of the parameters are fed through **go.line.ms** abstractions to smoothen their changes.

Here is a list of example parameter settings and the very different sonic effects they can have listed in order of delay time.

	Delay (ms)	LFO depth	LFO (Hz)	Invert	Decay (ms)	Dampen	Wet/dry mix
Delays	700	0			6000	0.8	0.4
Mad dub	300	0.03	1	Yes	4000	1	0.8
Garage echo	150	0			1000	0.5	0.3
Slap echo	60	0		Yes	1000	0.5	0.3
Tape flutter	30	0.1	3		10	1	1
Chorus	20	0.03	4		0	1	0.6
Didgerimetal	10	0.01	99	Yes	2000	0.15	1
Flanger	5	0.8	0.1	Yes	50	1	0.5
String	3	0.001	7		1000	0.75	1
Phaser	1.5	1.0	0.1		1	1	0.5
Toothpaste	0.3	0.6	1.0	Yes	12	1	1
Filter Wobble	0.1	1	5.0	Yes	2	0.5	1

You can select and morph between these using the **umenu** interface in the *delay_multi_effect.maxpat* patch. It's worth spending some time trying out different input sounds and testing and listening to the output to get a sense of these effects and how their parameters interact. Some of these are well-known "classic" effects; others are a bit more experimental. You may also find it interesting to set a high **param morph_ms** value to listen to the intermediate sounds as the patch "morph" between these examples.

We think it is quite amazing how many different sonic results can come from a fairly simple patch. Let's look at some of them more closely, working our way down from echoes to the microsonic realm of filters.

We hear clear individual repetitions with longer delay times of around 100ms to one second or more. Without feedback, this can seem like musical hocketing; with lots of feedback, it can produce a sensation of rhythm or tempo.

Slightly shorter delay times resemble tape-head or slapback echoes associated with devices such as the Watkins Copicat, whose image opened this chapter, and adding a little judicious LFO modulation can introduce some "tape flutter." Delays in the 20-100ms range with feedback can begin to fuse into trill-like trails, perhaps reminiscent of room echo, and adding some damping filtering will make them sound less metallic.

Below this range, we no longer hear individual repetitions, and the rhythmic effects turn into effects that we identify by their spectral content. As the delay time is shortened to around 10 - 30ms, a blend of dry and delayed sounds can appear to reinforce themselves (commonly referred to as "doubling") and add a slight amount of modulation to the delayed signal to introduce subtle changes in pitch will lead to characteristic "chorus" effects. Chorusing is similar to vibrato because it introduces subtle changes in pitch by modulating the delay time with an LFO. Varying the rate of the LFO will generate more phase shift (and perceived pitch modulations) of the original signal.

The span of 0.5 - 25ms corresponds to the realm typical of musical pitches (from 2000Hz down to 40Hz, respectively). If we set the feedback very high and feed the delay with bursts of noise, the delay's corresponding fundamental frequency will ring out like a resonating string. We'll look at many ways to improve this kind of string emulation later in this chapter.

Going down to around 1 - 10ms, the combination of the original signal with its delayed, modulated copy begins to emphasize and de-emphasize different frequencies present in the original signal. With a slow modulation of delay time and plenty of feedback, this produces the characteristic sweeping sound of "flanging." With even shorter delays, around 0.25 - 2ms, and with less feedback, it produces the characteristic whooshing effect of "phasing." The timing differences that result when mixing the original and the delayed/modulated signal cause a constantly changing phase shift between the two signals. As the relative phase between the signals is modulated, some frequencies of the sound become perfectly in sync, leading to constructive interference, while other frequencies go perfectly out of sync and cancel each other out. As the LFO modulates the delay time, these points of interference will change, resulting in a distinctly airy sweep.

Filtering with delay: comb filters and allpass delay filters

At a micro-sonic scale of around 0.05 to 5ms (corresponding to fundamental frequencies from 500Hz to 20kHz, or handfuls to hundreds of samples), the effects of delay transition into the realm of filters. These kinds of effects are also often described in block diagrams, just like the filters we already saw in Chapter 6. For example, a comb filter with both feedback and feedforward sections might be block diagrammed like this:

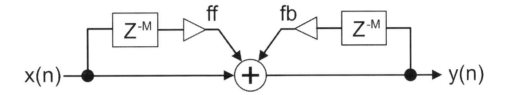

The Z blocks in the diagram use a superscript (Z^{-M}) rather than Z^{-1} to represent that these blocks delay the signal by *M* samples rather than 1 sample, which means we'll be using the **delay** operator rather than the **history** operator to translate this diagram.

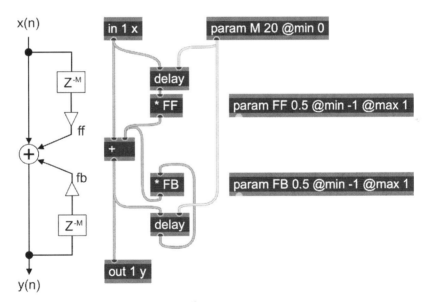

comb_filter.maxpat

If you use only the feedforward path (i.e., **param FB** = 0.0), it creates notches in the output spectrum.

If you use only the feedback path (**param FF** = 0.0), it creates *peaks* in the output spectrum of the sound.

Or you can combine both, creating both peaks and notches.

This should make it clear why it is called comb filtering: the spectrum looks a bit like a comb, with its peaks and/or troughs at evenly spaced frequencies. The specific frequencies where these occur depend on the delay length, with a peak at each whole number multiple of the delay's fundamental frequency and a notch halfway between each peak. So, if your delay period is 10ms, corresponding to a fundamental frequency of 100Hz, there will be peaks at 0Hz, 100Hz, 200Hz, and so on, and notches at 50Hz, 150Hz, 250Hz, and so on.

However, if the **param FF** and **param FB** coefficients are negative, then this flips around, with notches at whole number multiples of the fundamental frequency and peaks halfway between. This is because any of the delayed frequencies that are in phase with each other sum together, while frequencies that are out of phase with each other cancel out.

Modulating the delay time produces a characteristic zooming sound as these peaks and notches slide up and down the spectrum together. It works especially well with spectrally rich harmonic sources such as pulse waves for the input.

Enharmonic combs

Our next filter block diagram is drawn from a paper authored by Jae hyun Ahn and Richard Dudas,[4] which begins with the goal of using delay-based filters to create "enharmonic" comb-like effects. That simply means that the delay periods of the two delays can be set at different frequencies that are not necessarily whole number harmonics, producing more complex spectra. Trial and error showed that they could create an elegant and great-sounding enharmonic filter that also remains stable using the following block diagram:[5]

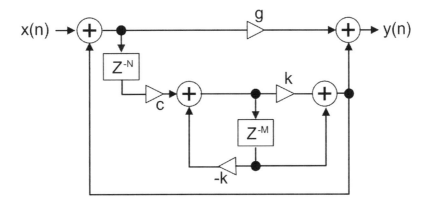

As before, we'll rotate this block diagram and replace blocks with gen~ operator equivalents. As before, we replace **param** coefficients with inlets that will allow us to modulate our filter at audio rates, rearrange it for a more easily visible signal flow, and add some clipping for patch hygiene.

Here is the resulting patch, with the nested allpass filter highlighted in a box.

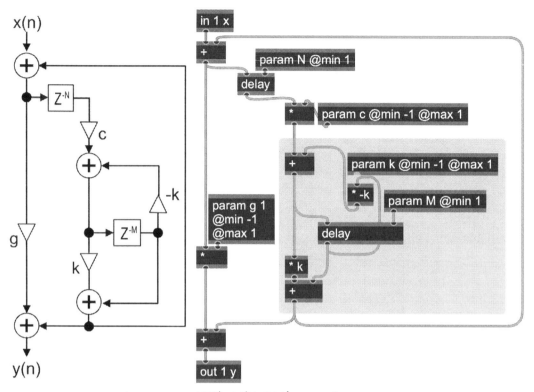

comb_enharmonic.maxpat

The ***comb_enharmonic.maxpat*** patch also shows an example of how to choose the two delay values using MIDI note semitones, which makes exploring the enharmonic output a lot of fun.

Strings

Delay times between 0.5 to 25ms and high levels of feedback can produce resonances evocative of string instruments. This method is commonly called Karplus–Strong string synthesis, after Kevin Karplus and Alexander Strong invented and analyzed it.[6] It is another kind of comb filtering but also a kind of dynamic wavetable synthesis in which the looping delay contents (the "tape") represent one period of an oscillating sound.

This patch can work as a tuned resonator for any input sound, but if the input is just a very short burst of noise, it will sound like a simple plucked string.

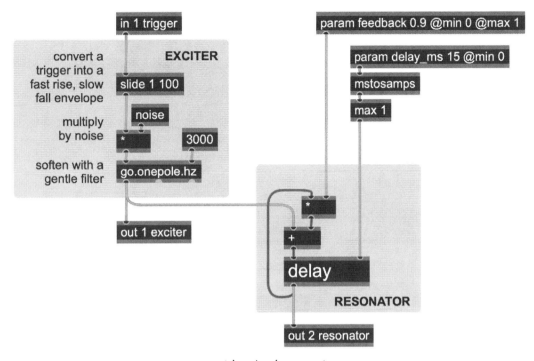

string_basic.maxpat

- The input **noise** is the *exciter,* which represents the input that sets the "instrument" in motion (like the interactions of the bow drawn across a string, a mallet striking a string or plate, or the interaction between a lip with a reed).

- The slowly decaying feedback **delay** acts as a *resonator,* which represents the physical system that the exciter acts upon. The pitch we set as the delay length is the lowest resonating frequency, but also any harmonic (any whole number multiple of the fundamental) can also resonate.

If we wanted to control this circuit with specific pitches, such as MIDI-style pitch numbers (in semitones), we would need a way to convert the pitch into an equivalent period in samples for the **delay** operator.

We can convert a MIDI-style pitch number into a frequency in Hertz using the **mtof** operator. A frequency in Hertz represents cycles per second, and so a reciprocal of this (using a **!/ 1** reciprocal operator) gives us a period in seconds per cycle. We can convert this period in seconds to a period in samples by multiplying by the **samplerate** constant. We can even merge these two operations into a single **!/ samplerate** operator.

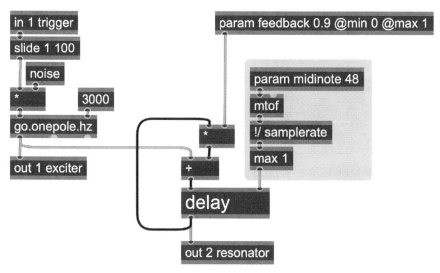

string_pitched.maxpat

The **param feedback** amount determines how long the string resonates (1.0 as infinite sustain, 0.9 or so for pizzicato), but this will vary according to the period of the delay. That Is, higher pitches with shorter delay periods will have shorter resonant decay times, and vice versa.

If this isn't desirable, we can use the same **t60**-based solution from *delay_feedback_decaytime.maxpat* (p.201) to set a decay time in milliseconds independently of the string length. Now the strings will decay over the same amount of time (**param decay_ms**) regardless of whether they are high notes or low notes.

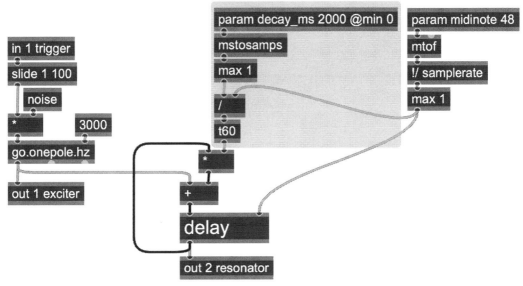

string_feedback_control.maxpat

What happens in the feedback loop?

We can refine this patch in several other ways, most of which involve placing more processing within the feedback loop.

1. With the feedback high and the delay time so short, it's a good idea to add a highpass DC blocking filter into the loop, just as we did earlier in the chapter (p.172). This is also realistic: a physical string can't accumulate DC endlessly, as the string is tied down to the body of the instrument, and the body dissipates this accumulated energy from the displacement of the string.

2. Changing the *sign* of the feedback also changes the sonic output: the alternation of positive and negative each time through the loop effectively makes the apparent period twice as long, sounding one octave lower (see the *string_inverted_feedback.maxpat* patch, for example). At the same time, this causes harmonic effects as the alternating positive and negative copies of the signal running through the loop largely cancel each other out. The result is a hollower tone of odd harmonics only, more characteristic of a wind instrument.

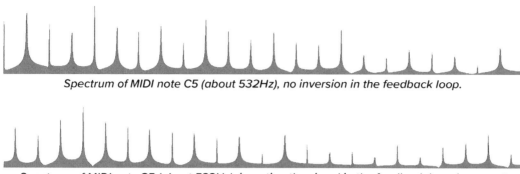

Spectrum of MIDI note C5 (about 532Hz), no inversion in the feedback loop.

Spectrum of MIDI note C5 (about 532Hz), inverting the signal in the feedback loop (apparent spectrum one octave lower).

Put another way, the resonant harmonic peaks of the spectrum of the inverted feedback case are exactly halfway between the resonant harmonic peaks of the non-inverted case. You might recall that we saw a similar phenomenon with positive and negative comb filter effects earlier in this chapter.

Damping

When you pluck a real string, the energy you impart to the system decays gradually, but the higher harmonics fade out sooner than the lower harmonics–the sound of the resonating string gets duller and duller after the initial pluck. We can emulate this easily enough by placing a lowpass filter into the delay loop, just as we did earlier in the chapter in the ***delay_feedback_filtered.maxpat*** patch.

However, the more subtle point is that using a lowpass filter will also impart some slight delay since, as we saw in Chapter 6, a low pass filter averages a signal with its own history.[7] Although it can be just a fraction of a sample, this delay is enough to cause the string's pitch to drop slightly, and the string will sound "detuned" — the more filtering is applied, the more the string's pitch drops.

We could compensate for this if we could estimate what the introduced delay will be and then shorten the core delay length by the same amount. The duration of additional delay a filter adds is dependent on the filter cutoff frequency and the particular filter algorithm we use. Unfortunately, the filter delay is also frequency-dependent — higher pitched tones may be delayed by slightly different proportions than lower-pitch tones (due to the filter's complex phase response). The mathematics required to derive this is beyond the scope of this chapter, but for the case of the most basic one-pole filter with a **mix** coefficient (damping factor) of *b*, then `2*log(1-b)` returns a close approximation to the required shortening of the delay time in samples. If we shorten the string length by this amount, we achieve a string simulation that can be damped without it going badly out of tune.[8]

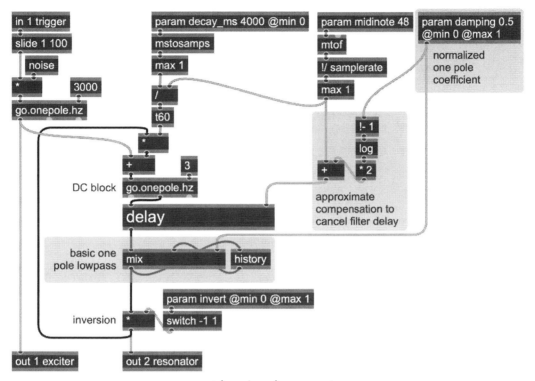

string_damping.maxpat

Cleaner interpolation for a consistent sound

Even if the damping filter is completely disabled (i.e., the **param damping** value is 0.0), you might notice that is sounds like there is still some damping happening, with the sound of the string after each pluck not just getting quieter but also becoming gradually duller as it fades away. You might also notice that this is stronger for some pitches than others. What's going on?

In fact, this inherent damping is a side-effect of linear interpolation inside the **delay** operator itself. Why is there interpolation here? Briefly, any delay length that isn't an exact whole number of samples requires some sort of interpolation to estimate the value between the sample frames of the delay's internal memory.

For example, if we wanted a delay time of exactly 7ms, we need a delay length of `samplerate * 7/1000` samples, which for a typical **samplerate** of 44.1kHz works out to be 308.7 samples. But our delay's internal memory tape is a discrete sequence of samples—there is no 308.7th sample! We could simply round this to the nearest whole number (by using **delay @interp none**), read the 309th value in the delay memory, and forget about the 0.7 part; but this will lead to distinct stepping or aliasing artifacts when our

223

delay times are very short or gently modulated, such as in chorus and flanger effects, and especially for our string emulation here. Instead, we must estimate what the value of the signal would be at fractional points between samples, which means using some kind of interpolation.

The simplest estimation is to draw a straight line between samples and read off the value at the desired point in between. This is linear interpolation, and it is what the **delay** operator performs by default. Linear interpolation is computationally quite inexpensive and very effective for most delay purposes. However, as we saw in the last chapter (p. 162) there is a close relationship between linear interpolation and low pass filtering; and with the very short delay times and high levels of feedback in string emulation, this low pass filtering effect becomes noticeable. To solve this problem, we need a form of interpolation that does not change the frequency spectrum. [9] Let's look at a couple of solutions.

In Chapter 6 (p. 174), we looked at a kind of filter that has no effect on the frequency spectrum: the allpass filter. This is typically described as a filter that applies a change of phase, but another way of looking at it is that it applies fractional sample delays. Theoretically, the allpass filter we looked at (**go.allpass**) can apply a delay between 0 and 2 samples' duration. If the desired delay is D samples, then the allpass coefficient can be calculated as $(D-1)/(D+1)$. So we could solve our problem by combining a regular, non-interpolating **delay @interp none** operator for the integer part and a **go.allpass** filter for the fractional part, which together should let us have any delay time we want.

There's just a slight wrinkle: the allpass filter's response becomes distorted at the extremes of its range and is better behaved between a range of about 0.3 and 1.3 samples' delay, so it's best if we can keep our use of the allpass filter within that range. We can ensure that by sending our desired delay time through a **wrap 0.3 1.3** operator for the allpass filter, and we can subtract that from our desired delay to get a remainder (that will always be a whole number) for the **delay @interp none** part. This works brilliantly, providing clean, unfiltered delays even at non-integer lengths.

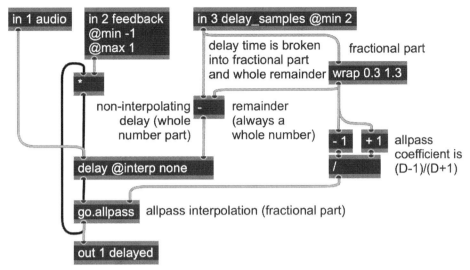

delay-interpolation-types.maxpat

Unfortunately, there's one more catch: if we want to *modulate* our delay time continuously, say with an LFO, we will find that in some circumstances, the allpass filter starts to resonate and become harsh or even explodes (<u>watch your ears!</u>). For example, this can happen if the LFO period is a simple whole number division of the delay time, such as one-half. If we're trying to emulate a physical string, this might not be a problem. Any physical modulation (such as from a whammy bar on an electric guitar) would be at a much lower frequency than the string itself. But for more exploratory synthesis, including audible frequency modulation of a string, we would need to handle this case.

The cheapest solution would be to add a saturator in the feedback loop, just as we did earlier in the chapter. You can see an example of this in the ***string_everything.maxpat*** patch.

Alternatively, we could try to tackle the cause of the problem, which is the feedback loops inside the allpass filter itself. Like almost all the filters we explored in Chapter 6, the allpass is an example of an Infinite Impulse Response (IIR) filter. It is infinite because it contains a feedback loop that operates on the histories of its own outputs. A different class of filters, Finite Impulse Response (FIR) filters, do not contain feedback and only operate on the histories of their inputs. That is, they only have feedforward paths.[10] FIR filters are often more expensive or require more data to achieve comparable results to IIR filters, but their avoidance of feedback paths means they are far more stable under modulation. This also makes them valuable for interpolation and resampling applications.

For the purposes of our delay interpolation problem, we can use an FIR filter that performs *sinc interpolation*. We'll look at what sinc interpolation is and why it works in more detail in Chapter 9 (p. 283), but briefly stated, the sinc function $\sin(x)/x$ happens to be an ideal smoothing curve for resampling without losing high frequency energy up to a certain point. In our patch below, we use an 8-point sinc interpolation, which means we read out eight non-interpolated samples from the **delay** operator, each spaced one sample apart, and multiply each one with an evenly spaced slice of a windowed-sinc function, shifted by the fractional part of the delay time, adding them all up for our output value.

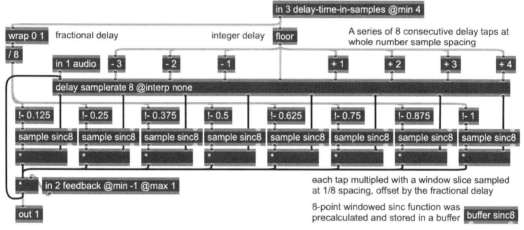

delay-interpolation-types.maxpat

This solution is more expensive than an allpass filter, but it does a very good job of preserving the spectrum up to `samplerate/4`. It is also far more robust under more extreme modulation as long as the modulation frequency is not higher than the fundamental frequency of the string itself. This may be a preferable solution if you want to explore very deep phase modulation, as we will see in the next chapter (p. 257).

We will return to look at more refined physical models in Book 2.

Chapter 8: Frequent Modulations

In this chapter we're going to look at some common (and less common) ways to modulate one oscillating signal by another, mostly at audio rates. This includes amplitude and ring modulation (AM and RM), frequency and phase modulation (FM and PM), and some interesting extensions to them. These methods are relatively simple and often computationally economical ways to generate interesting waveforms and spectral richness with smooth and continuous evolutions. Sometimes these subjects, and FM in particular, have an air of mystique or impenetrability. We hope to show not only how they are really quite approachable, but also through the flexible capabilities of gen~, how we can go beyond traditions to explore new and unusual algorithms and structures.

Amplitude modulation (AM) and Ring Modulation (RM)

One of the simplest things we can do with a signal is make it quieter, which means reducing its amplitude, which means multiplying every signal value by some number less than one. If the multiplier is a signal that varies over time, we can call it a "modulator", as it is modulating the amplitude of our original signal (which we call the "carrier"). This is known as amplitude modulation (or AM for short). This is what we are doing when we repeatedly envelope a sound, for example. An envelope typically runs from 0.0 (silence) to 1.0 (full amplitude) and back. That is, the modulator is *unipolar*.

Let's start with a simple bipolar sine wave at 100Hz (using a **cycle 200** operator) as the carrier:

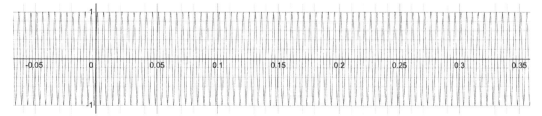

...and for the modulator, a unipolar sine wave at 5 Hz. We can make a **cycle 5** operator unipolar by sending it through a **scale -1 1 0 1** operator[1]:

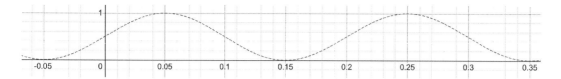

Then, multiplying these two signals produces our AM result:

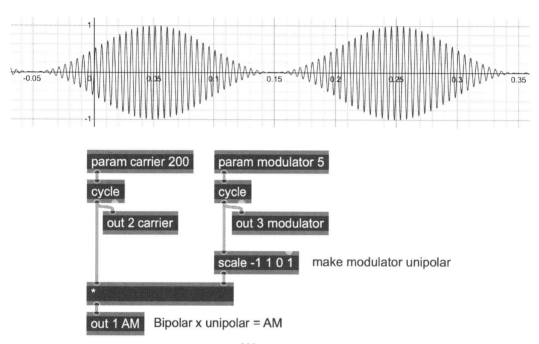

AM.maxpat

With the modulator frequency at 5Hz, the effect is a series of distinct sound events, like primitive notes. If you speed the modulator up to about 15Hz, it turns into a quite intense rhythmic tremolo effect. We'll look at reducing the intensity shortly, but first, try pushing the modulator frequency gradually upwards. At somewhere around 25-40Hz, the rhythmic sensation transforms into a kind of "fused" complex timbre. Above 40Hz, as you slowly keep rising, you may start to hear other tones appear, at certain points sounding like chords. With the carrier frequency at 600Hz, try modulator frequencies at 200Hz or 300Hz, for example. It's quite remarkable that with a single parameter we can evoke so many musical elements: note events, trill/tremolo, timbre, and chords.[2]

Sidebands

To understand what's happening here, we can have a look at the spectrum. Here is the carrier, a pure sine wave at 800Hz:

Here is the modulator, a pure sine wave at 200Hz:

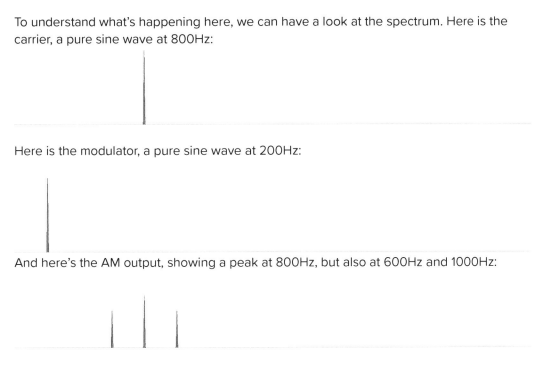

And here's the AM output, showing a peak at 800Hz, but also at 600Hz and 1000Hz:

Regardless of how we change the carrier and modulator frequency params, there's a copy of the carrier frequency present, a tone above, and a tone below it whose spacing increases as the modulator frequency increases. In fact, for sine waves, the frequencies of these "sideband" tones can be precisely predicted as:

```
CarrierHz + ModulatorHz

CarrierHz — ModulatorHz
```

Notice that the calculation can result in negative sideband frequencies. For example, if the carrier is 100Hz, and the modulator is 300Hz, then there will be sidebands at 400Hz and -200Hz. We can't hear any difference between positive and negative frequencies by themselves, but it can lead to waveforms interfering and cancelling each other out in unexpected ways. We'll also see this also for the other kinds of modulation in this chapter.

Ring modulation

Let's go back to the tremolo at 15Hz and reduce its depth. If we could make our modulator run between, say, 0.8 and 1.0, then the modulation *depth* would be decreased, and the tremolo effect would be more subtle.

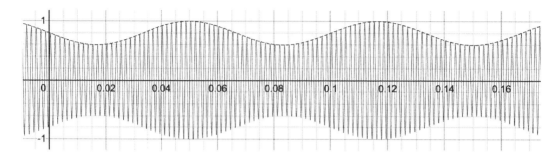

We can control this depth by modifying our **scale** operator to set the minimum value with a **param low** and thus map our original modulator's range (-1.0 to 1.0) to our desired range (**param low** to 1.0).

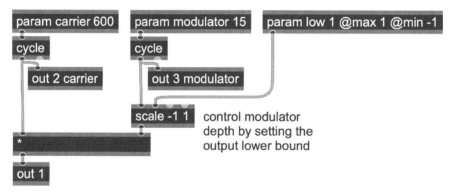

AM-depth.maxpat

Initially, there is no tremolo effect at all, but as we bring the **param low** from 1.0 down towards zero, the depth of the tremolo intensifies.

Turn the modulator frequency back up to 200Hz again. Now slowly push the **param low** further down all the way to -1.0 while watching the spectrum. You will see the "central lobe" at the carrier's 600Hz fade away toward zero, while only the sideband lobes at 400Hz and 800Hz remain (now slightly louder. At the point where **param low** equals -1.0, the **scale** operator is actually doing nothing at all: we are simply multiplying two bipolar oscillators, which is called *ring modulation[3] (RM):*

Here are some observations:

- Ring modulation (RM) is just a multiplication of two bipolar signals
- Amplitude modulation (AM) is a multiplication of a bipolar with a unipolar signal
- Amplitude modulation has the same sidebands as RM, mixed with the original carrier
- Amplitude modulation looks like a mix between RM and the original carrier

That last observation is mathematically correct, in fact. Call the bipolar carrier "C" and the bipolar modulator "M," then we can simply say that

```
RM = C * M
```

and

```
AM = C * ((M * 0.5) + 0.5)
```

Note that `((M * 0.5) + 0.5)` is the equivalent of a **scale -1 1 0 1** operator.

Doing a little rearranging:

```
AM = (C * M * 0.5) + (C * 0.5)

AM = (RM * 0.5) + (C * 0.5)  (because RM = C * M)

AM = (RM + C) * 0.5
```

That last expression is an exact average. So, we could actually express our blend from C to AM to RM as a more intuitive linear **mix**:

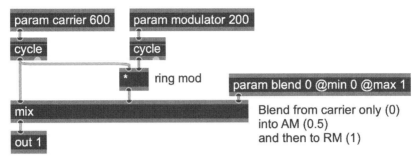

AMRM.maxpat

Beyond sinusoids

What happens if we start using waveforms other than sine waves for our carrier and modulator? The Fourier theorem says that any complex periodic signal can be described as simply a mixture (a sum) of plain old sine waves at different frequencies, amplitudes, and phases. What the spectroscope is showing us is an approximation of that mixture of sine waves. But most *interesting* waveforms need quite a large number of sine wave components, and since every single pairing of these between carrier and modulator creates two more sidebands, it can easily end up becoming a huge number of sidebands, and it can get complex very quickly. Still, if the carrier and modulator are harmonically related, and their component sine waves are harmonics, then many of those sidebands might end up overlapping such that the final waveform is likely to be harmonic too.

Frequency modulation (FM) and phase modulation (PM)

In the last section, we saw how speeding up a tremolo effect turns into the spectral effects of amplitude and ring modulation. In a similar way, speeding up a vibrato effect can open up the strange worlds of frequency modulation (FM) and phase modulation (PM).[4] As we'll see in this section, these two techniques are very similar to each other and have the same results in many cases.

Let's keep things simple by starting with sine waves again. This time, we're going to build a sine wave oscillator from a **phasor** operator rather than using the **cycle** operator. The main reason for this is that we're going to need to manipulate the sine wave oscillator at a finer level than a **cycle** operator affords.

Making this change will also make it easier to use waveforms other than sine waves later on as well. Here is our basic sine oscillator:

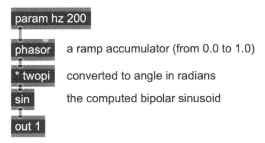

Sine.maxpat

The simplest PM and FM circuits use two of these oscillators — one being the "carrier" and the other the "modulator." Here is the main difference between PM and FM:

- In PM, the modulator is added to the angular phase before it enters the carrier's **sin** operator.
- In FM, the modulator is scaled to a value in Hz and added to the frequency before it enters the carrier's **phasor** operator.

In addition, in both cases, the amount of modulation added is multiplied by a parameter called the modulation *index* (or sometimes called the *depth*).

Here are the two circuits side by side, with PM on the left and FM on the right. As you can see, the difference between these two circuits is fairly minimal. The main difference is whether we are modulating the phase, or the rate of change of phase.[5]

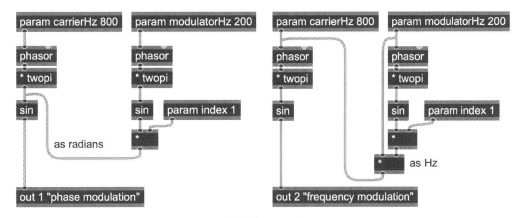

FMPM.maxpat

233

Sidebands

As it turns out, the spectra coming out of these two circuits are *identical*, regardless of what the parameters are. The waveforms also look virtually the same, however their relative phases may be different. And as long as the **param index** is fairly low, the spectra also look a bit similar to amplitude modulation, with a peak at the carrier, and symmetric sidebands above and below:

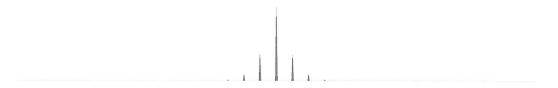

But for FM and PM, there are a lot more sidebands—and so the timbres and spectra of FM and PM are much more complex. For a carrier frequency of "C" and a modulator frequency of "M," the output frequencies are at the carrier C followed by pairs of sidebands at C+M and C-M just like AM/RM, but also at C+2M and C-2M, C+3M and C-3M, and so on. More generally:

        CarrierHz + k * ModulatorHz

        CarrierHz - k * ModulatorHz

Where k indicates the whole numbers 1, 2, 3, etc. For example, with a carrier at 1600Hz and modulator at 100Hz, the spectrum shows a strong central peak at 1600 Hz, sidebands above at 1700Hz, 1800Hz, 1900Hz, etc., and symmetric sidebands below at 1500Hz, 1400Hz, 1300Hz, etc.

The intensity of each of these pairs of sidebands depends on the modulation index in a complex way[6], but it is generally the case that increasing the index will increase the number of sidebands heard, with their intensity spreading out from the carrier frequency as the index increases, resulting in brighter and more complex sounds.

The spectra below show the spectrum with **param index** at 1, 4, and 10, respectively:

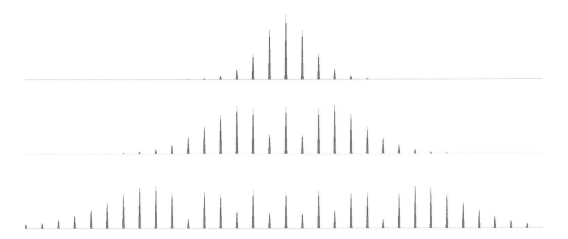

Therefore, many implementations use an envelope signal to control this modulation index and thus shape the PM or FM spectrum into an expressive event, such as rising quickly to a bright sound and then decaying more slowly to a duller sound, a timbral profile common to many musical instruments. We can extend our patch to support this by multiplying the **param index** with an **in 1** operator for the modulation signal input (and feeding an envelope of choice into that input). And while we are at it, why not also multiply the output with a related amplitude envelope to control the overall loudness of the event?

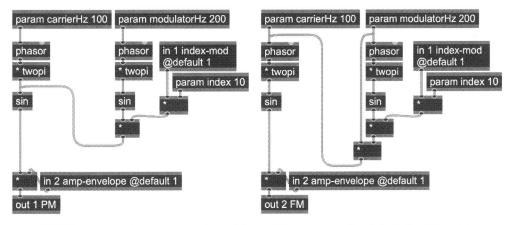

FMPM-enveloped.maxpat - on the left is the PM patch, on the right is the FM patch.

Frequency ratios and harmonicity

If you play around with the carrier and modulator frequencies in the ***FMPM.maxpat*** or ***FMPM-enveloped.maxpat*** patches, you may notice that some combinations of frequencies are more clangorous, metallic, bell-like, or enharmonic than others. Since sidebands appear at `C + k*M`, where `k` is some positive or negative whole number, it makes sense that the sidebands will form a more harmonic alignment with the carrier when the *ratio* of the modulator and carrier frequencies is made of simple whole numbers, such as 1:2, 1:5, 4:3, etc. This ratio is sometimes called the "harmonicity ratio." For example, when the modulator frequency is twice the carrier frequency (a ratio of 2:1), the resulting spectrum will contain only odd harmonics, much like a square wave.

But whole number ratios are not the only ones that can create harmonic partials. As John Chowning himself put it (on a post on the Cycling '74 forum[7]), it is better to think of there being a fundamental frequency (or pitch) control and to set carrier and modulator as multiples of that core frequency. That way, the spectral shape of the sound stays consistent as the core frequency (or pitch) control changes, and the sound will be harmonic if the carrier and modulator multipliers form a simple ratio (such as 3:2, 2:3, 3:4, 4:3, etc.). It is this ratio that defines the harmonicity. Following Chowning's recommendation, we can modify our patch to include separate fundamental frequency, as well as carrier and modulator multiplier parameters from this point onward.

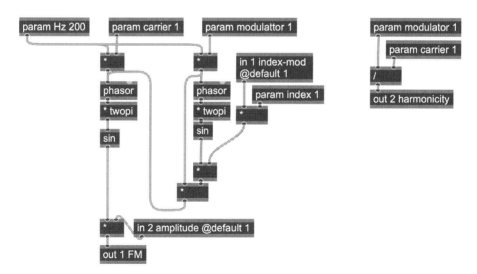

FMPM-harmonicity.maxpat (here showing the PM implementation).

It's also highly recommended to try ratios that are *almost but not quite* whole ratios, such as 1 : 3.01, as these slightly detuned frequencies will produce undulating "beating" variations that deepen the timbre. You could also add a tiny amount of noise (or one of the smooth random generators from Chapter 4 (p. 93) to the modulator frequency!

For some low carrier and high modulator parameter combinations, some of the sidebands will go "below zero." For example, if C=5Hz and M=10Hz, even the first sideband of C-kM is at -5V, the next at -15Hz, the next at -25Hz, etc. These sidebands don't disappear — they simply mirror around the zero Hz line and rise back up with their phase inverted (their waveform runs backward). For a symmetric waveform such as a sine wave, this is no different than an imperceptible phase-shift. While those negative frequency sidebands can add to the characteristically clangorous sound of FM and PM, something interesting happens when the harmonicity ratio is simple: the folded negative sidebands may line up with the regular sidebands, resulting in a harmonic sound.

Combinations (FM algorithms and beyond)

So far, we've only looked at patches with a single modulator oscillator feeding a single carrier oscillator. Historic hardware phase modulation synthesizers such as the Yamaha DX7 included more oscillators with a variety of "algorithms" to choose from, where the term algorithm really meant pre-defined configurations of a handful of ways of wiring these oscillators together.

In this section, we'll delve deeper into these as well as several other ways of combining oscillators through mutual modulation. This is another example of where gen~ offers great freedom: rather than being limited to selecting from pre-defined configurations, we can freely rearrange signal structures and explore new ones by inserting different processes between them, including single-sample feedback loops.

To keep things simple, we'll focus mostly on phase modulation, as it is slightly easier to construct and maintain pitch stability. Many of the patches include FM implementations, too.

Parallel carriers and parallel modulators

Parallel carriers refers to the technique of sending a modulation signal into more than one carrier and mixing the results together. Adding more carriers can be a relatively controllable way of producing coherent formants.

The following example blends two carriers with a linear **mix** operator:

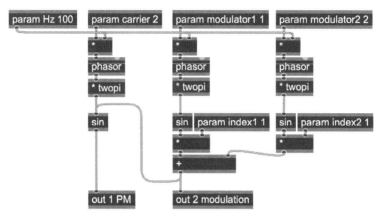

FMPM-parallel-carriers.maxpat

Similarly, we can easily combine multiple modulators together — here, for example, is two modulators routed into a single carrier:

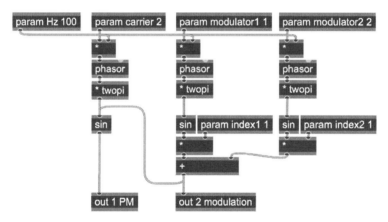

FMPM-parallel-modulators.maxpat

The ***FMPM-parallel-modulators.maxpat*** patch also shows the FM equivalent (they sound the same). For more movement, try carrier to modulator ratios that are slightly detuned from simple fractions, like 2:3.01.

Beyond sinusoidal modulators

We can use these patches to understand what PM and FM mean for more complex waveforms. Take a look at the ***FMPM-parallel-modulators.maxpat*** patch again. The modulation signal that goes from the + operator to the **sin** operator is just one signal (we can take a look at it from **out 2**), which has a waveform made from two sine waves added together. The PM or FM spectrum this produces creates a whole set of sidebands for each of those two sine waves.

From this, we can extrapolate that *any* waveform made up of a more complex combination of component sine waves will create a whole set of sidebands for each sine wave component. And, since the Fourier theorem shows that *any* periodic waveform can be created from a collection of sine waves, we now have a better idea of what to expect from more complex modulator waveforms.

One quick observation we can make is to note how quickly waveforms with significant high harmonics can produce sidebands at extremely high frequencies, which as we shall see can cause aliasing distortion. Accordingly, many PM and FM implementations restrict their oscillator waveforms to sine waves, waveforms whose harmonics fall quickly, such as triangle waves, or waveforms that can be band-limited to only include lower harmonics. We'll return to this later with respect to band-limiting signals.

Moving beyond basic sinusoidal modulators, we also start to hear differences between PM and FM. The ***FMPM-blending.maxpat*** patch demonstrates this using a triangle wave modulator (and also shows how we can blend smoothly between PM and FM using an equal power mixer).

Why does a non-sinusoidal waveform sound different for PM and FM? Remember that when we hear a sound, our sense of its pitch or frequency doesn't come from the size of the wave, but from how quickly it oscillates, that is, its *rate of change* (or, in mathematical terms, its *derivative*).

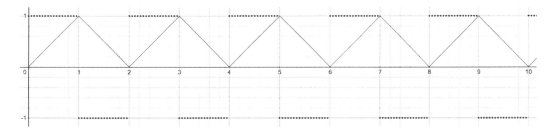

Let's keep things simple by choosing a slow triangle wave as a modulator (solid line in the graph above). The rate of change of a triangle wave is a positive constant when the triangle is rising and a negative constant when the triangle is falling; that is, the rate of change of a triangle wave is a square wave (dotted line above). So if you use a triangle wave modulator in PM, you will alternately hear a high pitch, then a low pitch, and so on. In contrast, with FM, we feed the modulator through a **phasor** operator first.

You may remember from Chapter 2 how we built the **phasor** operator from a process of counting, which makes it act like an integrator in mathematical terms: it converts the *value* at the input into a rising or falling *slope* at the output (i.e., it converts the input into a rate of change). So, our triangle wave modulator in FM directly produces rates of change of the carrier signal, alternately speeding it up and then slowing it down, which we hear as a rising and falling pitch, like a vibrato.

That's why the modulator directly shapes the pitch of the output in FM, but it is the modulator's rate of change (slope or derivative) that shapes the pitch of the output in PM. The reason we couldn't hear this difference with a simple sine wave modulator is that the rate of change of a sine wave is another sinusoidal wave[8]—this is part of what makes sine waves so special. But once you start using other waveforms, including even simple mixtures of sine waves, the differences become far more obvious.

To take this insight one step further, have a look at the second example in **FMPM-blending.maxpat**, and you'll see that even though we are using a skewed triangle wave modulator, both FM and PM sound identical. How? Because we fed the PM modulator through a lowpass filter (which, as we saw in Chapter 6 (p. 162), is a kind of integrator) and the FM modulator through a highpass filter (a kind of differentiator)! That is, <u>FM using a highpass filtered modulation signal is exactly the same as PM using the lowpass filtered modulation signal!</u>

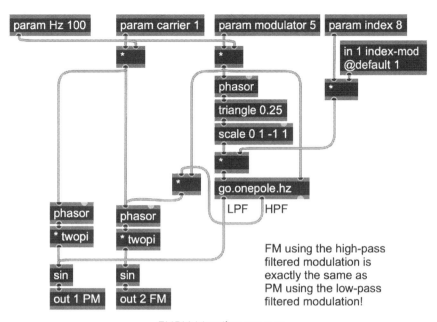

FMPM-blending.maxpat

Modulating modulators: cascade modulators

What if we use another PM or FM signal as our modulator? This is sometimes called series modulation or cascade modulation, as it simply means that our modulator is modulated by another modulator.

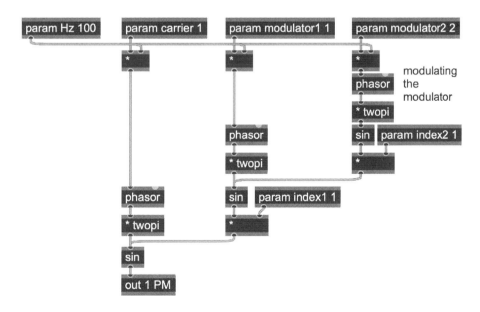

The ***FMPM-cascade-modulation.maxpat*** patch shows this PM implementation of cascade modulation, as well as a comparable FM implementation. Unlike simpler configurations, once the modulator's modulator's index (here, the **param i2**) is non-zero, the PM and FM versions respond differently—with the PM version producing comparably brighter spectra.

As with parallel modulators, cascade modulation is equivalent to a single modulator with a more complex and dynamic waveform, but it can achieve this complexity with far fewer oscillators. The timbral spectrum of the sidebands has a slightly recursive quality, as each sideband produced in the second modulator creates a whole set of sidebands in the carrier.

Cascading more modulators increases this recursive complexity.

Feedback modulation

Could we create a cascade of infinite modulators? Actually, this can be done very easily by simply feeding the carrier's output back through a **history** operator to become its own modulator.

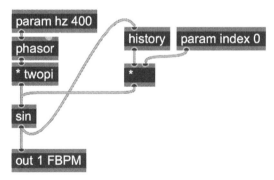

FMPM-feedback.maxpat

With an index parameter of zero, there is no feedback at all, and we hear the pure carrier sine wave. As the index is brought up to 1.0, the sine becomes increasingly skewed toward a rounded saw wave. Turning the index down to -1.0 will skew in the other direction.

Unlike the unusual distribution of often clangorous sidebands in typical multi-operator phase modulation, the sidebands have a more naturalistic exponential distribution with feedback modulation, and they are *always* harmonic.

But as we increase the index further, you can start to hear distortions appear. The feedback modulation patch is a very basic chaotic iterated system, and these distortions are examples of "hunting" phenomena in the chaos. Keep turning the index parameter up and it will eventually collapse into complete noise. This noise can be handy for a bright "strike" effect if driving the index with an envelope, but it sets in rather quickly.

The original patent for Yamaha's implementation by Norio Tomisawa[9] added a filter in the feedback loop to lessen the impact of this chaotic behavior; in the patent, this filter was a very simple average with the previous input (a finite impulse response filter), which allows the index to go up to about 2.0 without any chaotic disturbance; in gen~ it looks like this:

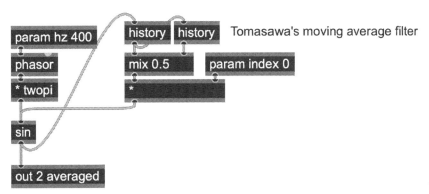

FMPM-feedback.maxpat

If instead we insert a one-pole lowpass filter such as the **go.onepole.hz** we built in Chapter 6 (p. 186) and tune it to a cutoff frequency somewhere between 200 to 4000Hz, we can push the modulation index much higher. However, as we lower the cutoff frequency, the output waveform becomes more spiky and less saw-like.

As an alternative, we can have the lowpass filter's cutoff frequency track the same frequency as the carrier, as in the following patch, which results in a very stable output even with a much higher index.

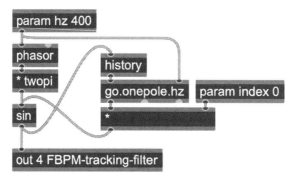

FMPM-feedback.maxpat

Feedback FM modulation can also be implemented in a similar way, but the behavior is rather different, leading to a spikier waveform.

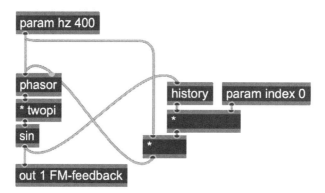

FMPM-feedback.maxpat

Unfortunately, the asymmetry of this waveform in feedback also effectively "detunes" the oscillator. We'll look at why (and how to fix this) in the next section.

Fixing FM going out of tune

If the modulator signal is not balanced around the zero line, which is to say that the average of the value of the modulation over time is not zero, then that deviation is called a bias or DC offset. Any such DC offset in an FM modulator will be heard as a detuning of the carrier. A tiny amount of very low frequency modulation might be desirable, as slight detuning can add to the warmth or "fatness" of a sound, but beyond this we may likely want to eliminate more significant detuning due to DC. We can suppress it quite effectively using a highpass filter[10] (such as the middle outlet of **go.onepole.hz**). For example, here's that solution applied to feedback FM:

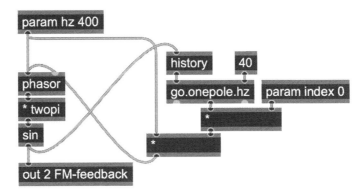

FMPM-feedback.maxpat

In this patch, we made the filter track the same frequency as the modulator, but you could also try using a fixed filter frequency tuned to the threshold of audibility somewhere between 10 to 50Hz. Regardless, it is generally best to place this filter *before* scaling the modulator by the modulation index so that the effects of envelopes are *not* filtered away.

Highpass filtering is not usually necessary for PM since a DC offset there leads to a change in phase rather than a change in pitch. But here's something very curious—if you compare the output and response of the feedback PM patch with the tracking *lowpass filter* and the feedback FM patch with the tracking *highpass* filter, they now look remarkably similar![11]

Cross-coupled feedback modulation

So far, our feedback modulation patches have had a single oscillator, but we can also create feedback with two (or more) oscillators, where each acts as a modulator to the other. In this "cross-coupled" feedback, either oscillator can be the output (or both).

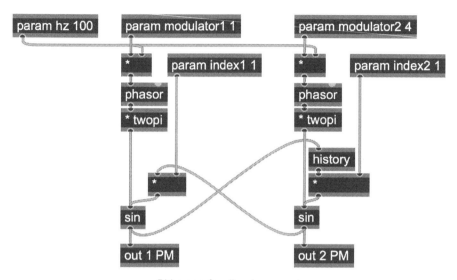

PM-cross-feedback.maxpat

As long as both index parameters are non-zero, this creates a feedback loop through both oscillators. The resulting waveform combines the saw-like spectrum of feedback PM with the complex spectrum of ordinary PM.

As with single-oscillator feedback PM, inserting a lowpass filter in the feedback loops permits much higher index parameters and more elaborate transitions into chaos. In between, it can sometimes jump between bifurcations of harmonics and other very expressive sounds. The feedback filter cutoff has a strong impact on the output spectrum.

For the following patch, we set the filter frequency parameters to be multiples of the modulator frequencies:

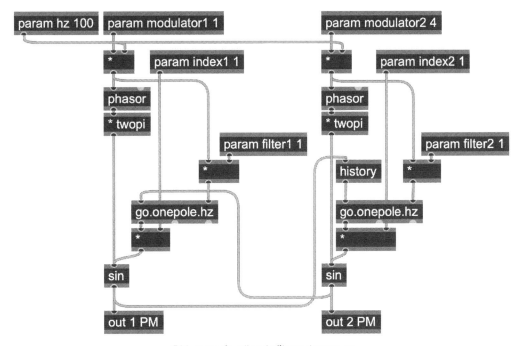

PM-cross-feedback-filtered.maxpat

Try setting the carrier frequencies to slightly detuned from a whole number multiples of each other to hear how this interacts with the beating frequencies.

Or, for something completely different: set one carrier at an audible rate (e.g., 50-100Hz) and high index (e.g., 100-200), and the other at a slow LFO rate (around 1Hz) and low index (around 4) and explore the complex soundscapes that ensue as you move the filter cutoff frequencies between 5Hz and 250Hz. The results can sound remarkably analog and can be surprisingly hard to predict!

Exploring hybrid algorithms

Most of the algorithm structures we have looked at so far are pretty lightweight in computational cost and can easily be extended and combined to involve more oscillators. But with an environment like gen~ why stop there? For example, what happens when we combine parallel, cascade, and feedback structures with other signal processors besides PM and FM, such as AM/RM, waveshaping, or other filters and delays? What happens when we introduce colored noise, chaos, quantized or smooth-stepped signals into these circuits? There's a huge range of possibilities to explore!

Index amplitude/ring modulation

Actually, we've already been doing some of this, more or less. We've seen that multiplying the **param index** with an envelope can create expressive sound events, but there's no reason to limit yourself to sending envelopes into that **in 1 mod-index** operator! Try throwing all different kinds of modulations in here, such as LFOs (for a classic 'wub wub' sound, see ***FMPM-lfod.maxpat***) and audio-rate oscillators. In fact, if you think about it, inserting an oscillator here is like *applying amplitude or ring modulation to the modulator* before it modulates the carrier!

Phase modulation: suppressing clicks

You might notice that, with phase modulation, making rapid changes to the modulation index can lead to clicks and distortions in the carrier. This makes sense: any sharp transients or jumps of *magnitude* in the modulator signal will become sudden jumps of *phase* of the carrier and cause skips in the output waveform.[12]

For example, in the following graph, the index of modulation (dashed line) is a stepped random signal whose steps cause the modulation signal (thin dotted line) to jump in magnitude. As a result, the phase modulation output (solid line) has skips and breaks in its flow that will be heard as clicks.

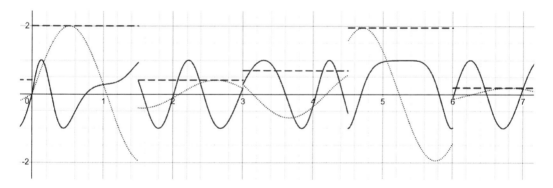

There are a couple of ways we can address this.

One way is to sneak in the index changes by updating it only when the modulator signal is crossing zero (i.e., the very moment at which the index scaling has no effect) using a zero-crossing detector and a **latch** operator.

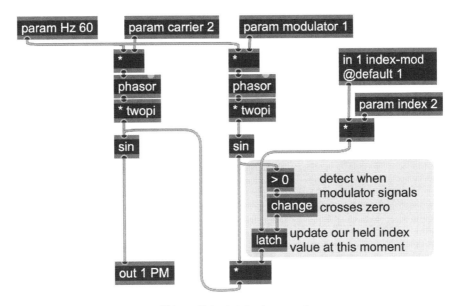

PM-noclicks-latched.maxpat

The technique of introducing a change in parameters at the point where the algorithm is temporarily silenced is one you've seen before in this book (for example, where we used it to change a delay time without adding a pitch shift in Chapter 7 (p. 209). For the phase modulation patch above, latching the index when the modulator is near zero, and thus having no effect on the carrier, quite effectively hides the discontinuities (at least, so long as the modulator has no significant DC offset).

An alternate method is to add a slew or lowpass filter to the index parameter before the modulation is added to the carrier to soften any jumps by spreading them out over time. The filter may need to be tuned to fit each application as needed since the more it suppresses clicks, the more it may also limit the brightness of the index modulation itself. In ***PM-noclicks-filtered.maxpat*** we chose a series of three stacked one-pole filters at around 500Hz as a reasonable tradeoff.

Waveshaping modulators

Take a closer look at almost any of the patches we've explored so far. No matter what we do to create our modulation, you can see that the resulting signal always goes through the **sin** operator just before the output, which means that the output will always be swinging between -1.0 and 1.0. Compared to creating sounds "additively" by mixing sine waves together, phase modulation and frequency modulation are much cheaper ways to produce a spectrum that is not only complex but also energetically optimal.

Try setting the carrier frequency to zero. Now the perceived pitch is entirely determined by the modulator, and increasing the index parameter creates an effect very much like wave folding or wave shaping.[13] In fact, for phase modulation, that carrier **sin** operator really is acting as a waveshaper: no matter what crazy modulations we throw at it, it ensures the output is wrapped within the -1.0 to +1.0 range. We could also try different periodic waveshaping functions here instead of a **sin** operator (such as a **triangle**, **sinh,** or **fold** operator), and we'll return to this notion when we look at wavetables in the next chapter,

Or, we can try adding more waveshaping operators between the modulator and the carrier. Changing the *shape* of the modulator waveform will change the spectral distribution of sidebands at different indices (in fact, that's part of what parallel and cascade modulation achieves). This spectral variation is especially apparent when driving the index with an envelope. The ***FMPM-waveshaping-modulator.maxpat*** patch shows an example using a unit easing-based waveshaper from Chapter 3 (p. 79) for both PM and FM. As usual, for FM, you probably want to add a highpass filter after any waveshaper to ensure that modulation stays centered at the zero line and thus minimizes detuning of the waveform.

Exponential FM/PM

Some analog synthesizers include both a "linear FM" and an "exponential FM" modulation input (and sometimes the linear FM is marked as "through-zero" or TZFM[14]). So far, what we have been doing in this Chapter corresponds to linear (through-zero) FM, where there is a linear relationship between the modulation signal value and the resulting frequency. In contrast, exponential FM effectively applies an exponential scaling function to a modulation signal before adding it to the carrier frequency. Exponential scaling has some perceptual advantages, as it more closely follows the curvature of perceived pitch (where increasing pitch by one octave implies a doubling of frequency).

We can emulate this frequency-doubling curvature in gen~ using the **exp2** operator, which is equivalent to raising 2 to the power of the input signal. In the following patch, we applied this after the index envelope scaling to intensify the effect:

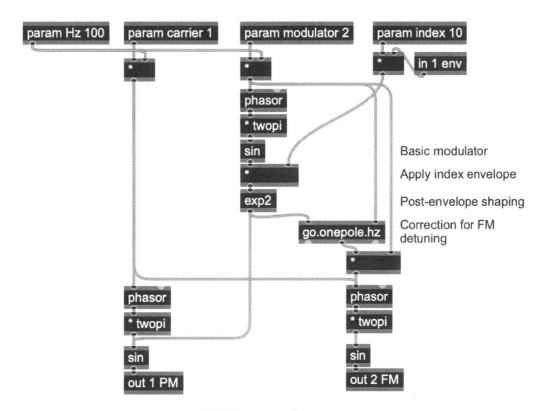

FMPM-exponential.maxpat

Exponential shaping tends to lessen the characteristic "glassy" sound of PM/FM as the index changes and instead imparts a more fizzy texture.

Note that the exponential function will only ever return a positive output. That's because the closer you get to zero, the flatter the curve gets, so you can never quite reach it. So, as the modulation index increases, the average value of the signal will get more positive. In the FM case, this would have caused the output to rise in pitch, but—as before—we suppressed detuning in the patch above by adding a highpass filter.

Using AM for asymmetric PM spectra

As we have seen, the spectrum of a sinusoidal PM patch is symmetric: with a sideband below the carrier for every sideband above the carrier. This can sometimes be problematic when the lower sidebands fold around zero, and in other terms, it is generally uncharacteristic of natural sounds. One way to break this symmetry is to use a modulator waveform that is not perfectly symmetrical. Another is to amplitude modulate the PM output with a waveform that is synchronized to the modulator.

In either case, it's not easy to design a modulation waveform to produce a specific balance of sidebands. But here's a really interesting exception: If we AM the output of the PM patch with a "raised cosine" window that is synchronized to the modulator frequency, it can completely remove *all* the sidebands below the carrier, leaving only sidebands above it![15] A raised cosine window for phase running from 0.0 to 1.0 looks like this (first in math, then in code):

$$e^{\;n\,(\cos\,(2\pi\;\text{phase})\,-\,1)}$$

```
exp(n * (cos(twopi * phase)) - 1)
```

The parameter "n" defines the sharpness of the window: the higher *N* gets, the thinner the windows get. Here is the graph of a raised cosine as a function of phase (the *X* axis), with a parameter "n" of 4:

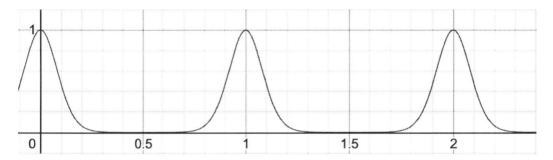

There is something particularly remarkable about this envelope function. If we drive it with the same phase as the modulator and set the parameter "n" to be exactly the same as the modulator index, and then we amplitude modulate the window with the phase modulation output, it perfectly cancels out *all* of the lower sidebands.

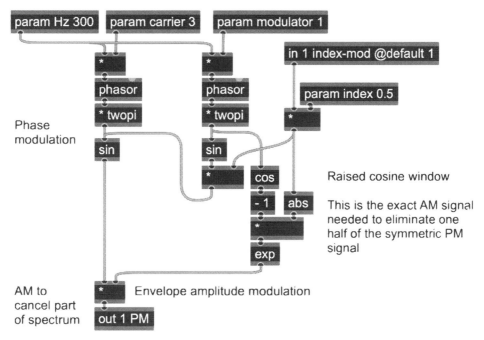

PM-asymmetric.maxpat

With a higher index, the resulting waveform begins to resemble an impulse train:

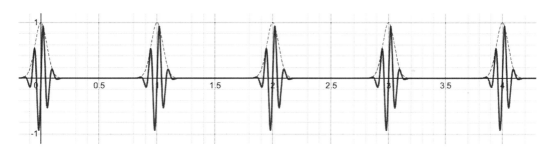

With a negative index, only the sidebands below the carrier pass through and all harmonics above the carrier are canceled out: a very alien sound.

Driving the **in 1** index modulator with an LFO or oscillator can produce some quite rich sounds.

Things that can go wrong

We noted earlier in the Chapter that adding filters can be very helpful in suppressing clicks in phase modulation and suppressing detuning in frequency modulation, but here are a handful more recommendations for better control of your modulation patches.

Removing inaudible frequencies to preserve headroom

All of the techniques in this Chapter lead to the generation of new frequencies as sidebands. It's quite possible that some of these sidebands appear in sub-audible ranges and even at zero Hz (DC); it is highly likely, for example, when carrier and modulator frequencies are very close to each other, which is especially the case for feedback modulation circuits! Any such sub-audible frequencies and DC offsets in the output will reduce the overall usable headroom of audio signals as they push it away from the zero-line. For this reason, you might want to place a **dcblock** operator or some other highpass filter tuned to around 10-40Hz *after* the carrier, just before the final output.

Aliasing and bandlimiting

We noted earlier in this Chapter that with AM/RM—and especially with PM/FM—using complex waveforms with significant high harmonics can very quickly produce sidebands at extremely high (and problematic) frequencies. But aliasing can be a problem even with pure sine waves. Although carrier and modulator signals cannot be above the Nyquist limit of **samplerate/2**, it's quite possible for the sidebands generated to end up much higher. And since no sampled digital system can represent frequencies above the Nyquist limit, they will be "folded" back down (aliased), which can cause undesirably audible side effects. We'll look at aliasing suppression in more detail in Chapter 9, but stated briefly here, the best way to avoid it is to constrain the input such that these frequencies are never generated in the first place.

In the case of AM and RM, it's relatively easy. Since the upper sideband is C+M, then the maximum possible frequency of any AM or RM effect is the maximum absolute frequency of the carrier plus the maximum absolute frequency of the modulator. This suggests three possible solutions:

1. Pre-filter both carrier and modulator to have no frequencies above samplerate/4 so that their combination of samplerate/4 + samplerate/4 can never go above samplerate/2. (See ***AMRM-bandlimited.maxpat***)

2. Oversample the AM/RM effect at 2x the normal **samplerate**, and downsample back afterward. (We will look at this kind of oversampling in Book 2.)

3. Or, if we have complete control over the waveforms, we can simply limit the total of the frequency parameters to never go above samplerate/2—such as by fading the inputs to zero when they approach the limit.

The first two options work with any waveforms and inputs; the third option requires that we know how to limit the inputs at the source.

The case of FM/PM is not as easy since far more sidebands are produced, and the mathematical Bessel functions that define the sideband intensities are quite complex. We can, however, point out a rule-of-thumb (known as the Carson bandwidth rule[16]) that pertains to the overall bandwidth when working with pure sine waves. This rule-of-thumb states that 99% of the signal energy in the spectrum is bounded between $C - M*(index+1)$ and $C + M*(index+1)$. With some additional refinements to handle negative parameters, the patching to implement this calculation looks like this:

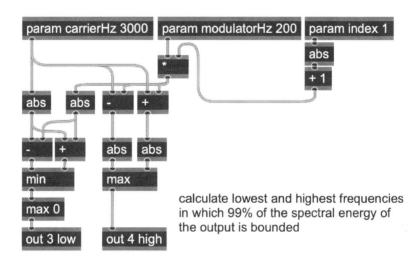

FMPM-carsonrule.maxpat

255

More usefully, we can rearrange this calculation to derive what the maximum possible modulation index can be within the Nyquist limit of samplerate/2, like this:

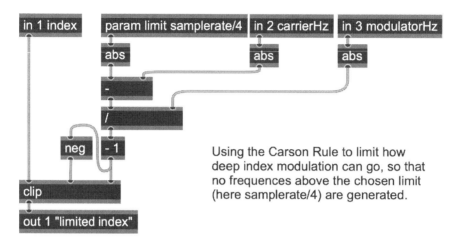

FMPM-carsonrule.maxpat

With these circuits in the **FMPM-carsonrule.maxpat** patch, you should be able to see how the param limit prevents the spectrum from going outside the defined upper bound, no matter what carrier and modulator frequencies you choose. For a slightly different approach, the **FMPM-carsonrule-filtered.maxpat** patch uses the rule to estimate a filter cutoff frequency to lowpass filter the modulation signal itself in such a way that it achieves a comparable limiting of the index; the result is a little less abrupt.

Remember, though: the Carson rule only works with pure sine waves. Different wave shapes, or more complex modulations, can easily introduce far higher sidebands. If these can't be predicted and prevented at the source, a lowpass filter might be a better compromise.

The **FMPM-antialias-filter.maxpat** shows a simple example of inserting a two-pole lowpass filter, tuned to match the available bandwidth, which greatly suppresses high aliasing modulator frequencies even for a harsh saw wave modulator.

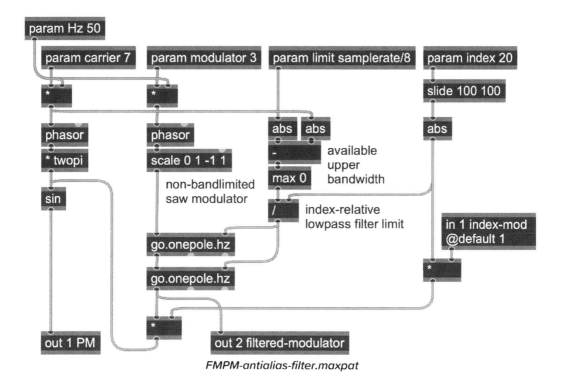

FMPM-antialias-filter.maxpat

Delay as phase modulation

In Chapter 7 (p. 208), we talked about how modulating a **delay** operator's delay time parameter can approximate the effects of Doppler shift: the rising and falling of frequencies when an object is moving toward you or away from you. Now you might be able to see how this is the same as phase modulation. Modulating the delay time alternately compresses or expands the data read out of it, just as a moving object can compress or expand physical wavefronts emanating from it, thus raising or lowering perceived frequencies. This compression and expansion of the waveforms is like the effect of adding a continuous modulator to the phase input of an oscillator: according to the modulator, sometimes we are reading ahead, sometimes reading behind. Put another way: if frequency modulation is like a singer with extreme vibrato, then phase modulation is rather like a singer with no vibrato, but who is moving very quickly toward you and away from you![17]

Since phase modulation is similar to a high-frequency Doppler shift, it makes sense that you can also use a variable delay to create phase modulation. We can certainly do this, but there are a couple of subtleties to work through first.

- Since the modulator signal normally represents a phase in *radians*, we need to convert that to an equivalent delay time in *samples*, which we can do by multiplying the modulator with **samplerate/twopi**.
- We might also want to scale this to the length of the carrier's period so that a phase rotation of pi radians will phase shift by half a cycle, which we can do by dividing by the carrier frequency.
- Since a delay can only read from the past, not the future, there's no such thing as a negative delay time. That means we can't handle negative phase modulation. Instead, we must raise our modulation signal to be always above zero by adding an appropriate constant offset—the simplest way being to stick a **+ 1** operator right after the modulator's **sin** operator. And as an extra precaution (in case of a negative index or carrier parameter), we can insert an **abs** operator right before the **delay** operator's delay time input.

It looks like the following patch when put together. On the left is a typical phase modulation patch that we have seen throughout this Chapter. On the right is a patch that produces the same sound by feeding the modulator signal to set the delay time of a **delay** operator.

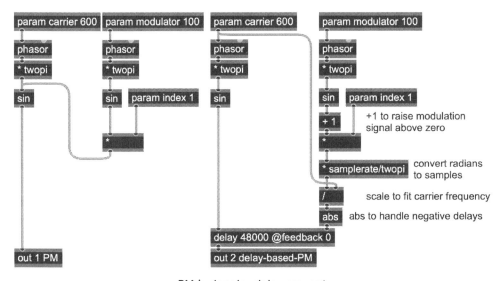

PM-is-doppler-delay.maxpat

Using a **delay** operator to implement phase modulation is more computationally expensive, but it does offer a unique advantage: it allows you to modulate *any* carrier signal, even one that you have no control over, such as a live audio input. However, it does then require that you *either* estimate the carrier frequency *or else* ignore this component of the delay time calculation and embrace phase modulation with a more arbitrary depth control.

More generally, we can use this insight to look again at delay-based circuits, knowing that we can introduce the various effects and transformations of PM through audio-rate modulation of delay time. For example, with a Karplus-Strong delay-based string model, dropping in a slight amount of delay-time modulation at one-half the string frequency can add some deliciously chorus-like subharmonic fuzz to the sound.[18]

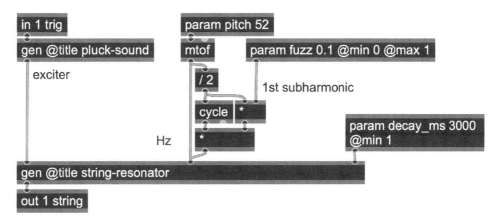

KP-FM.maxpat

However, for a more robust phase-modulated string model, the sinc-interpolated example at the end of chapter 7 (p. 223) is recommended. We also noted in that chapter how modulating the cutoff frequency of a **history** or **delay**-based filter at audio rates can produce interesting timbral complexity; you might now understand this a little better through the lens of frequency and phase modulation!

Blending harmonic oscillators

The clangorous timbres that enharmonic ratios produce can be absolutely wonderful noises, but sometimes we might want to focus only on purely harmonic timbres. In that case, it's tempting to restrict carrier and modulator frequencies to be simple whole number multiples of the fundamental frequency (where the "harmonicity" ratio forms simple fractions). It's easy enough to limit a parameter to whole numbers via a **floor** operator, but then we wouldn't be able to transition smoothly from one timbre to the next. As the parameter is changed, we would hear undesirable "stepping" in the output.

To solve this, and achieve smooth morphing between integer parameters, we can use a trick we have used several times in this book, such as the smooth bitcrusher in Chapter 5 (p. 157) and the mipmap level mixer we'll explore in Chapter 9 (p. 287). The trick is to simply use two copies of an algorithm, each using a different parameter value, and smoothly crossfade between them to emulate one morphing parameter. To transition between two neighboring integer parameters, we can use two copies of the algorithm and a trio of **floor**, **+ 1,** and a **mix** driven by the fractional difference to crossfade between them.

split input parameter "harmonic" into nearest whole numbers below (floor) and above (+ 1)

process both of these whole numbers

blend between the results using the fractional part of the parameter

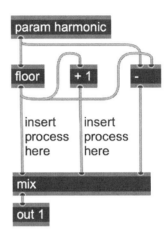

Now we can simply put our sine wave oscillators inside this structure to synthesize the two nearest harmonics. We can even save a little CPU (and gain a little stability) by having both oscillators driven by the same **phasor** input.

Synthesize the two nearest integer multiples of the base phasor's frequency

And blend them according to the fraction between

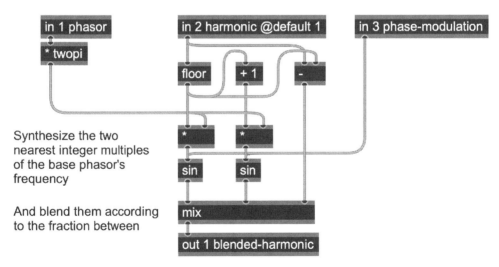

Harmonic.maxpat (and go.harmonic.gendsp)

This works because the multipliers coming out of the **floor** and **+ 1** operators are always whole numbers, and since **sin** repeats seamlessly every **twopi** radians, a whole number multiple of that *also* repeats seamlessly at the same point.

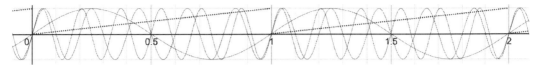

A fundamental phasor ramp at 1Hz (dotted line) and its harmonics at exactly 1x, 5x, and 6x this frequency (solid lines). Notice how all harmonics complete a cycle at the same time as the fundamental phasor at x=1, x=2, etc.

With the *Harmonic.maxpat* patch, try modulating the "harmonic" parameter up and down smoothly between 1.0 and 10.0, with all the decimal numbers between. Instead of hearing stepping, you will hear smooth transitions, sounding a bit like a filter sweep through the harmonic series. (We come back to this with Modified FM later).

Blended harmonic AM/RM and PM

We can plug this "blended harmonic" oscillator (which we saved as *go.harmonic.gendsp*) back into our various modulation algorithm patches. We can do this for either of the carrier and/or modulator oscillators. In the following AM/RM patch, we did both, using the same phasor for each.

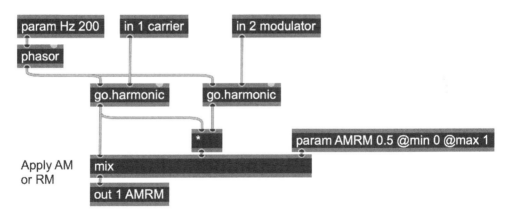

AMRM-blended-harmonics.maxpat

And we did the same for basic phase modulation here:

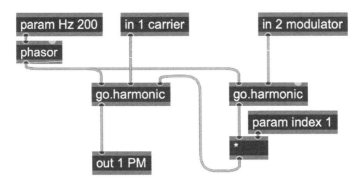

PM-blended-harmonics.maxpat

In both cases, the entire patch is now driven by a single **phasor**. The results have the characteristic complexities of AM/RM or PM and can be smoothly varied, but they avoid the enharmonic timbres because the frequencies are always whole number multiples of the fundamental phasor.

Try **PM-blended-harmonics.maxpat** with the carrier at 1.0 and the modulator around 1.15, and the index at 1.0, and you will get a soft saw-like waveform. Turning the modulator up to 2.0 produces a more square-like waveform. Turning up the index and modulator further produces sounds comparable to wavefolding. Adding some envelope, LFO, or oscillator modulation to the carrier and modulator inputs can lead to quite richly complex timbres while still maintaining a strong harmonic coherence. (If taking this modulation to extremes, it may be advisable to add a little lowpass filtering on them.)

Modified FM

The raised cosine window we saw in the asymmetric spectrum patch also does fascinating things with a blended harmonic oscillator. In this algorithm, called "Modified FM,"[19] a raised cosine window is driven by the same fundamental **phasor** that drives the blended harmonic oscillators, and both are combined by amplitude modulation.

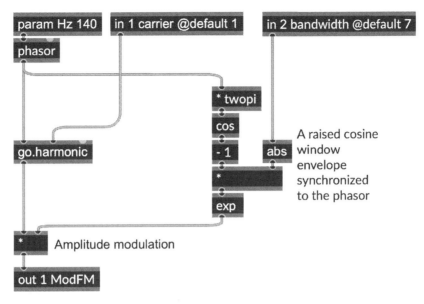

ModFM.maxpat

With this algorithm, turning up **in 2 carrier** operator shifts the center frequency up and down, much like a resonant filter, while modifying **param index** alternately narrows or widens the set of sidebands around this center frequency, much like a bandwidth or resonance control on a resonant filter. At certain settings, it can create a cheap band-limited approximation to an analog saw wave. At other settings, it can produce a characteristic acid-like impulse train, as below. The somewhat "vocal" formant quality has also led to its use for analysis-synthesis vocoding. We'll look at some other ways of creating impulse trains in Chapter 10.

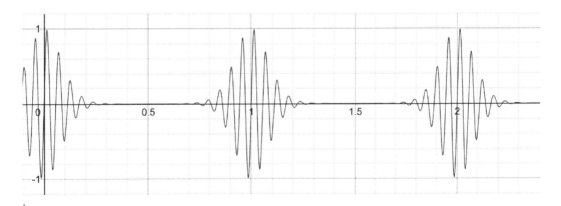

Chapter 9:
Navigating Waves of Data

In Chapter 2, we saw how to read and play a waveform stored in a **buffer** with a repeating **phasor** ramp by interpolated indexing using the **sample** operator. A **phasor**-driven **sample** patch like this is an example of a table-lookup oscillator, sometimes also called a wavetable oscillator:

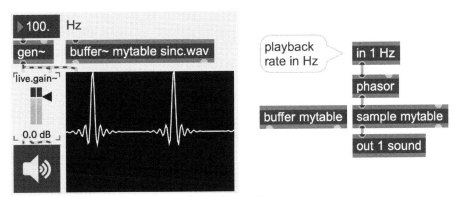

phasor_basic_table_oscillator.maxpat

The fundamental frequency of the oscillator is determined by the frequency of the **phasor** ramp itself, while the content of the **buffer** determines the actual shape (and thus timbre) of the oscillator. Since the **buffer** can have any combination of sample value data in it, the range of possible waveforms is practically infinite (although not all possibilities will necessarily sound interesting). Put another way, the **phasor** effectively navigates *a data space* that the **buffer** provides. In this chapter, we're going to look at a variety of different ways of organizing this data for greater variety, as well as a variety of different ways of navigating it.

Wavetables

The main drawback of a table-lookup oscillator, as in the patch above, is that the waveform's shape is always the same. It can feel sonically static and lifeless. If you wanted to switch between several different waveforms, you could have several other **buffer~** objects and sample players, but that's not very efficient or flexible. Instead, the approach usually taken with wavetable oscillators is to pack several different single-cycle waveforms into subsections of a single buffer and dynamically switch (or blend) between which subsection of the waveform is playing at any time. For example, if our single cycle waveforms are each 1000 samples long, then we could store eight different single-cycle waveforms end-to-end as slices of a buffer of 8000 samples' length:

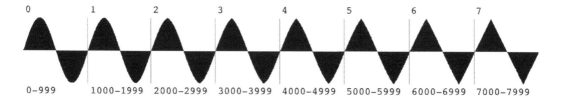

If we wanted to play the first waveform, we would need to loop over samples 0 to 999; if we wanted to play the second waveform, we would need to loop over samples 1000 to 1999; and so on. The **wave** operator is handy for that purpose. It takes a phasor signal at the first inlet to set the fundamental frequency and uses two additional inlets that specify the starting and ending sample positions of the sub-range of the buffer you want to play.[1]

To build a wavetable player, we'll need a **buffer~** containing several single-cycle waveforms. The software with this book includes a few example files, such as *wavetable64.wav,* which contains 64 individual waveforms. We can load that into our parent patch using a **buffer~ tables wavetable64.wav** object and reference this within a gen~ patch by adding a **buffer tables** operator. We can now read the data using a **wave tables** operator, driven by any unipolar ramp signal such as a **phasor** operator.

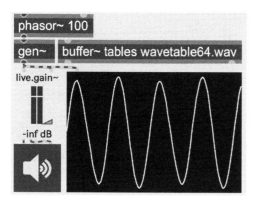
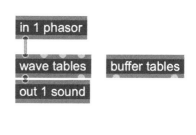

To pick out a specific waveform, we will need to set up the start and end sample indices of the **wave** operator. That means we need to know how many single-cycle waveforms the buffer contains, which we will provide using a **param N 64** operator. We also need to know how many samples are in each of the single-cycle waveforms. Since the **buffer** operator broadcasts the total number of samples it contains from its first outlet, we just need to divide this by number of tables (**param N**) to get the sample length per table. It's handy to store this result in a named **history** operator, (such as "**history len**") so that we can re-use that name "len" throughout the patch, just like we can with **param** operator names.

We'll also need an input to select an individual table (in this case, from 0 to 63), which we can ensure is a whole number using a **floor** operator, and we can constrain that to the available range of tables using a **wrap 0 N** operator. Now our start sample index is simply this table number multiplied by the waveform length ("len"), and our end sample index is the start sample index plus the waveform length again.

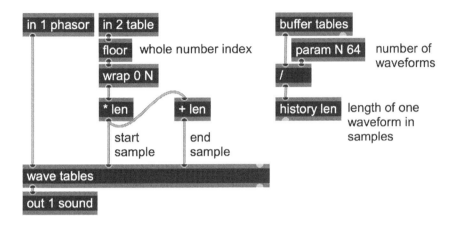

Morphing between waveforms

Using the patch above we can switch between waveforms just by changing the signal value at **in 2**. However, as this value changes you might also hear clicks if the waveform changes abruptly from one shape to the next. Wouldn't it be better if we could smoothly blend (morph) between the waveforms rather than having these sudden switches? We can use a technique we have now seen many times in this book and which we will be using again and again in this chapter: to compute the two nearest whole number values (to select our two nearest waveforms) and output a linear crossfade or mix between them using a **mix** operator.

For this, we need an input that can support fractional indices that are part way between one waveform and the next, so the first thing we need to do is get rid of the **floor** operator after the **in 2** table index input. To get the **mix** operator's crossfade factor, we can send the table index through a **wrap 0 1** operator, representing our position between two whole number table indices. We can also subtract this fractional part from our table index to get the nearest whole number table index to the left and add 1 to *that* to get the next whole number table index to the right. These identify the two waveforms that we need to mix.

This is simpler than it might sound. For example, if our index is 2.3, then our two nearest waveforms are at index 2 and at index 3, with a crossfade factor of 0.3 between them, meaning we will get more contribution from waveform 2 than from waveform 3.

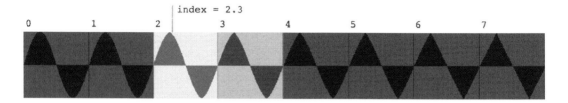

All we need is to repeat our **wave** operator twice, each working with one of the nearest table indices, and feed the results into the **mix** operator.

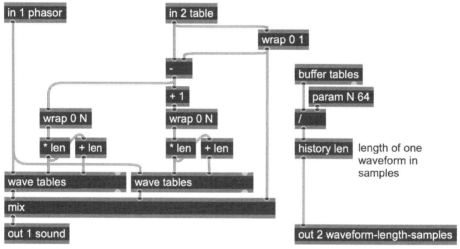

wavetable_1D.maxpat

Now we can plug in different kinds of modulation signals to the **in 2** table input (such as an LFO multiplied by **N**) and hear smoothly morphing waveforms!

2D wavetables

With the previous patch, we can only morph left or right, through the set of waveforms in the buffer. Wouldn't it be nice to be able to morph in more directions? For example, if our set of 64 waveforms was arranged not in a flat sequence but instead in a two-dimensional grid of 8 columns of 8 rows, where each "cell" of the grid contains a single-cycle waveform, then we could morph left and right and also up and down across this grid:

0	1	2	3	4	5	6	7
8	9	10	11	12	13	14	15
16	17	18	19	20	21	22	23
24	25	26	27	28	29	30	31
32	33	34	35	36	37	38	39
40	41	42	43	44	45	46	47
48	49	50	51	52	53	54	55
56	57	58	59	60	61	62	63

To select a cell within this grid of waveforms, we will need two index inputs—one to set our position across the columns (which we can call "X") and one for our position down the rows (which we can call "Y"). For a **buffer** containing 64 distinct waveforms in an 8x8 grid, there are eight possible indices per axis. So, now we will set our index range N to be 8, and we can compute the total number of waveforms as N^2 or $N*N$, which we will need to figure out what our single cycle waveform length ("len") will be. Our patch starts like this:

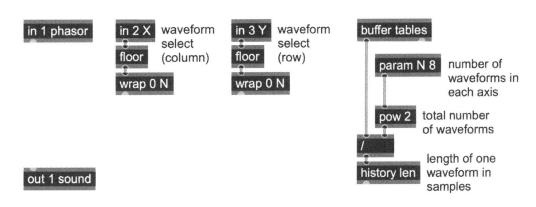

Notice that we used a **floor** operator to restrict X and Y to whole numbers for now (we'll add the blending back again later), and we added **wrap 0 N** operators to ensure they fit within the range of each axis of the 2D waveform grid.

Even though we are pretending that the waveforms are laid out in a two-dimensional grid, they are still all in a linear series in the **buffer**. We will need a way to take a 2D grid position (such as column $X=2$, row $Y=3$) and convert it into a 1D index into the waveform series. We can figure out what the 1D index is just by taking into account the spacing. The first row starts at index 0, the second row at index 8, and so on, up to index 56 in the last row. So, we can simply take our row Y position and multiply that by $N=8$ and then add our column X position to get the 1D waveform index. For example, if $X=2$, $Y=3$, then the 1D index is $3*8+2 = 26$.

Finally, to convert the 1D index into a sample start index for the **wave** operator, we can multiply it by the waveform length "len." The sample end index is always just the start index plus "len," just as we did before.

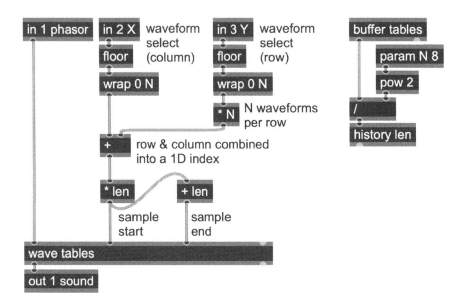

Morphing in 2D

Now, if we want to add waveform morphing, we can do it much as we did for the 1D wavetable. However, we now need to morph in two axes—blending vertically as well as horizontally over the waveform grid.

This means that we need to blend between the nearest *four* waveforms, which means we need four **wave** operators. For example, in the image below, X=2.8 and Y=3.9, which means blending between the four waveforms at indices 26, 27, 34, and 35 in the highlighted box.

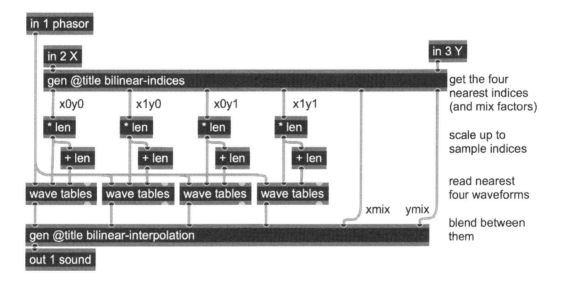

The output will be an appropriate linear mix of the four waves in the two axes, which is called "bilinear" interpolation. The overall structure might look something like the following patch.

First, we feed the X and Y inputs into a **bilinear-indices** subpatch whose job is to work out the 1D index of the nearest four waveforms and also the horizontal and vertical crossfade factors that we will need. These 1D indices are converted into sample start and end positions for the four **wave** operators, whose results are fed into a **bilinear-interpolation** subpatch to do the actual crossfading.

Let's fill out those subpatches. For the X input, we'll do the same as we did before: capture the fractional component with a **wrap 0 1** operator (which we also send out as a crossfade mix factor), subtract it from the X input to get the nearest column index to the left, and add 1 to get the nearest column index to the right. We added a **wrap 0 N** on each of these to ensure they are always in the valid range of columns. We do the same for the Y input, giving us the two nearest row indices above and below. Then, for each of the possible pairs of row and column indices, we can calculate the equivalent 1D index as before (using `index = X + N*Y`).

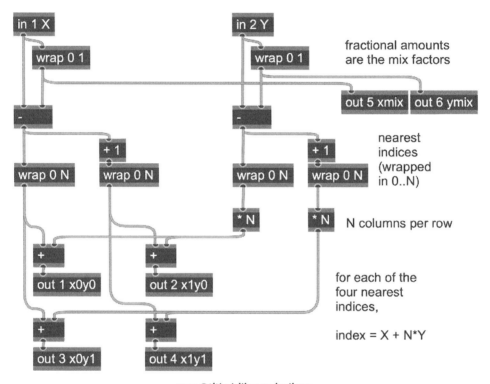

gen @title bilinear-indices

To perform the bilinear interpolation and blend between the four wave outputs in the **bilinear-interpolation** subpatch, we first apply blending in pairs across the X axis and then blend the results of these across the Y axis, using the corresponding "X mix" and "Y mix" factors accordingly. That is, we first blend across the rows and then blend the results across the columns. Even though we are blending between four waveforms, we only need three **mix** operators. That's because the X axis was already mixed down before we came to process the Y axis.

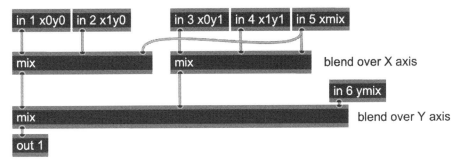

gen @title bilinear-interpolation

And with that, we can now smoothly wander all over the space of our 2D set of waveforms. This patch will respond pretty well already to some quite strong modulations: try plugging in a pair of LFOs for the X and Y inputs, or a pair of random walks, or one of the chaotic generators from Chapter 4 (p. 112), or indeed any pair of signals—we'll see more ideas for interesting orbits later in this chapter.

To make it a bit easier to try out different control signals, it would be handy if the X and Y inputs were expressed in a unipolar range, which we can do simply by multiplying unipolar inputs by N before feeding into the **bilinear-indices** subpatch:

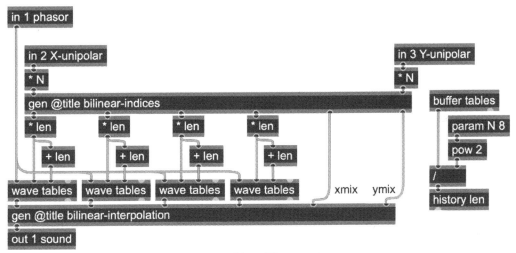

wavetables_2D.maxpat

3D wavetables

Now that we have seen how to extend from waveform selection over a 2D list into waveform selection over a 2D grid, we might have an idea how we could take this into waveform selection over a 3D volume!

First, we will need a file that represents a cubic volume of NxNxN waveforms. For example, the software with this book includes a wave file called ***3x3x3.wav***, which contains 27 single-cycle waveforms. Although they are stored in the wave file end to end in a linear arrangement, we can imagine those 27 single-cycle waveforms in a three-dimensional arrangement as a 3x3x3 cube, as in the following image:

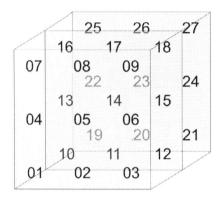

Dividing a 3D parameter space into cells like this is similar to the idea of the voxel[2] used in computer graphics. Each of the waveforms stored in our buffer can be seen as a point in a regularly spaced 3D grid. That means that we'll need three parameters (X, Y, and Z, for horizontal, vertical, and depth) to pick out an individual waveform, each in a range between 0.0 and 3.0. Any trio of X, Y, and Z parameters (three values in a range of 0.0 to 3.0) will result in a unique waveform as its output.

The numbers in the cube image above are the order of the waveforms within the wave file, which is to say, their 1D index. As before, we'll need a way to convert from a 3D X, Y, and Z coordinate into one of these 1D indices. Looking at those numbers in the image above, you can see that if you are moving horizontally right across the cube increases the indices step in ones; moving vertically up increases in steps of three (to make space for the X coordinates), and moving in depth into the cube increases in steps of nine (to make space for X and Y coordinates). So, the 1D index can be computed from the trio of X, Y, and Z positions using `index` = X + N*Y + N*N*Z.

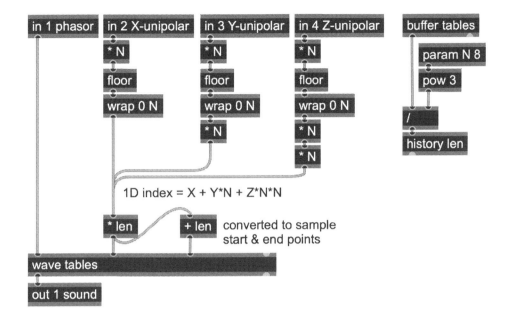

Here the number of tables is computed from the param **N** by raising to the power of 3 (cubing) using a **pow 3** operator in order to compute the total number of tables, and from there the length (**history len**) of each waveform in samples.

Morphing in 3D

As before, the morphing "space" between each of the waveforms in this grid can be filled in by interpolating between them; but now we will need to interpolate between the eight nearest waveforms!

This means we will need eight **wave** operators and eight sets of indices for the nearest waveforms to our desired point. We'll also need a way to blend those eight nearest waveforms together smoothly as you modulate along any or all of the horizontal, vertical, or depth axes. This is called *trilinear interpolation* because it crossfades through three axes.

Here is what the outer structure of our patch looks like:

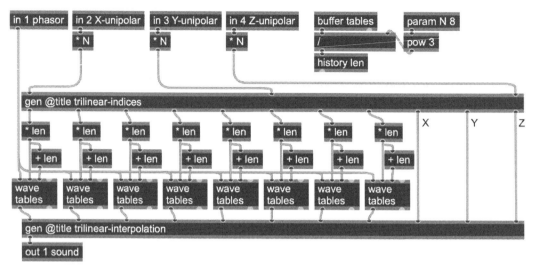

wavetable_3D.maxpat

The **trilinear-interpolation** subpatch replicates the same structure as the **bilinear-interpolation** patch, but now cascading the outputs of the *eight* **wave** operators through *three* layers of **mix** operators, one layer per axis. The first resolves the X axis, blending the eight waveforms into four; the next resolves the Y axis, blending these four into two, and the final stage blends these two along the Z axis, resolving into a single output signal that represents the 3D wavetable playback. Here is what that looks like:

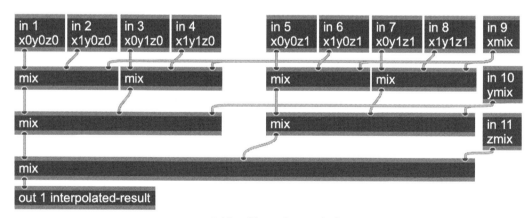

gen @title trilinear-interpolation

And as with the morphing 2D case, the **trilinear-indices** subpatch finds the nearest whole number indices in each axis, labeled in the following patch as x0 and x1, y0 and y1, and z0 and z1 (and the fractional parts are sent out of the patch for use by the trilinear interpolator).

Each of these indices is wrapped based on the number of waveforms per axis. Then, each possible pairing of these X, Y, and Z coordinates is passed through the function $index = X + N*Y + N*N*Z$ to compute the corresponding 1D position of the waveform in the buffer. You might notice that the full set of permutations of combining the X, Y, and Z values follows a binary pattern.

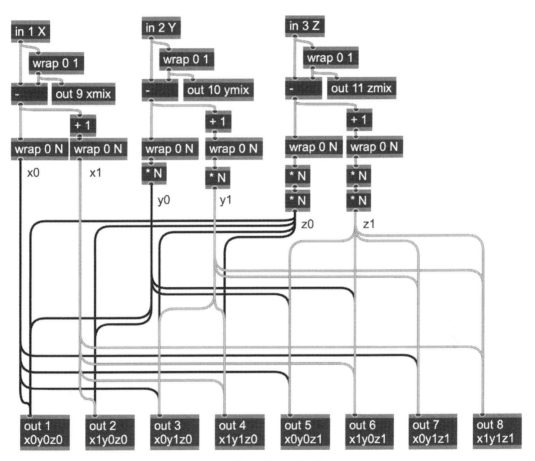

gen @title trilinear-indices

We now have a fully functioning, 3D morphing wavetable navigator! Since the number of waveforms per axis is set by a parameter, we could load a different set of waveforms (say, 4x4x4, or 8x8x8), and the only modification we need to make is updating the parameter **N**.

While we can explore the 3D wavetable by changing the X, Y, and Z inputs manually, this patch is tailor-made for modulation with signals at audio rates. The relations between the X, Y, and Z modulations will carve out different trajectories through the cube of waveforms. There are many ways we might consider doing this—perhaps, for example, using three **phasor** operators running at prime number rates for an aperiodic orbit.

Alternatively, we could use one of the chaotic attractor patches from Chapter 4 (p. 112), most of which already output three related signals. All we need to do is to scale the attractor patch's three outputs to the input range that the 3D wavetable patch requires, which we do in the ***wavetable_3D_attractor.maxpat*** example using **go.limits** abstractions and **scale** operators.

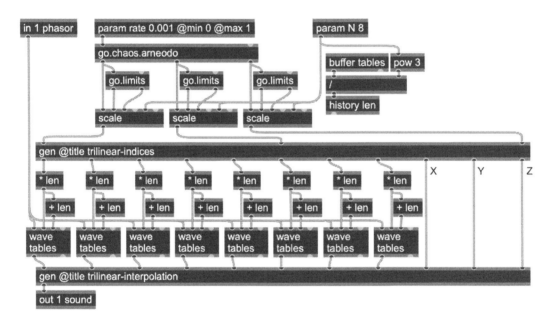

Generating wavetables

The ***wavetable_3D_attractor.maxpat*** patch also shows how the ***8x8x8.wav*** file itself was generated. We're providing this as an example of how you can generate wavetable data into a buffer procedurally using GenExpr code in a **codebox**.

In this patch, we generate the buffer one sample at a time so that the expensive computation it takes is spread over time. It only takes a few seconds to fill up the buffer, representing 8x8x8 = 512 waveforms of 1024 samples each. We work through the samples of the buffer using a cascade of **counter** operators. The first **counter** loops over the length of each waveform by means of the "len" argument. Its middle outlet outputs a trigger whenever it completes a lap, which is fed into the next **counter** operator. This one loops over **N** to account for each waveform in the X axis. Its lap trigger then cascades to another **counter N** for the Y axis, which cascades to a **counter N** for the Z axis. These four counts: the sample index "I" and the axis indices X, Y, and Z are fed into a **codebox**.

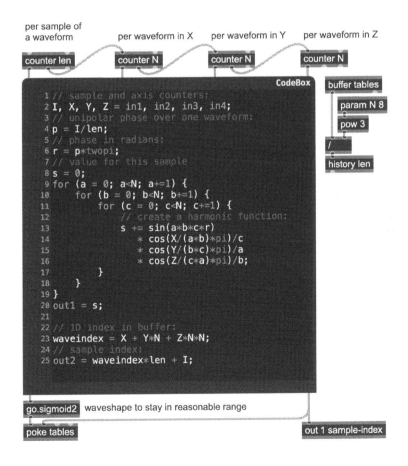

```
1 // sample and axis counters:
2 I, X, Y, Z = in1, in2, in3, in4;
3 // unipolar phase over one waveform:
4 p = I/len;
5 // phase in radians:
6 r = p*twopi;
7 // value for this sample
8 s = 0;
9 for (a = 0; a<N; a+=1) {
10     for (b = 0; b<N; b+=1) {
11         for (c = 0; c<N; c+=1) {
12             // create a harmonic function:
13             s += sin(a*b*c*r)
14                 * cos(X/(a*b)*pi)/c
15                 * cos(Y/(b*c)*pi)/a
16                 * cos(Z/(c*a)*pi)/b;
17         }
18     }
19 }
20 out1 = s;
21
22 // 1D index in buffer:
23 waveindex = X + Y*N + Z*N*N;
24 // sample index:
25 out2 = waveindex*len + I;
```

The outputs of the **codebox** are the sample value to write and the sample index to write it to, which feed into the corresponding inputs of a **poke tables** operator. We also sent the sample value through a **go.sigmoid2** waveshaper abstraction to get more saturated dynamics across the wavetables.

The internals of the **codebox** come in three parts. First, we convert the waveform sample index into a unipolar phase over the waveform and then a phase in radians, which is more convenient for use with **sin** and **cos** operations.

Second, we compute a sum of NxNxN sinusoidal harmonics, each weighted differently according to our X, Y, and Z coordinate in the 3D cube. When N=8, this means we are computing 512 sinusoids per sample of the wavetable. (That's a pretty expensive calculation, which is why this is worth spreading over time and saving into a wave file rather than computing it on demand!)

Finally, we compute what the actual index of this waveform should be in the 1D list, using the same `index = X + Y*N + Z*N*N` expression we have used previously. Then, to convert that to a per-sample index, we multiply by "len" and add the sample index "I."

You can replace the inner code with whatever functions you prefer to use to fill your wavetables, of course—it's up to you! When you have generated a wavetable you like, send a "writewave" message to the **buffer~** object in the parent patcher to save it to disk.

Band-limiting wavetables

So far, we've been reading from the buffer using **sample** or **wave** operators, Ih use linear interpolation to render a perceptually smooth output from what is actually a finite, discrete set of data samples. For some waveforms, that is good enough. But for other waveforms - particularly shapes with strong harmonic series such as saw and square waves - wavetables can introduce aliasing noise during playback, and linear interpolation alone won't prevent it. In this section, we'll look at why this noise appears and some strategies to address it.

First, why is interpolation needed at all? Since we can be playing the wavetable at many different rates (pitches), it is unlikely that the sample frames of real-time passing in the patch exactly line up with the sample points of the wavetable **buffer**. For example, if our wavetable is made of 64 samples, and our sampling rate is 48kHz (48000Hz), then the only frequency that they exactly line up is 48000/64 = 750Hz.

It looks like this:

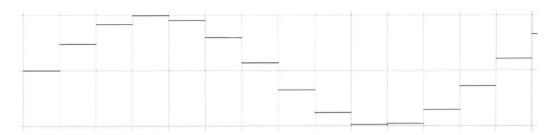

In the image above, the horizontal steps represent the data in the wavetable (representing a sampled sine wave), aligned with a density of 1.0: one wavetable sample per sample frame of real time across the X axis.

If we play the wavetable oscillator slower than 750Hz, the wavetable samples will be stretched out; if we play higher than 750Hz, they will be compressed more tightly together than the sampling rate. We can call this the relative sample density. For example, at 150 Hz, the relative sample density is 0.2 (as there is only one wavetable sample for every five samples of real time):

For most oscillator frequencies, this means we will have to *estimate* what the wavetable's data should be at fractional points somewhere between the actual data samples of the wavetable. That's what we use interpolation algorithms for. If we didn't use interpolation, the playback would follow the stepped graph above, which would be much noisier (try using a **wave tables @interp none** operator if you want to hear what this sounds like).

By default, the **sample** and **wave** operators use linear interpolation to estimate the value at any fractional point by taking a weighted average of the two nearest sample frames in the buffer. This emulates a simple ramp between samples, as represented with a dotted line in the following graph:

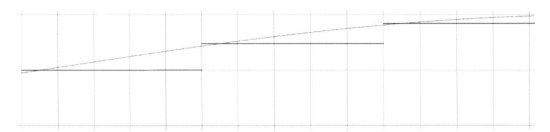

As you can see, linear interpolation does a reasonable job of filling in the gaps between wavetable samples, but it doesn't eliminate all of our noise problems. If we play through the **buffer** at a rate high enough that the relative sample density becomes large, so there are many wavetable samples per sample frame of real time, then we may end up trying to synthesize a signal that has more detail (higher frequency information) than can actually be rendered at the current sampling rate.

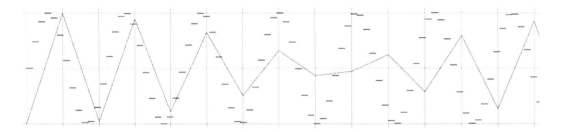

For example, in the graph above, the wavetable oscillator is playing at 5.9x the original frequency, with 5.9 wavetable samples for each passing sample frame of real time. This has far too much high frequency detail to render at the current sample rate. Notice that the interpolated output (the dotted line) no longer follows the original sine wave and even flips to be completely out-of-phase (upside down) part way through the graph. This inability to represent the detail, and the interference pattern that ensues from it, is an example of aliasing.

Note that this is not a limit of gen~, it is a fundamental property of any discretely sampled system. Whatever the sampling rate is, we cannot render any information that is more than half this sampling rate (the Nyquist limit). Nothing can appear to move faster than **samplerate/2**. The kind of aliasing that results from frequencies higher than the Nyquist limit is one of the most pernicious sources of undesirable noise in digital signal processing in general.

In the next chapter and moreso in book 2 we will be looking much more deeply into addressing the challenges of aliasing, but here we are going to work through strategies we can apply to wavetable playback. One of the first principles to know is that we can't filter out frequencies that have *already* aliased — we have to try to prevent those high frequencies from being generated in the first place (this is also called *band limiting* a signal). To address the problem with the wavetable playback, we want to avoid rendering a wavetable at a higher resolution than the current real-time sampling rate can support. We're going to do this using two strategies: a windowed-sinc interpolation filter and mipmapping.

Sinc interpolation

Let's start with sinc interpolation. We already saw in Chapter 6 (p. 162) that filtering and interpolation are very closely related. A linear interpolation or **mix** operation applies a weighted average, which will tend to smooth out differences (higher frequency detail) and preserve only the more similar, lower frequency parts of a signal. Another way of seeing this, which might not be as obvious, is that we are multiplying two samples of our wavetable by a two-sample triangle window and outputting the sum.

As we saw in Chapter 6 (p. 162), the linear interpolation of a **mix** operator means multiplying one sample by the unipolar factor "a" and the other sample by "1-a" and adding the results together. But here's yet another way to look at it: these two factors of "a" and "1-a" are simply intersections with the rising and falling edges of a two-sample triangle window! Imagine this triangle sliding across the data points of the buffer, always multiplying by the two nearest points that intersect with it and summing the result; this is exactly equivalent to linear interpolation.

Summing multiplied pairs of points like this is called *convolution*. Other kinds of interpolation, such as cubic, spline, etc., are also convolutions, but with different window shapes and usually summing more sample points. (We saw some of these when building smooth random signals in Chapter 4 on p. 93). The more points we use, the deeper the filtering can be; while the specific shape of the window determines the spectral distribution of the filter response. The filtering effect of linear interpolation spreads out widely over the frequency spectrum (decreasing by only -6dB per octave), which means it is not a good choice for suppressing aliasing noise. What we need is a filter that can attenuate high-frequency detail much more sharply without compromising the frequencies below.

Instead, we're going to convolve our wavetable with a windowed-sinc function, which can preserves energy well up to a certain point but soon silences frequencies above that point.

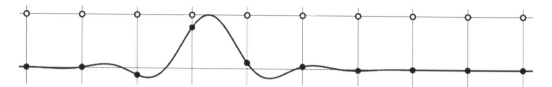

A sinc waveform can be generated using the mathematical function `sin(x)/x`, which has the characteristic rippled impulse shape in the image above. Since a pure sinc function is known to be bandlimited, then any convolution with it would also be bandlimited in the same way. Unfortunately however, the pure mathematical sinc function is infinitely long, and would need infinite sample points for convolution. Instead, we use a "windowed sinc" function, which simply means that the infinite sinc curve is tapered to zero after a certain number of ripples.

For our windowed-sinc wavetable patches we pre-calculated a sinc shape tapered using a Kaiser window for use with eight-point interpolation, which we stored in the ***go.sinc8.wav*** file in the software with this book. We can load this into our parent patch using a **buffer~ sinc8 go.sinc8.wav** object and reference it in gen~ using a **buffer sinc8** operator.

Using an 8-point sinc interpolation means that we will need the eight nearest consecutive sample points from our wavetable, which we can read using eight **peek** operators. We're using **peek** here because we explicitly don't want any interpolation at this stage of the patch; we're doing the interpolation ourselves next.

Each one of these **peek** outputs will be multiplied by a corresponding sample from the sinc8 buffer. We are using phase offsets and **sample** operators for the window because interpolating the window does make sense. The crucial part is that we should shift these samples in time according to the fractional interpolation factor we computed earlier.

Put together, it looks like this:

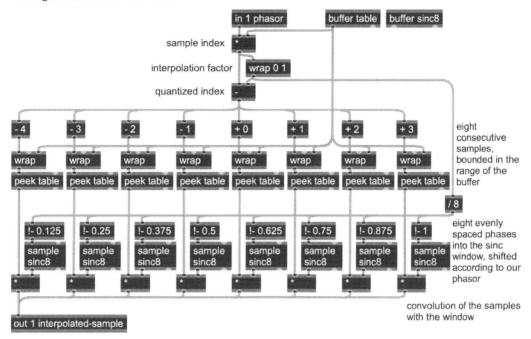

This is a dense patch, so let's walk through it step by step. First, our incoming phasor ramp is multiplied by the **buffer** length to get a sample index. We extract the fractional component of that using a **wrap 0 1** operator, which will be used as our interpolation factor. We subtract this fractional part to get a quantized integer sample index, which is then routed to a series of subtractions and additions for the eight nearest integer sample indices, and we use a **wrap** operator on each one to ensure it is within the bounds of our **buffer**. These indices are then sent to the eight **peek** operators to extract our nearest eight samples in the wavetable.

Meanwhile, the fractional interpolation factor is divided into eight evenly spaced slices between 0.0 and 1.0, to select the appropriate corresponding points of the window, sampled using the **sample sinc8** operators. Finally, each window point and wavetable sample is multiplied together, and the results are added up at the output to complete the convolution.

If the wavetable contains a saw shape and is played at around 450Hz, the spectrum will look something like the following:

The black spectrum in the image above is the sinc interpolated waveform. The gray spectrum is the linear-interpolated waveform. Notice how the linear-interpolated waveform has a lot of extra energy between the saw harmonics: these are the aliased frequencies that sound particularly awful when the pitch is modulated, and they are present throughout the spectrum.[3] On the other hand, the sinc interpolated waveform has a clean series of harmonics that remain strong over most of the significantly audible range, then taper down to zero before they hit the Nyquist limit, preventing aliasing noise. The best part of this is that it doesn't matter at all what the wavetable actually contains. The same band-limiting will apply!

But there's a problem we still have to resolve, which becomes apparent as we change the driving **phasor** frequency: the spectral filtering moves with it.

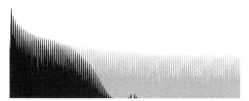

At around 200Hz, the sinc interpolation filtering is too strong, cutting out too many high harmonics

At around 850Hz, the higher harmonics are folding back to create audible aliasing

That's because our sinc filter is designed to work with a specific sampling rate; reading through the wavetable at a different phasor frequency means we are reading at a different sampling rate, and that would need a different sinc shape. It's expensive to compute these windowed sinc shapes continuously, so we're going to address this by extending our sinc interpolation with another technique called *mipmapping*.

Mipmapping

The technique of "mipmapping" is widely used in computer graphics to avoid the aliasing of high-resolution images rendered at low resolution output.[4] You've probably seen the result of aliasing in computer graphics in the form of Moiré patterns.

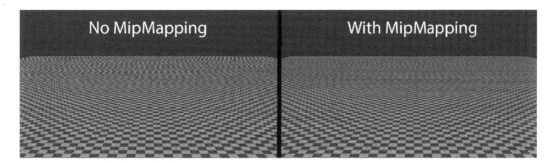

Look at the noise near the horizon in the image on the left (with no mipmapping) and compare this to the smoothness near the horizon in the image on the right (with mipmapping enabled).[5] In this graphic example, you see those noisy patterns because the detail in the checkerboard image far exceeds the sampling resolution of the pixels in the output image. Mipmapping helps solve this problem, and it can help us with our audio problems, too.

Here's how the graphics version of this technique works: a MipMap is a stack of versions of an original image, each of which is half the resolution of the version below. This forms a kind of pyramid, where each pixel of an image in one layer represents 2x2 pixels of the image in the layer below. Whenever we need to render the picture, we use whichever version has the closest resolution to what we want for the output, and we will know that it won't have too much detail to draw smoothly and thus won't get aliasing interference patterns.

We can use a similar approach to avoid aliasing in audio wavetable playback. Reading from a wavetable of a certain size at a certain frequency to render under a certain sampling rate is exactly analogous to reading from an image of a certain size at a certain distance under a certain rendering resolution. So, our MipMap can be a pyramid of wavetables, where each "higher" layer waveform has half the resolution of the one below.

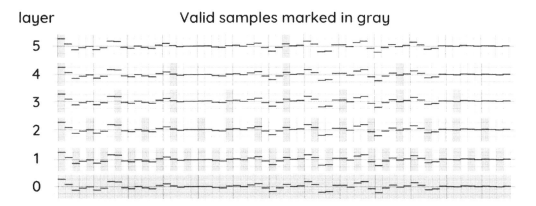

Starting from the bottom layer at full wavetable resolution, we could create the next layer above by simply "throwing away" every second sample (this is called "decimating"), giving us a waveform of half the resolution (half the total sample length). We can do that again and again for each layer going up the pyramid.

To keep our patch as simple and flexible as possible, we're going to compute the decimation on the fly during playback.[6] So, for the second layer, we want to read only every 2nd sample value (i.e., the even frames). For the next layer, we read only every 4th sample, i.e., only the data in samples 0, 4, 8, etc., and so on.

This sample spacing can be expressed as `pow(2, layer)`, or more simply as `exp2(layer)`. To apply this quantized spacing to our wavetable readers, we can use the same technique we have used for quantization elsewhere in this book: divide, convert to integer, then multiply again. That is, we divide our sample index by the spacing before we quantize it to an integer, and then multiply by the spacing again afterward (before each **peek** operator).

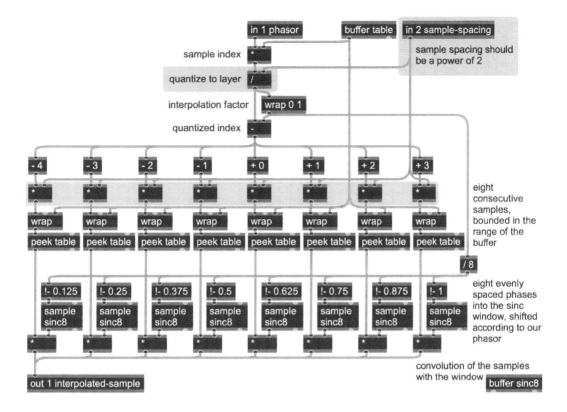

If you modify the **in 2 sample-spacing** control between 1, 2, 4, 8, etc. you will see the sinc filtering kick in at different octaves of the spectrum. So, all we need to do during playback is figure out which sample spacing (i.e., which waveform resolution) is appropriate for the playback frequency we are using to select the appropriate sample spacing to render at.

To do this, first we'll need to compute the relative sample density. This is just the rate of wavetable samples per sample in real time, so we can take our phasor's slope (using the **go.ramp2slope** abstraction) and multiply this by the wavetable resolution to get the density. We next want to quantize this to a power of two, which we can do with a sequence of **log2**, **ceil**, and **exp2** operators. And that gives us the sample spacing we need.

The patch is getting quite large now, so we'll put the sinc interpolation section into a **gen @title sinc-interpolate** subpatch, like this:

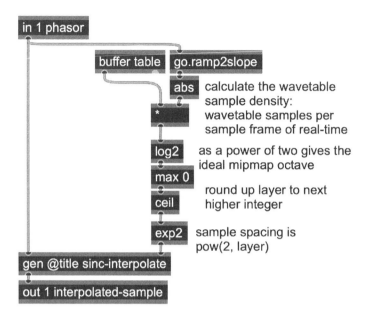

We also added an **abs** operator to ensure the patch works with phasors running backward and a **max 0** operator because zero is the lowest possible layer we can render.

Now, no matter what frequency we play the wavetable at, the aliasing suppression remains in the higher regions of the spectrum! There's just one more refinement to make. If you wiggle the frequency around, add portamento or deep FM, you may notice a distinct change as the wavetable switches from one-octave layer to the next. It would be much better if we could crossfade smoothly between the two nearest layers according to which layer is nearer.

Once again, we can solve this by running two copies of our sinc interpolator and mixing according to the fractional step between layers.

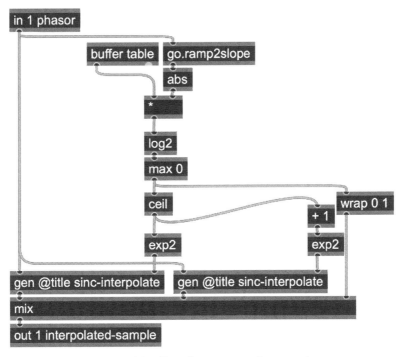

wavetable_sincmipmap_sample.maxpat

This patch can now be a drop-in replacement for a **sample** operator, and it will be bandlimited. What's more, this method remains bandlimited even under quite extreme audio rate frequency modulation, regardless of what data the wavetable actually contains!

With a little more patching, we can extend this to present the same interface as a **wave** operator. First of all, we'll need to add inlets to our sinc-interpolate subpatch to handle start and end sample indices, which feed into the **wrap** operators that constrain the **peek** operators.

We can then add inlets for the sample start and sample end positions in the main gen~ patch, and the difference between these will act as the effective resolution of the waveform.

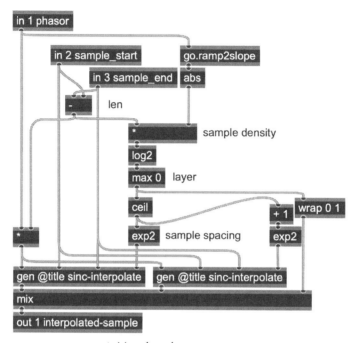

wavetable_sincmipmap_wave.maxpat

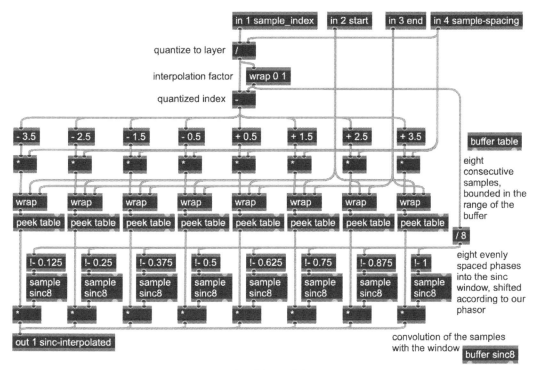

sinc-interpolate

Now, wherever we have used a **wave** operator before (including nearly all the wavetable patches in this chapter), we can replace it with our mipmapped, sinc interpolated subpatch above to get fully antialiased wavetable playback for any waveform, even while morphing between waveforms! Take a look at the ***mipmap_sinc_1D.maxpat*** and ***mipmap_sinc_2D.maxpat*** patches and explore applying deep modulation to them!

Wave terrains

As you modulate 1D, 2D, and 3D wavetables more deeply, you may observe that the output sound becomes more a function of the orbits through the space than of the content of the wavetable data itself. In this section, we're going to look at a closely related synthesis technique using 2D wave terrains, in which waveform data has almost entirely disappeared, and the orbits take center stage.

Wave terrain synthesis uses most of the same basic techniques as 2D wavetable synthesis, but in a slightly different way. Both include a dataset arranged over a 2D grid and an X and Y pair of signals to navigate this grid smoothly.

The primary differences are:

- In a 2D wavetable, each point in the grid contains an entire single-cycle waveform. For a wave terrain, each point in the grid is just <u>a single sample value</u>.
- Typically, the number of grid sample points in a wave terrain is much larger than the number of waveforms in a 2D wavetable. For example, rather than a handful of single-cycle waveforms in each axis, a terrain may have hundreds or even thousands of data points on each axis.

The term "terrain" comes from the intuitive sense that the sample value at any grid point can represent a vertical height above the XY plane, which could be visualized like this:

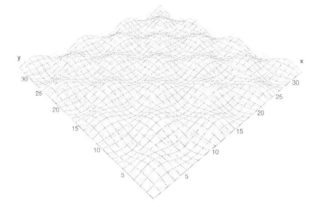

This particular terrain is a 32x32 grid of points, each of which has a height value computed as a function of `sin(x*pi/5) + sin(y*pi/5)`, but any resolution and function of X and Y can be used.

The wave terrain algorithm uses two signal inputs X and Y to determine our location on this map, and the output signal is simply the height of the map at this location. The X and Y inputs normally modulate fairly smoothly to create a continuous traversal over the terrain. And, whereas for a 2D wavetable, you would normally expect neighboring waveforms to be similar, so that traversal over the space of waveforms (wavetable morphing) is mostly smooth, then for a wave terrain, you would normally expect neighboring sample points to be similar, so that traversal over the terrain is predominantly smooth.

In this way, wave terrain synthesis allows us to generate all kinds of interesting evolving and complex waveforms, whether as audio signals or as lower-frequency control signals. In this section, we're going to look at a few different ways to generate interesting 2D terrains and explore some different ways to traverse these surfaces.

But first, we'll start with a basic terrain reader patch, which looks like this:

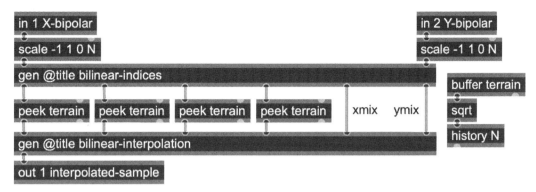

gen @title terrain-reader

As with multi-dimensional wavetables, our wave terrains will be stored in a regular one-dimensional **buffer** operator. We'll assume that our terrains are square, with the same number of samples across each axis, so we can calculate our resolution as the square root of the buffer length using the **sqrt** operator and store it in a **history N** operator so that the variable "N" is available for use throughout the patch.

To read from this terrain, we'll need a way to convert an X and Y coordinate into an index into the **buffer**, so we can read the data it contains. For wave terrains, it can be handy to work with bipolar signals for X and Y, so the first thing we do is convert these to axis coordinates using **scale -1 1 0 N** operators.

To interpolate between samples on the terrain smoothly, we can use the same basic approach as we did for the morphing 2D wavetables example: finding the four nearest indices, computing outputs at these indices, then crossfading the results. In fact, we can use exactly the same **bilinear-indices** and **bilinear-interpolation** subpatches as we used for the morphing 2D wavetables. Since the terrain contains only a single sample value at each of these points, we can directly feed the indices into four **peek** operators to retrieve the nearest terrain values and send those on to the bilinear interpolation. (We're using non-interpolating **peek** operators here because we'll be performing our own interpolation in the **bilinear-interpolation** subpatch.)

Now that we have a reader, we'll need to generate an X and Y pair of signals for its inputs. One of the simplest traversals we can try is a basic circular path (or "orbit"). Circular paths are popular for wave terrain traversal because they produce periodic results by definition.

The **poltocar** operator provides us with a simple way to generate a basic circular traversal. The name means <u>pol</u>ar <u>to</u> <u>Car</u>tesian coordinates, which simply means that it converts a radius and angle input into an X and Y output.

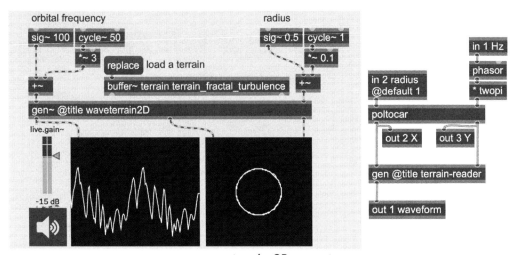

waveterrain_2D.maxpat

We specify the radius of the circle we want to create, as well as an angle in radians (ranging from 0.0 to 2π). In the patch above, we put this into continuous rotation by driving the angle input with a **phasor** scaled up to 2π radians using a *** twopi** operator.

Finally, we need some terrain data to load into the **buffer~ terrain** object. In the next section, we'll describe some ways to generate terrain data procedurally; but to get a quick start, we've provided a folder of audio files located in the ***media*** folder of the software that accompanies this book, generated at a 1024x1024 resolution.

It's worth exploring the orbital parameters to get a sense of how it changes the output waveform. The angular rotation of the **phasor** is what provides the fundamental frequency for the waveform at the output. There is often also correspondence between the radius and the brightness of the output sound—this is because, with a smaller radius, we are effectively moving over fewer distinct samples in the terrain—which is like reading from a wavetable with a lower resolution and thus less space for higher harmonics.[7]

Generating terrains

If you want to generate your own terrain, all you need is to create a function that computes the terrain's height value ("Z") from the 2D grid coordinate in X and Y. Then, with a bit of patching (and codeboxing), we can fill a **buffer~** with samples of this terrain function and save it to a wave file.

To start, we will want a **buffer~ terrain** object in the parent patch that uses the *@samps* attribute to set the number of samples in the buffer. The buffer length in samples should be a square of the dimensions of the terrain we want to generate. Generally speaking, a larger buffer size will generate a more detailed terrain whose output can have more high-frequency response when "read." For example, for a 512x512 terrain, we would use **buffer~ terrain @samps 262144**, and for a 1024x1024 terrain, we would use **buffer~ terrain @samps 1048576**.

As before, we can refer to this **buffer~** in gen~ using a **buffer terrain** operator and derive our axis resolution from the square root of its length using the **sqrt** operator, which we store in a **history N** operator.

We'll also add a **codebox** to do our computations to fill the terrain, which looks like this:

```
1  fxy(x, y) {
2      x1 = x*2-1;
3      x2 = tanh(sin(twopi*x*(1+y))+sin(4*pi*x));
4      return mix(x1, x2, y);
5  }
6
7  if (elapsed == 1) {
8      for (i=0; i<N; i+=1) {
9          for (j=0; j<N; j+=1) {
10             // normalized X and Y coordinates:
11             x = j/N;
12             y = i/N;
13             // compute Z according to X and Y:
14             z = fxy(x, y);
15             // sample index into the buffer:
16             index = j + i*N;
17             // write to the buffer
18             poke(terrain, z, index);
19         }
20     }
21 }
```

CodeBox   buffer terrain

sqrt

history N

Let's step through that code. First, we have the function `fxy(x, y)` that defines our terrain. You can put whatever mathematical calculations you want into here; all it needs to do is `return` a height value between -1.0 and +1.0 according to the current X and Y position. That said, you probably want to find a terrain that strikes an interesting balance of complexity—not so simple that it becomes boring, but also not too random that it becomes noise—the changes between one grid point and the next should be relatively small for the most part to create an undulating terrain. In the codebox above we just made up something that seemed interesting to us: a **mix** across the Y axis between a sawtooth wave (x1) and a **tanh**-waveshaped sum of two sines across the axes (x2).

Defining the function doesn't do anything yet—not until we actually invoke this function in the main body of the code. The main body starts with `if (elapsed == 1)`, which is just a simple way to ensure that all the code inside the next block (i.e. between the next "`{`" and the matching "`}`" brackets) only runs once. (The **elapsed** variable (and operator) always outputs the number of sample frames that have passed since the patch loaded, which will only equal one once.) If we didn't do this, the patch would be trying to regenerate the waveterrain on every passing sample frame, which is computationally expensive and unnecessary.

Inside this `if` block, we have two nested `for` loops: one stepping **N** times for each row in the Y axis, the other stepping **N** times for each column in the X axis, making the innermost body of code run **N**x**N** times altogether. Each pass through the innermost loop will calculate a different Z value for each XY point in the terrain and store it at the correct location in the buffer. The code first computes normalized X and Y coordinates (running from 0.0 to 1.0) by dividing both step counts by **N**. We'll use those normalized coordinates in the `fx(x, y)` function call to compute the height `z` for this particular grid cell. Next, we compute what the sample index will be into the buffer for this grid cell (i.e., where to write the value `z` to), which is the same calculation we used before for the 2D wavetable: `index = j + i*N`. And finally, we plug in the `index` and `z` value into a **poke** operation to write it to the **buffer terrain**.

Remember, you can use any function that refers to the X and Y values to derive the single Z value—feel free to experiment with functions of your own! If you find a terrain you like, send a "writewave" message to the **buffer~** object in the parent patch to save the data as a WAV file.

Basis Function Generator (BFG) terrains

As an alternative, we can also generate terrains by using the extensive matrix generation capabilities of Jitter. For example, the Jitter object **jit.bfg** can generate matrix data for a wide variety of interesting mathematical surfaces (BFG here stands for basis function generator). Working with Jitter is not the focus of this book, but this is such a useful source of terrains that we included an example patch to demonstrate generating landscapes for wave terrain synthesis.

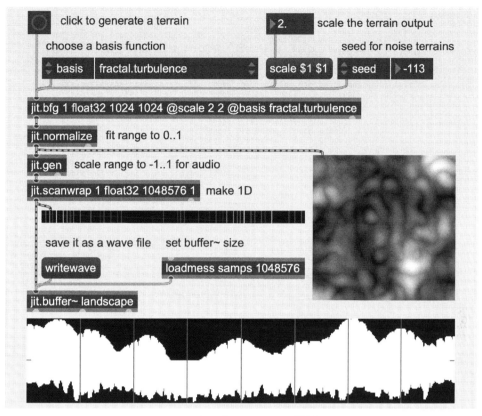

waveterrain_generate_BFG.maxpat

The **jit.bfg** object is configured to set the plane count (1), the matrix type (32-bit floating-point values), and the dimensions of the terrain (1024x1024). In addition, we set a default scaling value (@scale 2 2) and the basis function (@basis fractal.turbulence), which we can override with attribute menus.

When the button is clicked, the **jit.bfg** outputs a matrix, which we will process and convert to store in a wave file. First, we normalize the results to get an optimal spread of output values between zero and one and then use a **jit.gen** applying a **scale 0 1 -1 1** operator to scale the matrix contents to the -1.0 to +1.0 range we expect for audio. This outputs a 2D 1024 X 1024 single-plane matrix of audio-range values, which we convert to a 1D matrix of length 1048576 via the **jit.scanwrap** object, to be stored in a **jit.buffer~** object.

The useful thing about the **jit.buffer~** object is that we can treat it exactly like any **buffer~** object (we can even reference it by name for the **gen~** object's internal **buffer** operator, for example). This means we can send it the *writewave* message, which will let us save its contents to a .WAV file on disk.

Navigating data space

For the last section of this chapter, let's look at some more interesting ways of moving around a 2D data space by generating related X and Y signal pairs. We'll give these examples in terms of wave terrain synthesis applications, but bear in mind these same orbit generators can also be used for the X and Y parameters of a 2D wavetable patch or, indeed, any other algorithm that works with two related inputs.

Our first wave terrain patch used a circular orbit derived from a **poltocar** operator. While such circular orbits work fine for an initial example, there are many ways of making that circular traversal much more interesting. For example, we can nudge the orbit away from the center simply by adding more signals to the signal outputs of the **poltocar** operator.

We can extend this to a kind of parallel modulation approach and create a "double orbit" simply by adding two poltocar operations together. Setting the frequencies and radii to different values can produce interesting results, including paths like a moon orbiting a planet orbiting the sun, as well as much more extreme excursions!

However, when adding two orbits together, it's quite possible that the signals can go outside the -1.0 to 1.0 range that a wave terrain reader expects. To avoid this, we have a few options:

- We could send the results through **fold -1 1** operators so that the signals will mirror at the edges.
- We could send the results through **wrap -1 1** operators to have it jump around to the opposite edges or **clip -1 1** for hard clipping at the boundaries.
- We could apply any of the sigmoid waveshapers from Chapter 3 (p. 84) to *compress* the waves as they get nearer to the edges.

We could even use **param** and **selector** operators to vary the method we use:

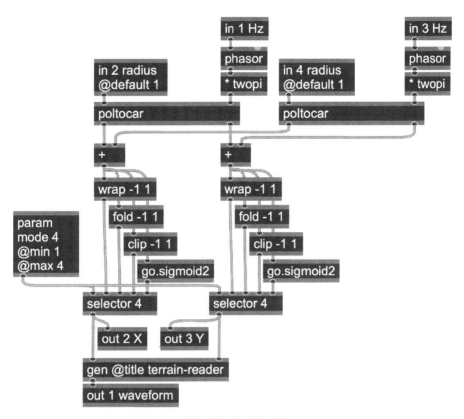

waveterrain_2D_doubleorbit.maxpat

Here are a selection of eccentric traversals this can produce:

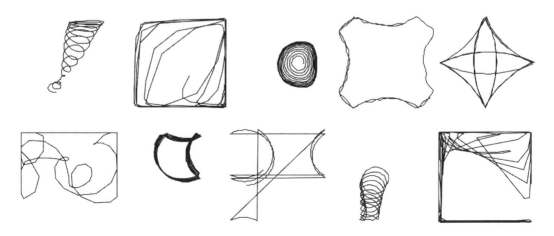

Circular orbits aren't the only choice. Any mostly smooth sequence of X & Y values in the range of -1.0 to +1.0 can yield workable results. For example, we can use simple accumulators into **fold** operators to produce a variety of triangle-like waveforms independently for X and Y:

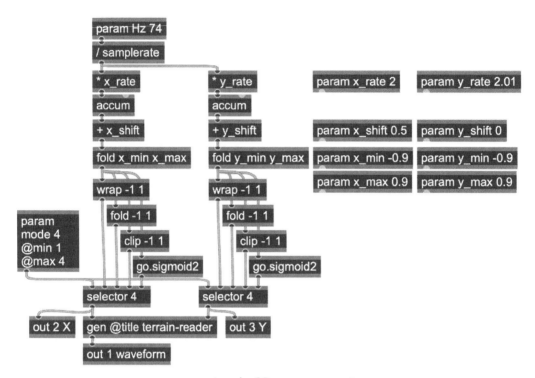

waveterrain_2D_carom.maxpat

As long as the X and Y rate parameters are similar, this patch will produce 45-degree angle traversals that appear to "bounce" off the min/max boundaries; but once the rates diverge, the angles change, and the diagonal shape breaks into weaving motions. Any modifications of the boundaries produce more complex patterns and will also "retune" the output. The caroming traversal can produce all kinds of results:

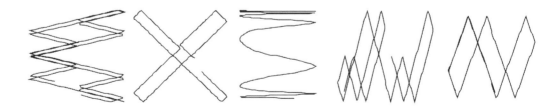

You might wish to experiment with having multiple versions of this patch traversing different areas of the same wave terrain at different rates.

Polygonal orbits

We've seen circular as well as diagonal orbits; what about traversals that describe regular polygons like triangles, squares, and pentagons? In fact, we can do this using a **phasor**-driven **poltocar** operator as before. The difference lies in the way we derive the radius input. If we can modulate the radius with just the right function, we can effectively inscribe the polygon within the circle—and it will inherit the periodicity of that circular basis too.[8] That is, we want a function that gives us the radius we need from the angle we have. You could think of this as a kind of precisely-tuned amplitude modulation or waveshaping of the radius.

The waveshaping will repeat N times around a circle for an N-sided polygon. For example, a triangle has three sides, so we need to shape the radius with the same curvature three times as we go around. To patch this up, we'll add a second **phasor** running at N times the angular frequency (which, therefore, also adds an audible harmonic). You can thus think of this **param N** as a modulator to carrier ratio.

We then apply some scaling math that lets us use this as the amplitude of the oscillator, which we send to the radius (left) inlet of the **poltocar** operator.

The equation of a unit polygon of *N* sides (and *N* vertices) in polar coordinates is the ratio of the angle between vertices (which is `cos(pi/N)`) and the current angle, which runs from `-pi` to `+pi` over each vertex:

`r = cos(pi/N) / cos(angle/N)`

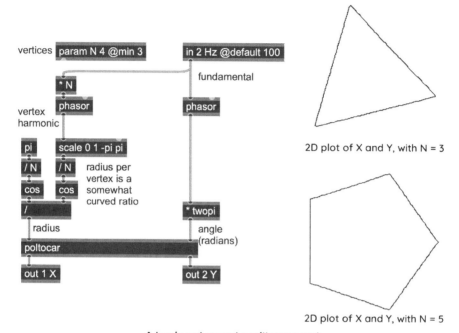

A basic polygonal oscillator patch

This can be extended in a few ways. There's no need to limit N to whole numbers. For example, if we set N=3.01, we will get a triangle shape that appears to spin in space, as each time around, it overshoots slightly. This is not unlike the benefit of slightly detuned oscillators and modulators we saw in Chapter 8. Suppose we don't want it to spin but instead want "partial" polygons. In that case, we can do the equivalent of oscillator sync and reset the vertex phasor to zero whenever the fundamental phasor resets.

We can also add a separate phase modulation offset "P" to the fundamental phasor output, which will effectively give us direct control over the rotation of the shape in space.

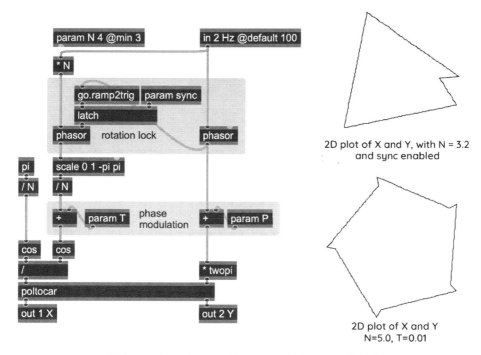

2D plot of X and Y, with N = 3.2
and sync enabled

2D plot of X and Y
N=5.0, T=0.01

Polygonal synthesis with sync and phase modulation

Adding a phase modulation offset to the per-vertex phasor (**param T** in the patch above) does something different. It "kinks" the straight side out, disrupting the output function in a way that repeats itself for each "section" of the polygon. It looks a bit like adding "teeth" to the shape.

Turning up this **param T** can easily make the shape expand beyond the -1.0 to +1.0 signal range, so once again we might want to add some kind of signal limiting here. And once we have limiting, it makes sense to add a **param drive** to push it.

For example, in the patch below we feed the potentially overdriven radius through a **fold** operator whose outer bound is 1.0 but whose inner bound is dependent on the angle, to keep the folding signal closer to the original shape's bounds.

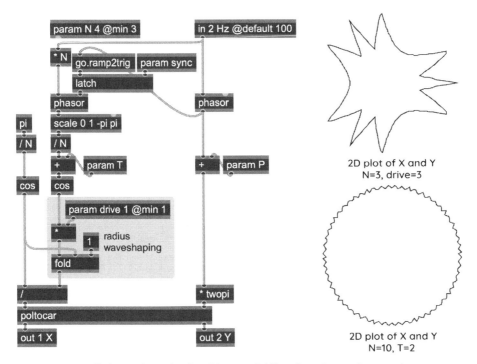

Polygonal synthesis with wavefolding, in polygonal.maxpat

There are lots of other things you could try in this kind of patch—perhaps sigmoid waveshaping to bow out the straight edges; perhaps bitcrushing/quantizing to step the radius; perhaps amplitude modulations, filtering, or any other signal processes! You can also try converting some of the **param** operators to regular **in** operators to feed with audio-rate modulations. Don't be afraid to experiment!

Although we've introduced these orbit generator patches for traversing 2D wave terrains or 2D wavetables[9], they are also very useful as modulation signals for other kinds of processes, such as frequency modulation and phase modulation patches, as well as for generating audio signals in their own right of course!

Taking things further

In this chapter, we've looked at many ways to generate more interesting waveforms by navigating data sources, and there are many ways you can take these ideas further.

So far, we have been using monophonic wavetables and terrains, but a **buffer** (or **data**) operator can be multi-channel, and so can the readers. For example, any of the **sample**, **wave**, or **peek** operators our patches used can be made stereo by adding an **@channels 2** attribute, or more simply adding the argument "2" after the buffer name, such as **wave tables 2** or **peek terrain 2**. Then, any patching downstream of these (such as the **bilinear-interpolation** subpatch) just needs doubling up to process each channel's output. We can also get interesting stereo output from a monophonic wavetable or terrain by running two copies of our patch side by side, feeding them related but slightly different indexing signals. For example, we run two **terrain-reader** patches and send the second **terrain-reader** the same X but an inverted Y (i.e., multiplied by -1.0).

As a wavetable's (or wave terrain's) data becomes more complex, it adds more higher-harmonic energy to a signal, sometimes at the cost of losing some of the fundamental frequency energy—this can be problematic for use as a bass, for example. A straightforward solution here is to add a simple waveform (sine, pulse, or saw) in parallel, driven by the same **phasor** that is driving the wavetable. (Or for wave terrains, using the same **phasor** that drives the angular rotation).

From the point of view of these core **phasor** operators, both wavetables and wave terrains become simply interesting functions of phase, just as was the case for the various frequency and phase modulation patches in Chapter 8. So, naturally, you can explore modifying those FM and PM patches, replacing the *** twopi** and **sin** operators with wavetable oscillators. There's an enormous amount of sonic complexity available here, and if you're using the sinc interpolated, mipmapped wavetables, they will handle pretty extreme modulation without aliasing. Similarly, you could explore some of the FM and PM structures for the polar (**poltocar**-based) oscillators. Simply adding frequency modulation to the radius and angle inputs can pick out some mesmerizing orbits.

Perhaps you might think about how to extend orbit generators to 3D to drive a 3D wavetable oscillator. Or, if you're feeling ambitious, think about how to generate and navigate 3D voxel terrain.

Chapter 10: Windows of Time

In this chapter, we'll be looking at how we can reset timelines and lifespans: using one process to determine the durations of another process repeatedly. What do we mean by timelines and lifespans? We've already seen examples of nesting timelines by subdividing and synchronizing ramps in Chapter 2. For example, even a simple repeating drum hit has at least three nested spans of time: the periodic tempo, the duration of the drum sound, and the period of the waveform that makes this sound.

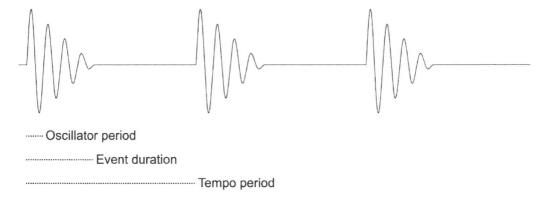

Note that two of these layers are periodic (the potentially endlessly repeating layers of the oscillator and the tempo), while the layer between represents a finite "window" of time (the lifespan of each event). In this chapter, we're going to dig deeper into these kinds of nested cyclic and windowed durations, right down to microsonic scales of pitches and timbre, producing a variety of formant, pulsar, polyphonic granular, and hard sync synthesis results.

Sync

Hard sync is one of the simplest examples of one process defining the lifespan of another—by literally cutting it short. Oscillator hard sync is a classic technique in analog synthesis in which one oscillator's phase (let's call it the "carrier") is reset back to the start whenever another oscillator (let's call it the "scheduler") completes a cycle.

A hard sync reset causes a jump in the phase of the carrier (so, in a way, this is also a special case of phase modulation). The reset jump will likely cut the carrier's waveform partway through one of its cycles, like this:

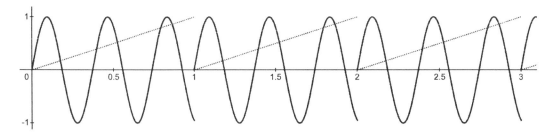

The graph shows a sinusoidal carrier oscillator at 2.7Hz (solid line) being hard synced by a scheduler phasor oscillator running at 1Hz (dotted line), producing a hard cut in the carrier waveform once per second. When listening to the carrier, hard sync produces a complex of the two oscillator tones. However, typically the scheduler's frequency is what we hear as the main pitch, while the carrier frequency shapes the principal formant or harmonic tone. Holding the scheduler's frequency constant while sweeping the frequency of the carrier creates a tearing or zippering sound—that's what people usually think of as the characteristic sound of hard sync.

A tentative hard sync patch in gen~ might look something like the following patch:

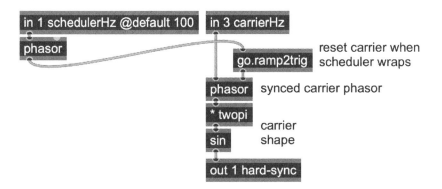

Here, we derive triggers from the scheduler **phasor** using a **go.ramp2trig** abstraction and use those triggers to reset the carrier **phasor** back to zero using the **phasor** operator's right inlet. This does work, but it will likely suffer from aliasing noise. Even if the carrier is a smooth sinusoid, the periodic hard sync cuts in the waveform will produce a lot of high-frequency harmonics in the same way that the large jumps in sawtooth and square/pulse-shaped waveforms do. The strength of these harmonics produces the desired brightness of a saw/pulse or hard sync sound. They are also problematic for digital synthesis. as they can very easily lead to harsh aliasing noise. At the end of this chapter, we will return to develop an understanding of this noise and build a solution to suppress it, but first, we will look at a much simpler related synthesis technique known as *windowed sync.*

Windowed Sync

Windowed sync is a variant of oscillator sync popularized by digital phase distortion synthesizers. It eliminates most of the aliasing problems of a hard sync cut point by simply fading out the carrier waveform right at the moment the sync cut happens. Perhaps this might seem like cheating, but it's quite pragmatic, cheap, and effective.

All you need to do is amplitude modulate the carrier using some kind of envelope or window function that fades down to 0.0 right at the cut point, like this:

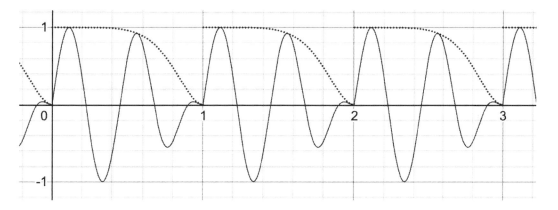

In the graph above, a smooth window function (dotted line) derived from the scheduler phasor is used to amplitude-modulate the synced carrier waveform such that the amplitude falls to zero at the sync point (solid line).

Here is what that might look like as a patch:

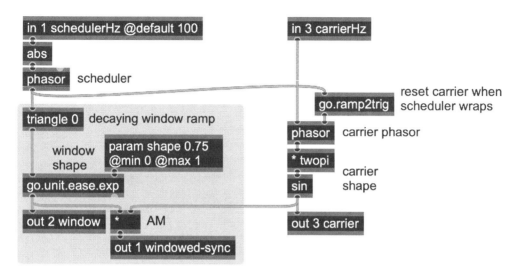

To create the window, we invert the unipolar scheduler's **phasor** so that it runs from 1.0 down to 0.0 as a linear decay shape (using a **triangle 0** operator) and then apply a **go.unit.ease.exp** abstraction to produce a curved envelope shape similar to the graph above. You can try substituting this shape with other options from the unit shapers in Chapter 3. This window output is then multiplied with the carrier waveform and output at **out 1**.

If you compare the windowed sync sound of **out 1** with the raw hard sync signal at **out 3**, you will be able to hear how windowing has suppressed a lot of the harsh aliasing, without losing too much energy at the lower harmonics. Here are the two spectra compared (windowed sync in black, raw hard sync in gray):

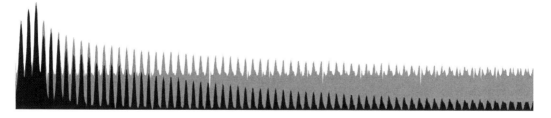

Sweeping the carrier frequency above the scheduler frequency now sounds a bit like a filter, where the carrier frequency picks out which harmonic resonates the most. In fact, it picks the next harmonic in the series for each multiple of the scheduler frequency. For example, if the scheduler frequency is 200Hz, the harmonics are picked out one by one when the carrier is 200Hz, 400Hz, 600Hz, and so on. So, rather than specifying the carrier frequency independently of the scheduler frequency, perhaps we should take inspiration from what we learned in Chapter 8 and work with a carrier-to-scheduler *ratio*. In this case, we may prefer to set the carrier as a *formant multiplier* of the scheduler frequency.

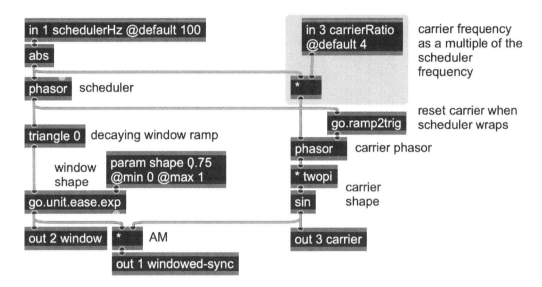

Sub-sample accuracy

There's one more important refinement to make. If you listen carefully at higher scheduler frequencies, you might still hear some aliasing noise. The source of this noise is still the carrier **phasor** reset, but the reason is a bit more subtle. Specifically, we shouldn't be resetting the phase of the carrier exactly to *zero* but to some value near-zero that properly reflects the ideal phase at that point. That's because the ideal reset probably happens *somewhere between one sample frame and the next*. If we zoom right down to the sample level, we can see that an ideal scheduler phasor (dotted line in the following graph) wraps somewhere between actual sample frames. Within the sample frame in which the phasor wraps (marked in gray), the sample value is slightly above zero.

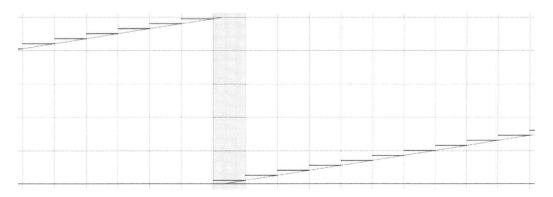

In contrast, when a **phasor** operator is reset by a trigger to its right inlet, it always resets to zero exactly. Although the difference looks small, it can have quite a significant effect on the sonic quality of the output (and we'll be seeing the importance of subsample offsets like these again and again throughout this chapter).

To fix this in our patch, we'll have to replace our carrier's **phasor** operator with an equivalent accumulator, using the same **history**, **+**, and **switch** operator set we've seen since Chapter 2. That way, we can control what value it resets to. This accumulator counts using a slope that is relative to the scheduler's slope (which could be derived via **go.ramp2slope** abstraction or simply by `schedulerHz/samplerate`). And as the crucial step for subsample accuracy, the accumulator's **switch** operator doesn't reset to zero but to a phase that is *relative to the scheduler's phase* whenever the scheduler itself wraps.

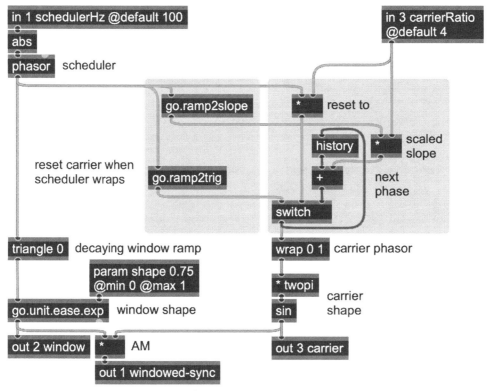

windowed-sync.maxpat

And with that, we have a very effective windowed-sync patch. With the scheduler at a low frequency, e.g., 100Hz, and the carrier exponentially ramping down from a high to lower frequency (e.g., 2000Hz to 100Hz), it can be a little reminiscent of a classic Roland 303 acid sound.

One of the neatest things about this method is its generality. Practically any envelope shape can be substituted here, and any carrier waveform, so long as *either* the start of the carrier waveform *or* the start of the envelope waveform begins at zero, and the envelope ends at zero. You could try swapping out the sine carrier shape with a wavetable oscillator from Chapter 9, for example, or an FM oscillator from Chapter 8.

In fact, we already saw a somewhat similar patch to this toward the end of Chapter 8. The last Modified FM example also performed an amplitude modulation of a carrier waveform with a window function (in that example, a raised cosine shape), leading to a sound with strong formant qualities. In that example, the more the window shape is squeezed, the more silence appears between the blips, and the more the formant is expressed.

Pulsar Synthesis

As we saw back in Chapter 2, we can take a phasor ramp and multiply it by some number greater than one to get a ramp whose slope is steeper. If we then use a **clip 0 1** operation to limit this steeper ramp into the 0.0 to 1.0 range, we get a shorter ramp that nevertheless still recurs at the original rate:

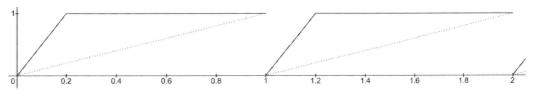

Dotted line: A scheduler phasor at 1Hz.
Solid line: The same phasor multiplied by 5 and clipped between 0 and 1.

We can apply this idea to our windowed sync patch in order to insert silence between grains, simply by scaling and clipping the scheduler **phasor** before it is shaped into a window, and using a **param windowRatio** to set the scaling factor:

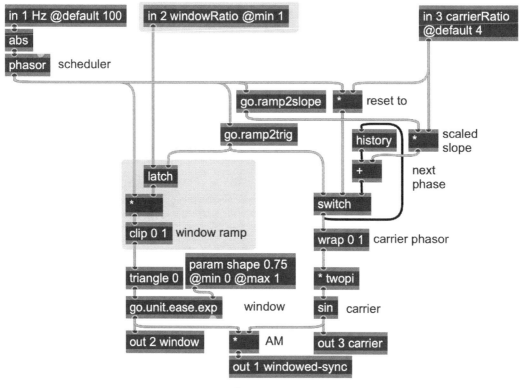

pulsar.maxpat

It's quite remarkable how much this patch can sound like a resonant filter, with the carrier ratio determining the resonant peak and the window ratio (and shape) of the resonance, even though there is no filter involved, and all we are actually doing is inserting silence!

What we have created here is also a form of synchronous granular synthesis known as *pulsar synthesis.*[1] Granular synthesis encompasses a variety of techniques that mostly involve scheduling many tiny particles of sound rather like clouds of tiny notes with durations in ranges of milliseconds. Each grain is typically a combination of two components: a carrier signal (which could be synthesized, read from a buffer, read from a delay, etc.) and an envelope to define the overall amplitude shape. That is, much like the diagram at the start of this chapter, granular methods usually incorporate three layers of schedulers, envelopes, and carriers. We'll be exploring several granular examples in this chapter and more granular techniques in Book 2.

Pulsar synthesis is a specific kind of granular synthesis that uses *synchronous* scheduling, meaning that grains are scheduled at a periodic rate that imparts a fundamental frequency to the sound. Within this period, there is a grain called a *pulsaret*, followed by a period of silence. That is, the duration of the sounding pulsaret is typically briefer than the period of the scheduler. The ratio of these two durations creates the effect of a duty cycle[2], and modulation of it creates an effect related to pulse-width modulation. If the carrier is pitched, it will likely have a higher frequency than the scheduler, and this can convey a formant frequency.. The way the length of the window duty cycle shapes the spectrum is easy to understand. With a longer window, more cycles of the underlying carrier waveform can be heard, and thus the more the carrier frequency dominates the sound (which is what evokes the character of a resonant formant filter). Conversely, as the window becomes shorter, fewer cycles of the carrier can be heard, until the waveform becomes more of a blip whose wide-band spectrum depends more on the window shape itself.[3]

Pulsar synthesis is quite a general technique: the carrier can be an arbitrary finite sound, and any window shape can be used for the envelope. For example, in the following patch, we modified our ***pulsar.maxpat*** patch to use a variable Tukey window shape and added another harmonic oscillator routed to act as an FM modulator of the carrier for a much more complex sonic output. It's well worth exploring extensive frequency modulation of the inputs of this patch.

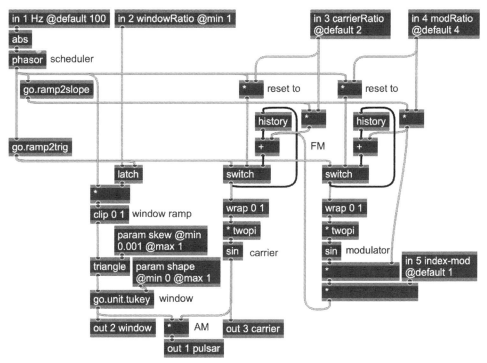

pulsar_fm.maxpat

When the event duration is longer than the fundamental period

Why is **param windowRatio** limited to **@min 1**? A ratio less than one would imply a duty cycle greater than one, which means that the envelope duration becomes longer than the available time in the scheduler period. With the patches we have built so far, this would simply mean that the envelope would never reach the end before a new envelope begins, truncating the waveform mid-cycle and losing the benefits of the windowing.

There are a couple of alternate strategies we could try here. First, we could prevent any new envelope from starting until the current envelope has actually completed, which will create a kind of subharmonic effect. Alternatively, we could modify our algorithm to support multiple overlapping grains at once as a kind of polyphony. We'll look at both of these solutions in the next sections.

Suppressing retriggers (subharmonics)

The first way to allow grain windows that are longer than the scheduler period is simply to prevent the scheduler from starting a new window until the last window has been completed. (This is similar to the behavior of envelope generators that will not retrigger until the current envelope completes). To do this, we will first need to decouple the window ramp generation from the scheduler ramp in just the same way as we already did for the carrier.

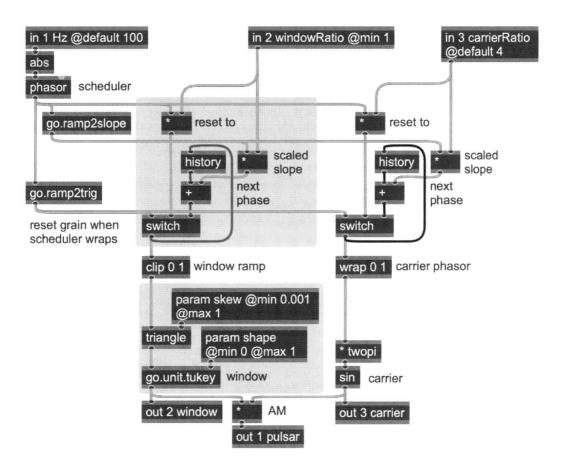

Now that the window ramp runs independently of the scheduler, we can suppress a new grain from being started by bypassing (zeroing) the scheduler's **go.ramp2trig** triggers. Our goal is to suppress these triggers only while our window is busy ramping. We know our window envelope is still busy *if the window ramp phase has not reached 1.0 yet*, which means we can test the ramp phase using a **< 1** comparator.

We can use this logical condition to suppress the scheduler's **go.ramp2trig** triggers with an **and** and a **not** operator. In other words, our grain envelope (and carrier) ramps will only be reset if the scheduler triggers <u>and</u> we are <u>not</u> already busy.

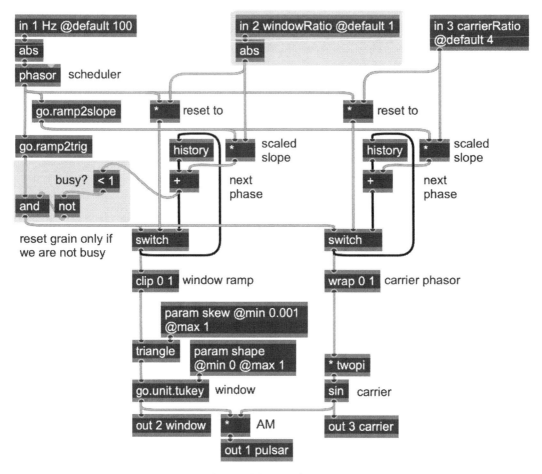

pulsar_subharmonic.maxpat

Now, while **param windowRatio** is greater than 1.0, this patch behaves as it did before, but if you bring the **param windowRatio** below 1.0 toward zero, you will hear the frequency halve, then divide into thirds, quarters, and so on, picking out the *subharmonic* series of the fundamental scheduler frequency. If the scheduler frequency is fairly low, say around 100Hz, then these subharmonics will quickly enter the temporal space of rhythms.

To hear the subharmonics as pitched tones, try setting the scheduler frequency high, say around 1000Hz, and then slowly bring the **param windowRatio** down from 1.0 to 0.5, then 0.3, then 0.2, etc. The envelope generator is no longer completely subordinate to the scheduler phasor but can also ignore it when it is already busy.

Polyphony (distributing event triggers)

What if, instead of truncating or suppressing long event windows, we wanted them all to play out fully, overlapping on top of each other like the notes of a polyphonic instrument? In this section, we'll look at one method to do this and another one later in the chapter. We'll first describe things in terms of note-playing because it makes an easier analogy, but we will then translate it to the grains of granular synthesis.

Strictly speaking, the operators of a gen~ patch, like all serial computing systems, can only process one thing at a time. So, just as we need at least three fingers to play a three-note chord on a keyboard or three singers to sing three-part harmony, we can imagine that we would need a separate signal process, or "voice," for each potential overlapping note for a polyphonic patch. One of the simplest ways to achieve this is to make a copy of a subpatch for each voice. Then, if we have some kind of scheduler producing triggers for note events, then all we need is an algorithm that will distribute each new trigger to one of the voices.

The simplest distribution algorithm just sends each new event to the next voice in turn (sometimes called the "round-robin" method), which could be done with a **counter** and **gate** operator like this:

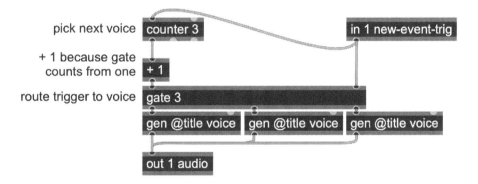

However, this algorithm isn't very practical if some notes are short while others are long: a long-held note may be cut off too soon as its voice is reused for another note, even if there were other voices not busy playing anything. It would be better if we could delegate this responsibility to the voices themselves so that a voice could say the equivalent of "Sorry, I'm busy, let me ask the next person." Then, we can pass each new event trigger to the first voice, and if this voice was already busy playing a note, it would pass the event trigger on to the next voice, and so on, until the new event trigger reaches a voice that isn't already busy and *can* start the new note.

We already saw with the subharmonic pulsar synthesis example how we can use the envelope to determine whether a patch is busy playing an event and to ignore new triggers if it is. We can use essentially the same logic control here, simply using a **gate** operator to determine whether to handle a new event trigger within the voice subpatch (if the voice isn't busy) or route the trigger to an outlet for the next the voice subpatch (if the voice *is* busy). A simple example might look like the following:

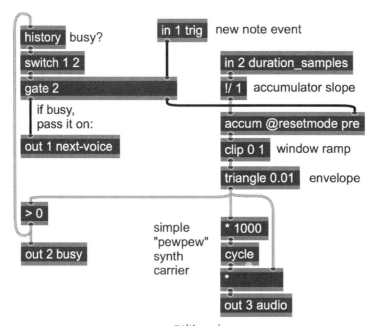

gen @title voice

The core of the patch is the **accum** and **clip 0 1** operator pair that ramps from 0.0 to 1.0 over the duration of an event. The slope of the ramp is set from the duration in samples via a **!/ 1** operator, and the ramp is shaped into a fast attack, slow decay envelope here using a **triangle 0.01** operator. As long as this envelope's output is greater than zero (via the **> 0** operator), we know the voice is currently busy.

This "busy" state is fed back via a **history** operator to control the routing of a **gate** operator, to either handle the input trigger inside the patch (by restarting the accumulator) or, if busy, to pass it on to the **out 1** for the next voice. We highlighted the trigger signals with black patch cords to make this structure clearer. (The bottom part of this patch just derives an enveloped sine sweep from the window ramp itself—it's not important to the polyphonic method here, it's just something simple so that we can hear that it is working.)

We can now duplicate this voice subpatch several times and chain them together.

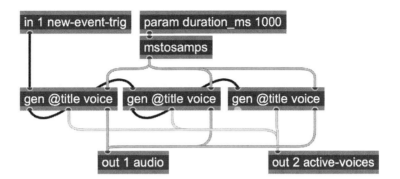

Notice how the parameters are sent to all voices, and all the voices' audio outputs are added together at **out 1**. Summing up the "busy" states of each voice subpatch (from their 2nd outlets to **out 2**) also tells us how many voices are active at any time. The trigger signals (again here marked with black patch cords) are routed from one voice to the next as they pass along any trigger they can't handle themselves.

You could trigger the events from a MIDI input source, any of the random trigger generators we saw in Chapter 4, or sequencers from Chapter 5. This patch can now play up to three overlapping sounds at any time without cutting any off midway. To increase the maximum polyphony, just add more voice subpatches!

Polyphonic notes

The voice subpatch can be practically any synthesis algorithm; all it needs is some way to indicate whether it is busy or not and the trigger handling/forwarding subcircuit. However, the more voices we add, and the more controls we add to each subpatch, the more spaghetti-like our patching can become.

Here is a little trick to simplify things: if we store the shared controls into named **history** operators in the parent gen~ patch, then these names will be available to reference in subpatches (and the same holds for **param**, **buffer**, and **data** operators).

For example, in the following patch, we store both the required slope and frequency as **history slope** and **history freq,** respectively, for a requested note duration and pitch.

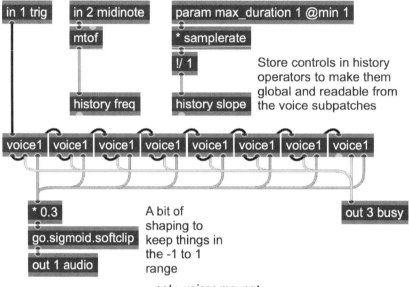

poly_voices.maxpat

We also increased the number of voices, and we saved the voice subpatch as an abstraction on disk next to the main patch (with the name ***voice1.gendsp***) so that we only ever have to modify one subpatch, and all the others will update accordingly. We also scaled down the output and applied a wave shaping soft limiter to the combined audio output. When many notes overlap, it's quite possible for the total signal amplitude to go outside the -1.0 to +1.0 range, so a bit of attenuation and limiting may be a good idea for any kind of polyphonic patch.

Here's the **voice1** subpatch, making reference to the **history slope** and **history freq** values by name (and adding a bit of random deviation for interest):

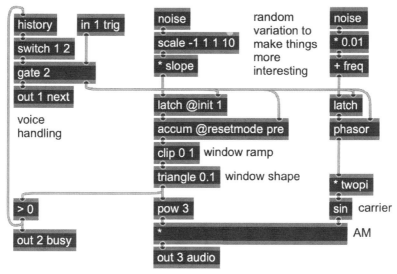

voice1.gendsp

Granulation

To bring things back toward the microsonic realm of granular synthesis, let's build a voice that plays microsonic snatches from a wave file stored in a **buffer src** operator. A starting patch might look something like this:

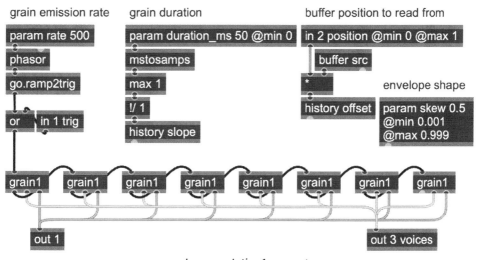

poly_granulation1.maxpat

The trigger source is a phasor fed into a **go.ramp2trig**, but there's also the option of external triggering via the **in 1** operator, combined via the **or** operator to let either trigger source pass through. The grain parameters include:

- a grain duration that is converted from milliseconds to a per-sample ramp slope and made global via the **history slope** operator
- a relative position from the audio buffer (via **in 2**), which is converted to a sample index and made global via the **history offset** operator
- a global envelope shaping option via the **param skew** operator

All of these global names ("slope," "offset," and "skew") are referenced inside the *grain1.gendsp* abstraction, which looks like this:

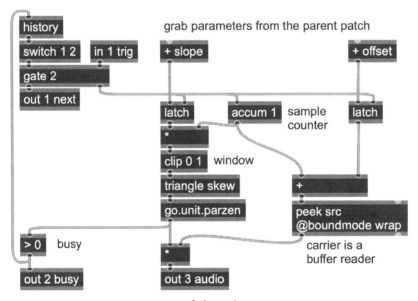

grain1.gendsp

The voice handling here is unchanged. The core is now a sample counter (the **accum 1** operator) that is reset to zero whenever a new grain starts, adding one for every passing sample frame. This is multiplied by the *slope*, as captured at the start of the grain via a **latch** operator, and clipped into 0.0 to 1.0 to create the envelope ramp. The envelope is shaped by a triangle that references the global skew parameter, and we shaped it using the **go.unit.parzen** window unit shaper. The sample accumulator is also used to read from the **buffer src**, shifted by the global "offset" parameter (also **latch**ed to hold it constant throughout the grain), and fed into a **peek src** operator with **@boundmode wrap** to ensure reading off the end of the buffer will wrap around to the beginning.

Asynchronous and stochastic grains

Patches like these respond really well to the introduction of randomized deviations to their parameters. Iannis Xenakis, the pioneering composer of microsound, argued strongly for the introduction of stochastic and probabilistic organizations of individual grains to re-introduce the micro-fluctuations and variance of timbre that make real acoustics sound more alive than electronic sounds made of pure harmonics.[4]

For example, even very slight deviations (on the order of 0.1%) in the buffer offset, so that each grain is reading from a slightly different part of the buffer, can completely transform the sonic character of the result. Meanwhile, deviating the emission rate very quickly eliminates any sense of *pitch* from the scheduler, which instead turns into a kind of probabilistic *density*. Note that emission rate and emission density are both concepts of frequency, but one is regular (and pitched), and the other one is irregular (and unpitched).

Here are both of these variations in the ***poly_granulation2.maxpat*** example:

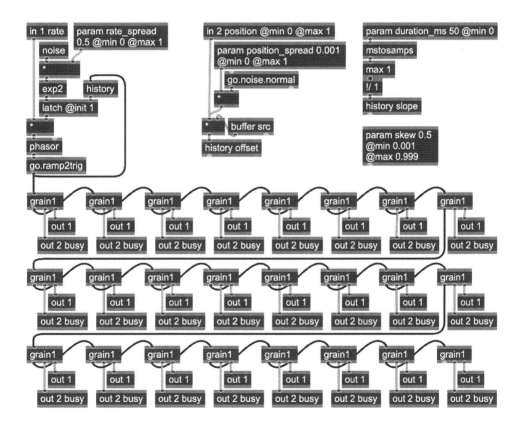

With a low emission frequency of around 1-10Hz, durations of around 100-200ms, and a fast attack skew of 0.1 or less, this will create clear percussive events. Softening the skew to an even 0.5 and increasing the emission frequency to around 100Hz or higher will start to create a dense, cloud-like sound. Bringing the duration down to below around 20ms, the original content of the buffer will seem to fragment into tiny particles of sound.

There are lots more refinements we can add to this, including adding randomized amplitude per grain, randomized stereo pan and width, variable playback speed per grain with deviations, and so on. For the most part, this is just an extrapolation of the techniques we've already explored, and several of these ideas are demonstrated in the **poly_granulation3.maxpat** example. You could also try embedding some of the wavetable or wave terrain ideas from Chapter 9 into the grain patch to give each grain a unique trajectory through data space!

But there's one more detail we'd like to address. If you turn all the stochastic parameters to zero, set the grain size to just a couple of milliseconds, and set the emission rate to an audible pitched frequency, you might notice the noise of aliasing recurring again. We'll look at that next.

Subsample-accurate events from phasor ramps

The polyphonic patches we have created so far trigger grains with sample-accurate timing, in the sense that the trigger aligns each grain to the precise sample frame during which the phasor ramp wraps. This is already much more precise than typical "control rates" and MIDI timing. But the smaller the grains get, and the faster they are spawned, the more the sound can transform into a pitched oscillator; and as we saw with windowed sync (and pulsar synthesis) earlier this chapter, at these rates, being sample-accurate just isn't accurate enough. At these rates, the fractional subsample locations of events become very important, and we need to locate each event precisely *within* a sample frame with *sub-sample* accuracy.

Let's zoom right in to where the scheduler phasor wraps and take a look at the grain envelope it causes:

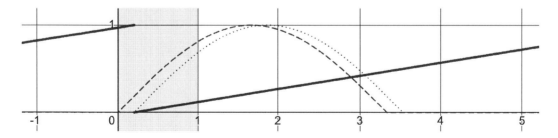

In this graph, the horizontal axis represents the passing sample frames in real-time, and the solid line is the continuous high-frequency ramp that our **phasor** operator is emulating.

The gray-shaded region is a specific sample frame in which the phasor has wrapped, causing a trigger, and the dashed line shows a grain envelope caused by this trigger, as our patch currently produces. But for a pure tone, the grain window should be aligned to the ideal ramp, as marked by the dotted line.

We dealt with this problem previously in a somewhat ad hoc way, but it would be great if we could build a more general-purpose abstraction to extract subsample-accurate events from phasor ramp schedulers. What we need is a way to extract what the subsample offset of the ramp actually is during the trigger so that we can properly align the grain window, carrier waveform, and any other dependent processes.

There's a simple way to calculate this: if we divide our phasor by its own slope, we'll get a ramp with a slope of 1.0.[5] Such a slope counts by one for each passing sample frame of time. Then, in the exact sample frame that the phasor wraps, the first value will always be some number between zero and one, giving us the fractional number of samples since it wrapped (and also giving us a trigger for free).

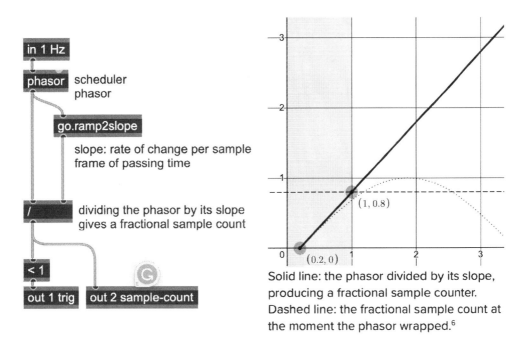

Solid line: the phasor divided by its slope, producing a fractional sample counter. Dashed line: the fractional sample count at the moment the phasor wrapped.[6]

There are a few subtleties to deal with, though. First, we have to ensure we're getting a steady rate of change of the ramp even through the transition, which we handled using the **go.ramp2slope** abstraction we created back in Chapter 2 (p. 46).

Unfortunately, this patch doesn't work for a phasor running downwards (with negative frequency), as it will focus on the values near the top of the ramp rather than near zero. We can fix that simply by subtracting one from the phasor to recenter it, but only if the slope is negative.

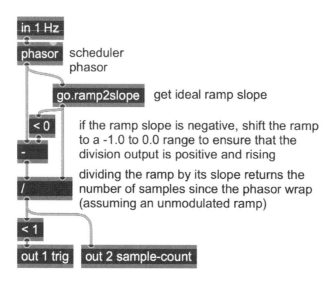

Up to now, this algorithm assumes that the phasor's slope isn't changing. That actually doesn't matter for the first sample after the phasor wrap, but beyond that, simply dividing the accumulated phase by the current slope won't accurately tell you the samples since the wrap. We can fix this easily enough by grabbing the fractional count at the wrap as we have above and storing it with a **latch** operator, and also restarting a sample counter using an **accum 1** operator at the same time. Adding both the **latch** and **accum 1** outputs together will give an accurate fractional measure of the number of samples since the last phasor wrap.

There's also one more condition we might want to handle. If we ever set our phasor's frequency to zero, then we shouldn't be sending any triggers at all; but if we happened to do this right in the midst of a transition, the sample count might be less than one and our algorithm would be outputting triggers (and potentially spawning new grains) continuously—not at all what we want! We can fix this simply by adding a condition to the trigger that the sample count is less than one **and** the slope is not zero.

Here is the final patch with both of these refinements added. This is another one of those highly reusable algorithms, which we have saved as the **go.ramp.subsample** abstraction.

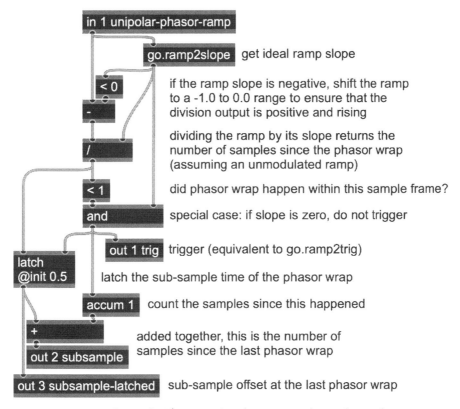

ramp-subsample-trig.maxpat and go.ramp.subsample.gendsp

We'll be using this abstraction in the last few examples of this book, but you can see it put to use immediately in the ***poly_granulation3.maxpat*** example, where it replaces the **go.ramp2trig** abstraction and sends its subsample variable into a **history subsample** operator, ready for use in the ***grain3.gendsp*** voice subpatches.

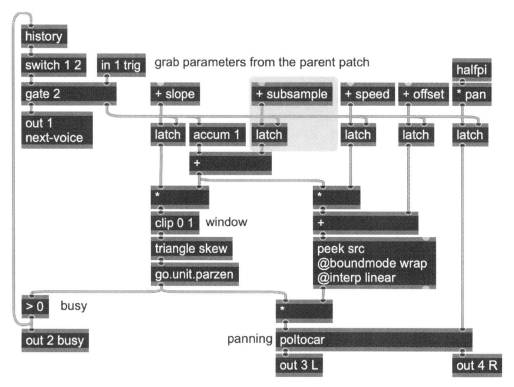

grain3.gendsp

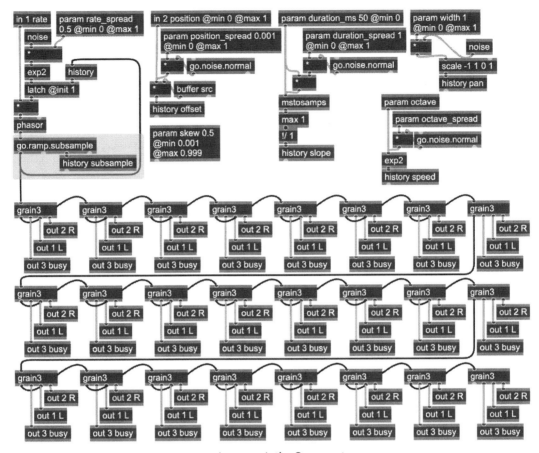

poly_granulation3.maxpat

Overdubbing the future

The strategy of passing an event on if a voice is busy works very well for overlapping events of variable durations, such as polyphonic note playing.[6] However, this strategy has a predetermined maximum polyphony (the maximum number of concurrent notes, grains, or processes). If we wanted to create very dense clouds of extremely microsonic particles, there's an alternate strategy that might perform better, which we will explore in the next section. Before we get to that, we need to take a little detour.

If you think back to the multi-tap tape loop analogy we saw in Chapter 7, we had a single writer head, a single eraser head, and several reader heads, each of which was *pulling data from the past*. What if we arranged our tape loop differently, with only one reader, but instead many writers to throw sounds *different distances into the future,* to be heard later once the tape winds around to the reader.

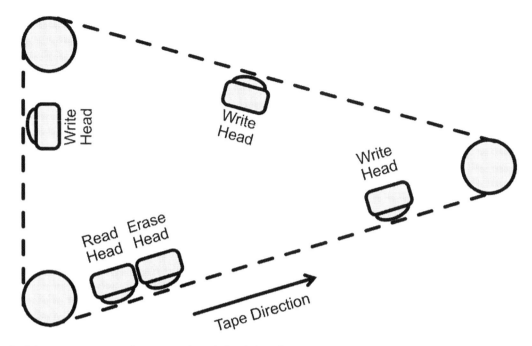

In this arrangement, the eraser head sits right after the reader to destroy sounds after they have been played. Each writer overdubs (adds) with the existing sound on the tape, accumulating many possible sound events, much like writing data into a score to be performed later. This is a kind of "overlap-add" algorithm since multiple writers can generate events that overlap with each other, and their sounds are added together.

For our tape, we can use a **buffer** or **data** operator. We'll use a **buffer** operator for now so that we can visualize the contents of the tape in a Max or RNBO patch. The length of the **buffer** determines the maximum time that we can project sounds into the future. The tape speed is locked to real-time, moving at one sample frame of the **buffer** for each sample frame in real-time.

That is, at any time, the current sample index of the read head is a whole number between zero and the sample length of the buffer, and it increases by 1 for every sample frame of passing real-time, wrapping back to zero when it reaches the length of the buffer. The **dim** operator, or the right outlet of the **buffer** operator, will tell us what this length is. For the read index counter, we can use a **counter** operator.

The read head and eraser head are both located at this position, but we need to be careful that erasure happens after reading; a simple way is to chain the final outlet of the **peek** operator, which passes the sample index, into a **poke** operator, and write a zero to the tape at that location. This ensures that the erasure happens immediately after reading the value of the tape at that point.

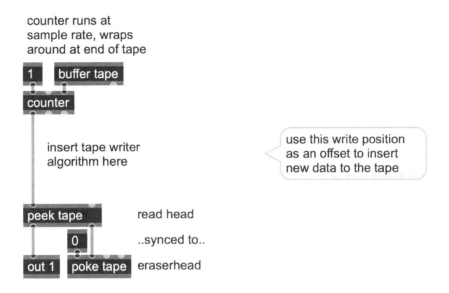

counter runs at
sample rate, wraps
around at end of tape

use this write position
as an offset to insert
new data to the tape

insert tape writer
algorithm here

read head

..synced to..

eraserhead

All we need to add now is one or more writer heads, using more **poke** operators at different positions on the tape.

Since the tape moves at 1 sample of the **buffer** per sample frame of real-time, then if the write head was positioned ten samples ahead of the read head (at `readindex+10`), we would be throwing our sound ten samples into the future, giving us a 10 sample delay between writing and reading. Similarly, for any future time N, we should write to `writeindex = readindex+N`.

Again we need to be careful to wrap around the tape, which **poke** can do automatically for us via **@boundmode wrap**. And, in case there's already some data on the tape there, we will want the **poke** to overdub (add) rather than replace, which we can do by setting the fourth inlet's value to one.[7]

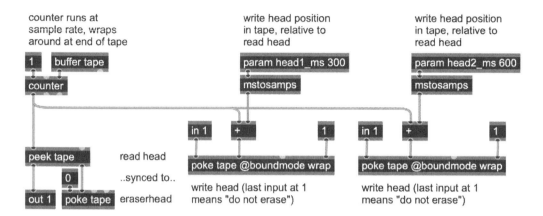

And that's all we need to be able to throw sounds into the future. We can add as many of these write heads as we like, all writing to different places in the future, and we'll hear the complete mix of them coming back.

There's a catch, of course. We can't arbitrarily modulate the delay times. If we tried to modulate the writer position N, we would end up with some probably awful noise as the incoming waveform's samples get scattered and mixed haphazardly around the **buffer** tape.[8] However, we *can* handle *sporadic stepped* changes of N, and there will be no noise so long as the waveform being written is zero (or very near zero) at the moment when N changes. We can even force this to happen whenever we want by briefly "ducking" the incoming waveform. Fading it to zero, changing N, and then fading it back in. In this way, the sound being written to the tape fades to silence at the start and end of any section being written. Put another way; this means we should be *windowing* the source sound. This points us back toward our real reason for exploring this "future-writing strategy" as an alternative method for implementing granular synthesis.

Whole grains at once

Imagine that we had hundreds of write heads instead of just two, with each one scrubbing just a few milliseconds' worth of enveloped sound onto the future tape at once. Hundreds of writers would mean a lot of patching, but we'll get around this by using **codebox** and using a `for` loop to write a whole grain at a time instantaneously.

The tape playback and erasure circuit remain the same: a counter wrapping around the tape length and being fed through some algorithm that writes to the tape and then to the read head and the erase head. The actual grain generation algorithm will be written into a **codebox** operator sandwiched between the read counter and the reader and eraser heads. That algorithm will also need a scheduler input to know *when* to write a new grain.

Let's start with a simple **phasor** operator running into a **go.ramp2trig** abstraction to turn the phasor signal into a series of triggers, routed into the codebox:

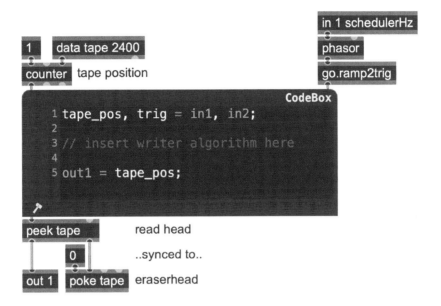

So far, this patch makes no sound, but it can be the basis for many different microsonic patches as a template. From this point on, nearly everything will happen inside the codebox. To design the algorithm, let's start by writing pseudo-code, which just means breaking the problem into steps using plain language first to think them through and then converting these steps to real code once we have the bigger picture figured out.

First, when a trigger arrives, we want to overdub an entire grain onto the tape, all at once. In pseudo-code, the general structure is this:

```
if it is time to trigger a grain,

    overdub an entire grain to the tape,
    starting from position tape_pos
```

An entire grain is made up of a series of samples, which we have to generate one by one, so let's expand that pseudo-code a little more:

```
if it is time to trigger a grain,

      for each sample step of the grain

            generate the grain's next sample,

            overdub it to the tape,
            starting from position tape_pos + step
```

Let's expand the grain generation. We know that grains are usually some carrier signal multiplied by some envelope signal:

```
if it is time to trigger a grain,

      for each sample step of the grain

            generate the carrier's next sample,

            generate the envelope's next sample,

            overdub carrier * envelope to the tape,
            starting from position tape_pos + step
```

We know an envelope is a function of the grain *phase*, which typically runs from 0.0 to 1.0 over the length of a grain. We can get this by dividing the grain's sample **step** by the grain's length.

Let's also start turning some of the pseudo-code into something a bit closer to GenExpr syntax:

```
if (trigger grain) {

    for (step from zero to grain length, stepping by 1) {

            phase = step / length;
            envelope = something derived from phase
            carrier = something

            poke (carrier * envelope) to the tape
                    at position (tape_pos + step),
                    being sure to overdub,
                    and wrapping around the tape boundaries

    }

}
```

That is, on each sample frame, the code will check whether it is time to generate a new grain. If so, it will use a **for** loop to step over each sample of the whole grain. For each step, it computes an envelope as a function of the position through the grain and uses it to multiply with a carrier sound. It overdubs the result onto the tape at the appropriate place. All of this happens within one sample frame of real-time as if the tape head whooshed by writing an entire grain onto the tape in a single instant.

Let's fill in the remaining gaps. For now, we can set the length of the grain to 5 milliseconds, converted to sample frames:

```
length = mstosamps(5);
```

For most envelope shapes we'd need to know how far we are through a grain, which we can compute using

```
phase = i / length;
```

That will give us the envelope phase, which rises from zero to one in a straight line. We can then shape this into a triangle shape using `triangle(phase)` or a softer sinusoidal shape using `sin(pi*phase)`.

```
env = sin(pi * phase);
```

For the carrier sound, we can generate a simple sine wave as a harmonic multiple of the grain period using the grain phase like this:

```
harmonic = 8;
carrier = sin(twopi * phase * harmonic);
```

Finally, we need a **poke()** call to write on the tape. This one has a lot of arguments corresponding to the same inlets as well as the attributes of a **poke** operator in a patch.

The first argument is the buffer or data to write to, which in our case is `tape`. Next is the value to write, which is just the carrier sound modulated by the envelope. Next is the position to write, which is the current tape head position plus the step into the grain. Next is the channel offset, which is zero since our tape is mono. The fourth argument is the amount of the original signal to preserve, which should be 1 so that the poke overdubs rather than replaces existing audio; this is the crucial argument that makes the overlap-add work. And finally, we need an attribute to make sure that if our write position is beyond the end of the tape, it wraps around back to the beginning again, via `boundmode="wrap"`:

```
poke( tape,                    // the buffer or data to write to
      carrier * env,           // signal to write
      tape_pos + step,         // position on tape
      0,                       // tape channel 0,
      1,                       // overdub
      boundmode="wrap" );      // wrap around ends of tape
```

If we modify this a little bit to turn the length and harmonic values into parameters, we get the following patch, which should make a chirpy sound:

```
1  tape_pos, trig = in1, in2;
2  length = mstosamps(len_ms);
3  if (trig) {
4      for (step = 0; step < length; step += 1) {
5          phase = step/length;
6          env = sin(pi*phase);
7          carrier = sin(twopi * phase * harmonic);
8          poke(tape,
9              carrier * env,          // signal to write
10             tape_pos + step,        // position on tape
11             0,                      // tape channel
12             1,                      // overdub
13             boundmode="wrap");      // wrap at end of tape
14     }
15 }
16 out1 = tape_pos;
```

Why did we limit the **param len_ms** to **@max 50**? Because that's as much data that can fit into our tape, that's the longest grain the tape can support. More importantly: since the CPU has to do the work of computing the grain all at once within a single sample frame of passing time, longer grains can cause higher CPU spikes. It's a good idea to set a limit on this to prevent audio dropouts that might happen if the CPU is too busy computing a very long grain.

The method described in this section is appropriate for microsound applications where grains are shorter than typical note lengths and more numerous than typical note polyphony. If you need to work with very long grains (approaching note lengths), this whole grain at once method probably isn't a good approach, and the polyphonic voice method earlier in this chapter would be better.

Subsample-accurate grains

As we've seen before in this chapter, the subtle difference in subsample accuracy is essential for scheduling higher frequency synchronous granular synthesis. Let's replace the **go.ramp2trig** with a **go.ramp.subsample** abstraction, which will give us the same triggers as before, as well as the subsample offsets we need. In the **codebox,** we will define a new variable called "subsample," assigned from in3, and connect the abstraction's 3rd outlet to the 3rd inlet of the **codebox**. We use this subsample variable to initialize step = grain_pos in the **for** loop. So, instead of counting from zero, our for loop will start counting from the appropriate fractional subsample location:

This is still a relatively simple patch, but it already pays off, especially with the intensive modulation of the phasor scheduler.

For some much more involved examples, you can look at the ***granola*** patches in the book's software package, which extend this patch with additional parameters and different carrier waveforms. The ***granola_buffer.maxpat*** example demonstrates reading from a buffer in a similar way to the polyphonic granulation example earlier in this chapter. The ***granola_glisson.maxpat*** demonstrates a more complex synthesized waveform in the form of "glisson synthesis", where each grain is a glissando from one pitch to another.

A bandlimited saw with hard sync

As a final example of the importance of thinking in subsample times, let's circle back to that challenge we raised at the start of this chapter: how to produce waveforms with hard cuts like sawtooth shapes (and pitched phasors), as well as general hard sync effects, without causing unpleasant aliasing noise. There are plenty of different approaches to creating bandlimited oscillators, including using oversampling, using bandlimited impulse trains (BLIT), bandlimited steps ("BLEPs"), etc., with various benefits and trade-offs that we will delve into in Book 2. But to close this chapter, we're going to describe a different method that performs remarkably well for how cheap and flexible it is.[9]

This is a somewhat subtle patch, so it's going to be helpful to understand what it solves and why it works before we start to build it. Let's start back at the beginning with a classic phasor ramp, whose ideal, continuous form looks like this:

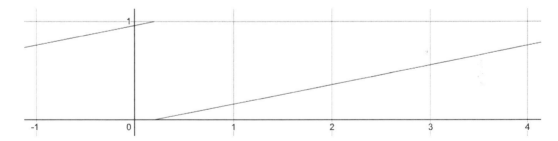

That graph is *ideal* because it is continuous, with infinite resolution. In practice, we only have the resolution of the sample rate, so, zoomed into the level of the sample frames, our typical **phasor** algorithm approximates the ideal graph by stepping with each sample frame, like the dashed lines here:

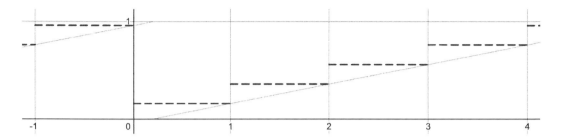

But there's no way that an actual loudspeaker's diaphragm can instantaneously jump from one position to another like this—it has to move continuously, just like an interpolation. The simplest imaginable path without instantaneous jumps is a straight line between each sample, like the dotted path below:[10]

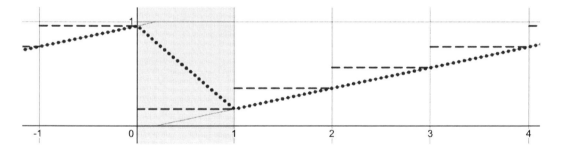

Compared to the *ideal* phasor, we can see that it diverges for exactly the one sample where the transition occurs (which we have shaded in gray). Everything that we are going to do is focused on changing this one sample frame.

Take a closer look at the values of the phasor where it enters and exits the gray region. You'll notice that these points are not symmetric: it enters very close to 1.0, but when it exits, it isn't nearly so close to 0.0; that's because the transition itself doesn't align perfectly with the sampling rate. That slight deviation might not seem like much, but over many cycles of the phasor, it can add up to a big sonic difference.

To make this visually very obvious, in the following graph we have set the phasor frequency much higher:

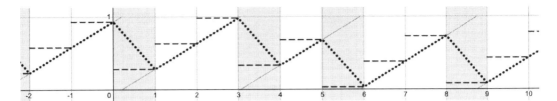

You can clearly see that with each gray-shaded transition sample, the *apparent* phasor (dotted line) that joins up our sample values enters and exits at quite different positions, creating an impression of irregular harmonic periods. These divergences thus introduce unrelated audible frequencies into the sound of the phasor, which is a form of digital aliasing noise.

The good news is that with these observations, we already have everything we need to solve the problem:

- We know that we can't actually render an instantaneous jump of the phasor; we must instead *always* have a sloping line of (at least) one sample's duration.
- We know that aliasing occurs because the ramp values during a transition depend on the relative alignment of the phasor wrap with the sampling rate, not the timing of the phasor itself.

So, what if, instead of trying to synthesize an impossible ideal phasor, we synthesize a function that already has the single-sample slope requirement embedded into it? And, to make this independent of the sampling points, what if we place that slope precisely centered on the ideal phasor's transition point rather than the sampling grid?

That is, if we try to synthesize this waveform:

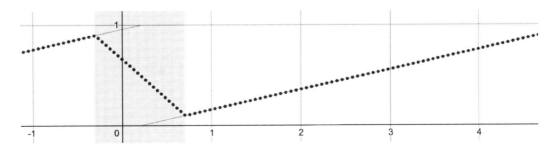

Notice that the dotted path is still exactly the same as the ideal phasor outside of the gray zone. The gray region of the transition sample is no longer aligned to the sample points but is instead exactly centered on the phasor's ideal transition. The entry and exit points of the gray zone are always symmetric.

Even at the same high frequency we used earlier, this waveform remains regular and balanced. And since no slope is ever steeper than what can be achieved in a single sample frame, this waveform *can* be rendered in digital samples without creating lots of aliasing:

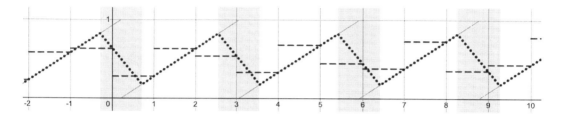

The gray zone itself is still only one sample frame long, which means that there's only one sample we need to change. And all we need to know to compute that change is the following information:

- The phasor value at the entry and exit points of the gray region exactly half a sample before and after the *ideal* transition. These points define the start and end of the single-sample downward ramp of the transition.
- The subsample position where the transition occurs so that we can extract the value of that downward ramp in the right place.

Time to get patching! We can start from the non-antialiased phasor we have seen since the start of this book:

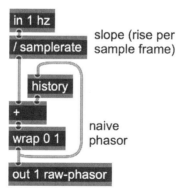

We want to know the values of the ideal ramp that this phasor represents, one-half a sample frame before and after it has a transition. The value half of a sample *after* a transition is pretty simple: since the phasor rises by a known slope for each sample frame, then half a sample frame after it wraps it will have risen by slope * 0.5. Except if the ramp is running in reverse; in that case, it will have fallen to 1.0 - (slope * 0.5). Then the value of the phasor one-half of a sample *before* a transition is just the mirror of the state half a sample *after*.

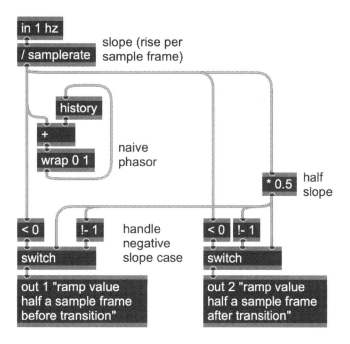

So, for example, if the phasor frequency is equal to `samplerate/5`, then the ramp value half a sample before a transition is 0.9, and the ramp value half a sample after a transition is 0.1. These are the highest and lowest values our antialiased phasor can reach and the entry and exit corner points of the gray region.

All we need to know now is the subsample location (i.e., the fractional sample count) of the ideal transition relative to our sampling grid so that we can get the value of the ramp between these two corner points. As we learned with the subsample ramp trigger in the granular scheduler, we can get the fractional sample count of a ramp by dividing the ramp's value by its slope.

To handle both rising and falling ramps, we can first recenter the phasor in the -0.5 to 0.5 range. Then we project half a sample ahead (by adding half a slope) to get our transition point and then divide by the slope. That will give us the fractional sample count of up to half a sample before or after the ideal transition.

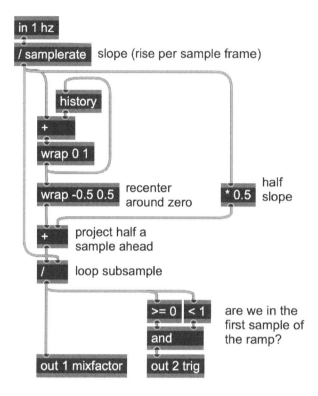

As a bonus, we can also use this fractional sample count as our trigger detection, just as we did with the **go.ramp.subsample** abstraction. Simply: if we are in the first sample frame of a phasor's ramp, then the fractional sample count will be between zero and one, which means we are in the gray zone, and we can output a trigger when that happens.

Now we can put everything together. When we are in the gray zone (i.e., the trigger fires at **out 2**), we want to replace the basic aliasing phasor with a new value that is taken instead from a replacement ramp between the entry and exit points of the gray region. We can use **switch** operators to swap in these values when the trigger happens.

And since the replacement ramp we are inserting is linear, we can simply crossfade between them using a **mix** operator, using the fractional subsample time as the crossfade factor.

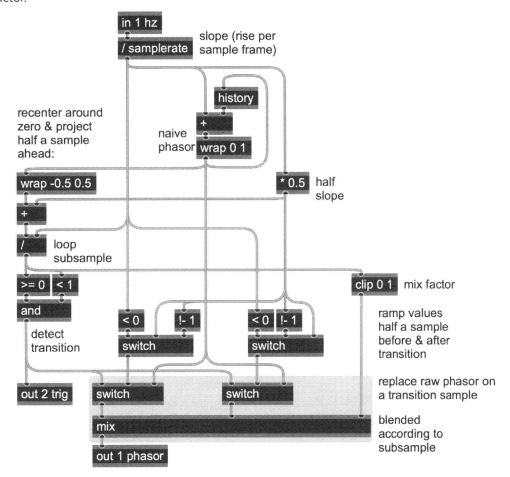

And that gives us exactly the output of the sampled antialiased waveform we wanted! It results in a unipolar ramp with far less aliasing than a **phasor** operator, with no latency, and at very little computational expense.

The following spectrum shows both—the standard **phasor** operator in gray and our antialiased phasor here in black - running at around 2500Hz:

You can immediately see how the black spectrum has a clearly defined shape with far fewer aliasing harmonics than the gray, aliasing phasor. The principal harmonics hold their strength well going up the spectrum, keeping the brightness of the sawtooth sound present, but the aliasing harmonics fall quickly to zero on the first reflection back and are practically inaudible, whereas the gray basic phasor continues to produce aliasing frequencies reflecting several times over the spectrum. It's not perfect antialiasing, but it is remarkably practical and effective for its simplicity.[11] It can also handle deep frequency modulation and, as we shall see, can be extended to support hard sync and some wave shaping. It all came down to creating a waveform in which no slope is sharper than a single sample and aligning those transitions to the ideal shape of the waveform rather than to the sampling grid.

Adding hard sync

First, we will need another oscillator as the hard sync source. With analog synthesizers, that would typically be some kind of trigger generator, but we will work with another phasor ramp here. Why? As we have seen throughout this chapter, it becomes essential to think about fractional sample counts and subsample accuracy for pitched oscillators, and hard sync is no exception. When a hard sync phasor reset happens, does it happen at the start of a sample frame, at the end, or somewhere in between? To specify that kind of accuracy, we can't rely on trigger signals alone.

Instead, here we are going to reuse the subsample-accurate ramp transition detector we built earlier in this chapter as the **go.ramp.subsample** abstraction. The first outlet of this abstraction gives a trigger when a transition occurs, while the 3rd outlet gives us the fractional offset of that transition within a sample frame. So, for the raw (aliasing) synced phasor, we can insert a **switch** operator to reset the phase when the **go.ramp.subsample** trigger occurs, and the value we reset it to is the subsample offset multiplied by the slope.

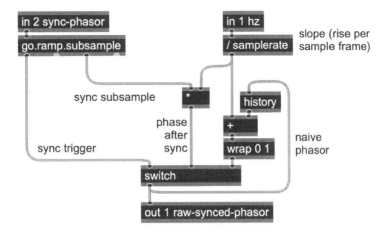

That subsample offset will also stand in as our mix factor for the antialiasing **mix** operator when a sync trigger occurs. But first, we need to compute the ramp phases half a sample before and after the sync event. This is a little more complex now since a sync event could happen *anywhere* during the ramp's progress. But we can figure it out by working back from the current ramp's value (before the reset) or forward (after the reset) by reusing our **go.ramp.rotate** abstraction from Chapter 2, and using the subsample offset multiplied by the slope to know how far to rotate:

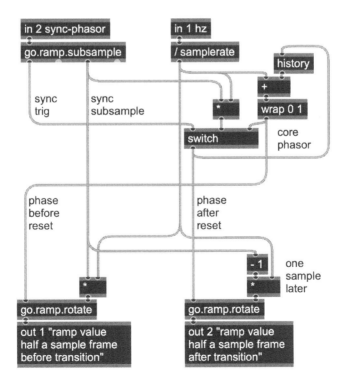

Now we just need to integrate these revisions with our antialiased phasor. This is mostly just careful plumbing and the insertion of a **switch** operator to select between the subsample offset of a normal phasor wrap transition versus a hard sync transition:

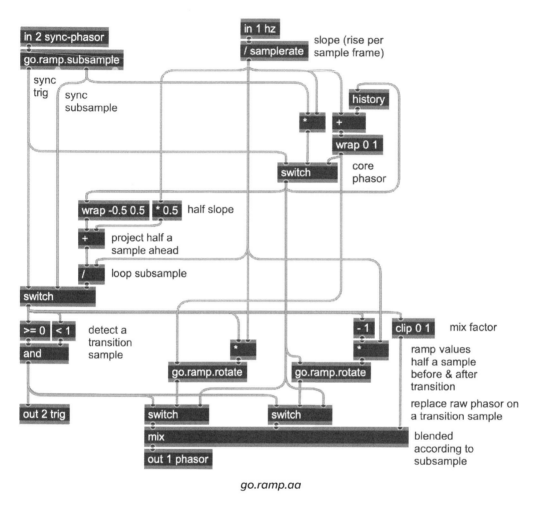

go.ramp.aa

And that gives us a very reliable antialiased phasor ramp that supports subsample accurate hard sync as well as deep frequency modulation, both up to audio rates!

Shaping

There's one more neat thing we can do with this patch. We can apply some unit shaping curvatures to the signals between the **mix** operator and the **switch** operators at the bottom of the patch. So long as the unit shapes start at 0.0, end at 1.0 and have no sharp cuts of their own, then the output of the patch will remain pretty well antialiased.

Some examples of unit shapers you can try here include **go.unit.arc2**, **go.unit.triangle**, **go.unit.tukey**, **go.unit.cubic**, **go.unit.ease.exp**, **go.unit.ease.sine**, etc. The *ramp_antialiased.maxpat* patch shows an example of chaining two unit shapers for a relatively complex waveform. Here are some example shapes (with the transition and sync triggers overlaid in gray), along with the corresponding aliased (gray) and antialiased (black) spectra:

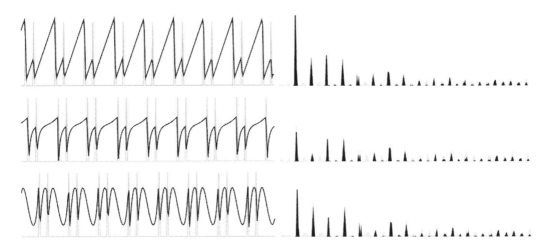

Here are a few more example waveforms and spectra using deep through-zero frequency modulation, including the ramp itself, as well as the ramp providing the hard sync signal, which this patch handles very well:

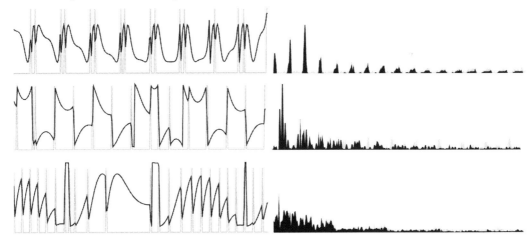

Naturally, you can try substituting this oscillator into some of the FM structures we encountered in Chapter 8 or perhaps with some of the ramp division modulations we met at the end of Chapter 2.

Onward

When we began this book, we spoke about developing habits of thought ("things to think with") to guide you in approaching seemingly very different audio topics. Some of these habits are pragmatic, formulated in the creation of abstractions that you can use again and again when solving, while others are more strategic, such as translating problems into more conducive representations; conceiving time in terms of ramps rather than as discrete events; thinking of unit slopes as fundamental rates of change, and unit shapes as a means to give them contour; considering audio processing not just at the sample level, but at the subsample level; understanding the patterns of modular ratios whether they apply to rhythms, pitch quantizations, FM tones or formants; using tape machines as metaphors for audio processing, whether as delays, filters, or granulators; and so on. Moreover, the patching examples we've created in writing Book 1 are not intended to be "finished solutions" so much as suggestions that we hope will point you to a much vaster array of possibilities. We strongly urge you to spend some time combining the different concepts and patches we have explored throughout this book before moving on to those in Book 2. There is an immense and fascinating world here yet to explore. Have fun experimenting!

Endnotes

Chapter 1: Patching One Sample at a Time

[1] Technically speaking, this isn't always true: if gen~ can analyze your patch and realize that a signal can be updated less frequently and still produce the same result, it will do so, as one of the many kinds of optimizations it performs to ensure your patch is more efficient. Since the result however is exactly the same as if the signals were always running at audio-rate, it's clearer to think of them in those terms.

[2] Since gen~ operates primarily with 64-bit floating point numbers, there are hardly any limits on the numeric ranges of signals — the range depends on what they should be used for, and what limits you create by patching. For example, you can set limits of a **param** operator by defining the *@min* and *@max* attributes. Or you can limit any signal's range using a **clip** operator (among others).

[3] Note that gen~ offers a few handy operators for converting between standard units, including MIDI note numbers and frequencies (**mtof** and **ftom**), samples and milliseconds (**mstosamps** and **sampstoms**), amplitude and decibels (**atodb** and **dbtoa**), degrees and radians (**degrees** and **radians**), and multipliers and decay times (**t60** and **t60time**).

[4] Note that testing *equality* with signals can be fraught with unexpected behaviour. First, with the resolution of 64-bit floating point numbers, and the temporal resolution of tens of thousands of samples per second, it is highly unlikely that one unknown signal will be precisely equal to another. Even something that is apparently "silent" could in fact just be an imperceptibly quiet signal, and never exactly equal to zero, for example. Testing equality probably only makes sense when working with stepped integer and logic kinds of signals. When working with audio signals, or signals derived from external controls, it usually makes more sense to work with comparisons and thresholds.

[5] If you prefer to use something other than this convention, you can also insert an appropriate logical comparator operator before the inlet, such as > 0 for a greater than zero convention or >= 0.5 for greater than or equal to 0.5. One reason you might choose to do this is when working with audio or control signals that are unlikely to ever be precisely zero.

[6] https://docs.cycling74.com/max8/vignettes/gen_topic and https://docs.cycling74.com/max8/vignettes/gen~_operators

[7] For example, as we will see in Chapter 7, whenever you see a block labeled Z^{-1} in a filter block diagram, you're looking at a place where you can use a **history** operator.

[8] As Heinz von Foerster would say, it is what turns a trivial machine into a non-trivial machine.

[9] For the more mathematically inclined among our readers, this is a function mapping an input domain to an output range. The domain is the set of all values for which a function is

defined, and the range of the function is the set of all values that the function produces as output.

[10] Why? The reason is that "branchy" code can often be less efficient, and unpredictably spiky, than non-branchy code. We are often asked whether to use `if()` statements to select between different processing paths. But it is often better to simply compute both paths, and use a **switch** or **selector** operator to choose the result. Modern CPUs can run much faster if they can predict which path of operation is most likely, and using `if()` or looping branches can confound that prediction. Doing a few extra math operations is much less costly than a prediction miss. Moreover, `for()` and `while()` loops can have unpredictable times, which can lead to spiky CPU usage. If you can lay out the operation over a sequence of sample frames instead, you will get more constant CPU performance. This is especially important to avoid audio glitches when running at low latencies, or when exporting gen~ code for embedded computing hardware.

[11] In fact, in its early development, some of the built-in operators that gen~ now provides were originally prototyped and developed in this way.

[12] If you were curious: the title of this book is a mishmash of two reference points whose spirits inspire us. First, there is the term "Organized Sound" attributed to the composer Edgard Varèse almost a century ago as he proposed a music of "sound as living matter" and "musical space as open rather than bounded". (Arguably, he was describing his own compositions as organized sound largely to side-step questions from the public whether his compositions *were* music, but it has long since come to be used by many as a definition *of* music.) Second is the cybernetic and evolutionary sense of "generating and organizing" as used by Brian Eno to contrast a more experimental approach to composition and the arts, with an interest in self-regulating and self-generating processes and riding the dynamics of systems.

Varèse, Edgard, and Chou Wen-Chung. "The liberation of sound." Perspectives of new music 5, no. 1 (1966): 11-19.

Eno, Brian. "Generating and organizing variety in the Arts." Studio International 192, no. 984 (1976): 279-283.

Chapter 2: Modular (Arithmetic of) Time

[1] The **gen~** object also includes other operators to handle and convert this rate into other forms: for example, **mstosamps** will tell you how many sample frames are represented by *N* milliseconds, and **sampstoms** will calculate the duration in milliseconds of a number of sample frames.

[2] In mathematical terms, this is also a discrete integrator: the patch is performing integration of the binary signal of the toggle. The word "integration" here is a fancy mathematical term for the process of adding slices to find the whole. Our discrete integrator adds a set amount to the stored value with each sample frame and stores the result. What it integrates is the rate of counting per sample frame. That might not seem very intuitive, but we will see how important this is in Chapter 6.

[3] The **switch** operator normally has three inlets but adding a *0* as an argument to the operator changes the number of inlets. The **switch** operator acts like many other operators in gen~ in that adding an argument *replaces* an inlet. The **switch** operator is also called the **?** operator, so don't be surprised if you see it under that name in someone else's patch.

---

⁴ Note that the **accum** operator's reset input can behave in two different ways, depending on the setting of the **@resetmode** attribute. It simply has to do with whether a reset trigger happens before the accumulation, or after. The default setting is **accum @resetmode post**, which sets the count to zero after adding the left Input. This means that the **accum** will always output zero while the 2nd inlet is nonzero. In contrast, an **accum @resetmode pre** will zero the count before adding the left input, so the output will have already started the new count when the reset happens. Again, the point is that the **accum** operator can perform *two* actions within a sample frame (count and rewind), and the *@resetmode* attribute sets what order these happen within the sample frame; "post" will apply the reset <u>after</u> the count, and vice versa. In our history and + version of accum, **@resetmode pre** means that we route the **+** to **out 1** rather than routing the **switch** to **out 1**.

⁵ We can also dynamically associate a gen~ **buffer mybuf** with a different **buffer~ play_me** by sending the message *mybuf play_me* to the **gen~** object. This technique is really useful because we can have multiple named **buffer~** objects in the parent patch and link them into the **gen~** object using nothing more than a message.

⁶ You might recognize this from the modulo operation, or **mod**. However, we recommend using **wrap** rather than **mod** because of the way that they handle negative inputs. The **mod** operator in gen~ follows the behavior of modulo as found in most programming languages, which rounds toward zero (known as "truncated modulo"), whereas the **wrap** operator follows the mathematical behavior in which division rounds toward negative infinity (known as "Euclidean modulo"). The first important difference is that **wrap** is guaranteed to always output values that are between the low and high limits, even with negative inputs, whereas the **mod** operator does not have this guarantee. The second important difference is that the direction of movement passing through **wrap** is always preserved, whereas **mod** will mirror directions when values pass through zero. For most musical applications the **wrap** behavior is usually preferred.

⁷ By default, the **sample** operator performs linear interpolation: a method to create a weighted average between samples, as a kind of estimation of where the wave would be, which counters the aliasing effect. We'll look at this more in Chapter 6.

⁸ It is also the tempo-clock equivalent of phase modulation synthesis, which we return to in Chapter 8!

⁹ The **rate~** object in Max and RNBO, and their replication in gen~ as the **rate** operator, can also do this kind of clock division. However, it can produce values outside the 0.0 to 1.0 range, in some cases. For this reason, we will use the **go.ramp.div** abstraction in this book, which always outputs within 0.0 to 1.0.

¹⁰ This pattern can be produced even more simply by multiplying the input phasor ramp by 8/3 and feeding that into a **wrap 0 1** operator; but as we will see in the next patch, it can be useful to have the intermediate signals that the multiply, wrap, and divide sequence of operations gives us.

¹¹ This is a form of multi-operator frequency modulation, but using ramp waves rather than the more usual sine waves. We'll look at phase and frequency modulation in much more depth in Chapter 8.

Chapter 3: Unit Shaping

¹ Radians are a measure of angle widely used in mathematics and programming. There are π (pi) radians in a semicircle and 2π (two * pi) radians in a circle. So, to convert from degrees to radians, multiply by pi/180 (or use the **radians** operator), and to convert from

radians to degrees, multiply by 180/pi (or use the **degrees** operator). The use of π is so common that there are **pi**, **twopi**, **halfpi**, and **invpi** ($1/\pi$) constants available in gen~.

[2] Compare this shift to the phase shifting of the **go.ramp.rotate** operator we saw in the previous chapter.

[3] Note that this is not the same as an "equal power" mixer. Even if we apply unit shapers to create nonlinear crossfade curvatures, the **mix** operator is still applying a weighted average of the two input amplitudes. For an "equal power" mix, which balances energy rather than amplitude (where energy is approximately the square of the amplitude), you can use the **go.equalpower** abstraction.

[4] The **go.unit.arc** unit shaper abstraction converts a unipolar ramp into a variety of curves by tracing a circular arc with different distance metrics according to the shape parameter. When the shape parameter is 0.5, a linear ramp goes through unchanged, For shape < 0.5 or shape > 0.5, it traces distance using a power scale that gives convex or concave arc sections. At the limits of 0.0 and 1.0, it becomes square shaped.

[5] Note that some window functions do not quite reach zero—including the Hamming function and the Gaussian and raised cosine under certain parameter combinations.

[6] Here's another interesting difference between filters and waveshapers: While most filters' responses also depend on their previous inputs or outputs, waveshaping doesn't. Waveshaping processes are entirely memoryless: the same input will always immediately give the same output, and the function is randomly addressable. This might seem an obscure difference, but there are some applications where it can be beneficial or even essential that a process Is free of history: for example, applying timbral effects to waveform data in a wavetable oscillator, or to Individual grains In a granular synthesizer.

[7] Most input signals are more complex that sinusoids, but if you know what their highest significant frequency content is, then you can compute the highest significant frequency of the waveshaped output would be, by multiplying by the waveshaper's degree. Alternatively, you could use this insight to limit the bandwidth of the signal going into the waveshaper. For example, if you don't want the waveshaper of degree 3 to produce any frequencies above 15kHz, then you could pre-filter the source signal at 15/3=5kHz before waveshaping it. In practice It Is more complex than this, as you'd also want to take Into account the weights of the harmonics to determine how much prefiltering to do.

[8] Interestingly, this endlessly differentiable smoothness is one of the features that has made sigmoids among the commonly used activation functions in artificial neural networks.

Chapter 4: Noise, Uncertainty, and Unpredictability

[1] If this is a subject that interests you, you might find the following to be worthwhile reading:

Maurer, John A. "A brief history of algorithmic composition." Unpublished manuscript. Available at https://ccrma.stanford.edu/~blackrse/algorithm.html (1999).

Loy, Gareth. "Composing with computers: A survey of some compositional formalisms and music programming languages." In Current directions in computer music research, pp. 291-396. 1989.

[2] For almost all purposes, it makes no difference to us whether a signal Is pseudo-random or truly random, as the results are practically indistinguishable. However, given the same initial value (the "seed"), a pseudo-random algorithm will generate the same sequence of random values every time, and that can be a problem. The **noise** operator in gen~ is

seeded according to clock time when a patch is loaded, so this should be different every time; all **noise** operators share a common generator, which ensures that each distinct **noise** operator in a patch will generate a different new value. For the curious: gen~ uses the Xoshiro256+ algorithm from Blackman, David, and Sebastiano Vigna. "Scrambled linear pseudorandom number generators." ACM Transactions on Mathematical Software (TOMS) 47, no. 4 (2021): 1-32. (See http://prng.di.unimi.it)

[3] For more detail about these different interpolation types, including the specific underlying algorithms used, take a look at the ***gen~.interpolation.maxpat*** patch in the Max Gen examples folder.

[4] Why **fold**? It acts like a kind of "reflection" off the edge boundaries. We could have used **clip**, but this would have had the signal sticking to the boundaries too often, and thus would bias the resulting random distribution to those bounds. Using **fold** maintains a perfectly even distribution while still limiting the values within these bounds.

[5] Named after the Hungarian mathematician George Pólya.

[6] Another way of implementing this would be to shuffle the pack whenever the discard pile becomes the new deck; but we like the pick a card at random method as this performs the shuffle gradually over time rather than all at once.

[7] The **go.zerox** abstraction simply detects when any Input signal rises from zero or below to above zero, and outputs a single-sample trigger at that point. The use of zero crossing detection in many different applications is explored in Book 2.

[8] It might seem as though bypassing the code using an `if` block would be more efficient, but this isn't necessarily the case. With the way that modern CPU architectures work relies on a lot of instruction prediction at the machine-level, which can be confounded by "branchy" code like `if`, `for`, `while` etc. It can often turn out that performing a few extra seemingly unnecessary operations is faster than conditionally bypassing them.

[9] The chaotic equations that we're demonstrating here and through the patches included with this book can be found among the amazing array of systems on Jürgen Meier's Homepage at http://www.3d-meier.de. Look under the Tutorials tab — particularly, the links labeled *Attractoren I*, *Attractoren II*, and *Attractoren III*. Jürgen collects information on attractors and provides source code (and the all-important starting x, y, and z and dt parameters for attractors that other references sometimes omit). We all owe him our thanks.

Chapter 5: Stepping in Time and Space

[1] Of course, pitches are not completely steady for many real instruments, with glides, vibrato, and other curvatures around a steady pitch. The same is true for dynamics, as well. We saw some examples of adding pitch glides Chapter 3, and we look at another way to embellish step functions with fluidities later in the chapter.

[2] Interestingly, this sequence length can be computed using a variation of the Euclidean algorithm, which we will encounter later in this chapter.

[3] See http://www.birthofasynth.com/Scott_Stites/Pages/Klee_Birth.html, http://www.synthpanel.com/modules/cgs13v2_gated_comparator.html, http://www.synthpanel.com/modules/cgs32_infinite_melody.html, https://thehordijkmodular.blogspot.com/search/label/Rungler, https://musicthing.co.uk/pages/turing.html, and https://mutable-instruments.net/modules/marbles/

[4] Incidentally, the technique of applying different weights to delayed copies of a signal is a kind of feedforward filter, often described as convolution with a finite impulse response (FIR). The data we have in the buffer is the impulse response, and a single trigger at the input of the shift register is the finite impulse that evokes this response.

[5] Adding more stages can have an exponential impact on the length of these sequences; for example, a 20-bit shift register can produce a sequence of over a million steps. The **noise** operator in gen~ uses the Xoshiro256+ algorithm that includes a combination of xor, shift and binary rotation movements of several 32 bit sequences to produce a total period of $2^{256}-1$ steps (see http://prng.di.unimi.it). That's more steps than there are atoms on Earth.

[6] At the heart of the octave-to-frequency conversion is an **exp2** operator, which is shorthand for raising 2 to a certain power; the inverse operation (from frequency to octave) has at its heart a **log2** operator, which tells you what power of 2 the input is. It makes sense really, since rising by one octave means doubling the frequency.

[7] A "normalized frequency" slope representation Is simply frequency/samplerate. This represents how much a unipolar ramp would rise over one sample frame, i.e. what we would need to feed the kind of ramp generator we built back in at the start of Chapter 2. A normalized frequency of 0.1 means a frequency of **samplerate**/10: it will complete a unipolar ramp every 10 sample frames.

With filters and frequency modulation patches, we may prefer use another kind of normalized frequency representation of "radians-per-sample", which is simply the unipolar normalized frequency multiplied by **twopi** (2π). Feeding a radians-per-sample ramp into a **sin**, **cos**, or **poltocar** operator will produce one cycle for every **twopi** radians.

[8] The period of a periodic waveform in seconds is 1/frequency in Hz, and the frequency in Hz is 1/period in seconds. A period in milliseconds (ms) is 1000 times the period in seconds. A period in sample frames is **samplerate**/frequency in Hz, and a frequency in Hz is **samplerate**/period in seconds. To convert between milliseconds and samples, we can use the **mstosamps** and **sampstoms** operators.

[9] In fact, the **go.unit.lfo** unit shaper abstraction is really just a simplified version of this smoothed quantizer, operating over a single unipolar step.

Chapter 6: Filters, Diagrams, and the Balance of Time

[1] Just remember that the "a" input (the 3rd input) should always be between 0.0 and 1.0 if you want the result to stay on the line between X and Y. In patching situations where the "a" value comes from a source whose range you don't know, you can add a **clip 0 1** operator right before the 3rd input to make sure of it.

[2] We already used this design pattern when creating the **go.unit.trapezoid** abstraction (as subtract duty, multiply, add duty) in Chapter 3 (p. 100), as well as the easing function and asymmetric bipolar shaping templates (in the sequence **scale** in—<*shape*>—**scale** out) and normalized bipolar shapers (as amplify, shape, attenuate). We have also used it when creating the **go.ramp2steps** ramp quantizer in Chapter 2 (p. 66), for the **go.random** abstraction in Chapter 4 (p. 142), and for pitch quantization in Chapter 5 (p. 196). Those last three examples all use the same approach (**multiply** by N —**floor**— **divide** by N).

[3] T60 is not the only possible measure of a characteristic decay. In analog circuitry one of the classic exponential decays is the release of voltage from a capacitor in an RC (resistor-capacitor) circuit. The decay is often measured by the time in seconds for the voltage to fall by a factor of e^{-1}, which is about 37%. This time, measured in seconds, is called *tau*, and

is related to the cutoff frequency as tau = 1/(twopi*freq). Here is a direct relationship between frequency and characteristic time of decay.

[4] The **t60** operator actually implements `multiplier = exp(log(0.001)/duration_in_samples)`, while **t60time** implements `duration_in_samples = log(0.001)/log(multiplier)`.

Interestingly, if we use a decay level of exp(-1) as the decay level used in RC circuits, and knowing that these have a time constant tau in seconds of 1/(twopi*frequency), we end up with `multiplier = exp(-twopi*freq/samplerate)`, which is precisely the same coefficient calculation we used for the simple lowpass filter earlier!

[5] For a far more accurate emulation (also implemented in gen~), see Parker, Julian, and Stephano D'Angelo. "A digital model of the Buchla lowpass gate." In Proc. Int. Conf. Digital Audio Effects (DAFx-13), Maynooth, Ireland, pp. 278-285. 2013.

[6] A vactrol is a device that combines a light-dependent resistor (LDR) in close proximity with a light source (usually an LED) to process the control signal. As the control signal rises, the light gets brighter, making the resistance of the LDR reduce and thus letting more audio through. Vactrols are interesting because the relationship between the light source and resistance is neither instantaneous nor linear: the more voltage is supplied to the LED, the faster the response of the LDR. Thus, the resistor does not instantly change state when the LED turns on — it takes a little time for the resistance to fall. Similarly, turning off the LED does not change the resistance instantly to full — it takes some time to decay.

[7] We noted already that the lowpass one-pole is a kind of "leaky" integrator, and conversely, the highpass is a kind of leaky differentiator, in that it reveals more about the slope of a signal than its position. A constant input has no slope and zero output from the highpass; a noisy input will reveal the slopes of the jumps up and down. This shouldn't be a surprise: we are taking a weighted average between the original signal, and the differentiated (x[n] - x[n-1]) slope of that signal. The coefficient sets up to what degree we are balancing the signal against its own changes!

[8] For a freely available online example, look at the W3C Audio EQ Cookbook, adapted from an article by Robert Bristow-Johnson: https://www.w3.org/TR/audio-eq-cookbook

[9] For example, among the lowpass, highpass, bandpass, resonant bandpass, notch, and allpass designs, the computation of the a0, a1, and a2 coefficients are all exactly the same. All of these filter types convert the desired cutoff frequency into the equivalent radians per sample and use both the sine and cosine of this value. Similarly, all of these filter types compute a value called alpha and the Q factor in exactly the same way. In fact, the only significant differences between the filter types are how the b0, b1, and b2 coefficients are computed from alpha and the cosine of the radians per sample.

[10] This patch is effectively similar to the **filtercoeff~** external in Max and RNBO.

[11] The discrete implementation of the bilinear transform maps an infinite possible frequency range to a discrete range up to samplerate/4, which thus warps higher frequencies downward. Instead, the coefficient calculator limits our frequency range up to samplerate/4 and applies a tan-derived function curve to "pre-warp" the frequency and adequately compensate for the warping. (For a more explicit explanation, see https://www.native-instruments.com/fileadmin/ni_media/downloads/pdf/VAFilterDesign_2.1.0.pdf#page=69)

A side-effect of this is that the trapezoidal filters will tend to attenuate frequencies toward zero as they approach the Nyquist limit (samplerate/2). That might itself be desirable, but if not it can be circumvented by oversampling the filter, as we shall see in Book 2.

[12] For an example, see Parker, Julian, and Stephano D'Angelo. "A digital model of the Buchla lowpass-gate." In Proc. Int. Conf. Digital Audio Effects (DAFx-13), Maynooth, Ireland, pp. 278-285. 2013. A further discussion of resolving "impractical" block diagrams can be found at https://www.dsprelated.com/showarticle/990.php

[13] One of the perennial questions about gen~ that has come up on user forums is "How do I make the equivalent of Max's **line~**?" This section shows how!

Chapter 7: The Effects of Delay

[1] Note that throughout this chapter we use the **delay** operator to process audio signals, but it can of course be used to process any kind of signal, not just audio.

[2] This capability of the **delay** operator is enabled by default, but it can be disabled by setting **@feedback 0** on the **delay**. Why would you want to do this? With feedback *enabled*, the **delay** operator cannot produce a delay shorter than 1 sample in length since at least one sample of delay is needed to allow feedback (just like with **history**). With feedback *disabled*, the delay time can go right down to zero samples. Practically, the difference is whether the reads happen before or after the writes. If you look at the code view, you'll see the corresponding `delay.read()` and `delay.write()` instructions change order with **@feedback 1** and **@feedback 0**.

[3] For more on this subject, see Dattorro, Jon. "Effect design, part 2: Delay line modulation and chorus." Journal of the Audio engineering Society 45, no. 10 (1997): 764-788.

[4] Hyun Ahn, Jae, and Richard Dudas. Musical Applications of Nested Comb Filters for Inharmonic Resonator Effects. In Proceedings of the 2013 International Computer Music Conference. Ann Arbor, MI: Michigan Publishing, University of Michigan Library, 2013.

[5] Incidently, this diagram is an example of a *nested* filter. All that means is, one or more elements within a diagram is replaced by another block diagram, thus nesting one filter response within another. If you look closely, you might recognize the inner structure of this diagram (with the **-k** and **k** coefficients) is practically the same as the allpass filter we saw in the previous chapter (p. 207), but with the Z^{-1} **history** operation replaced by a Z^{-M} **delay** operation. We'll see more allpass delay structures in Book 2.

[6] Karplus, Kevin; Strong, Alex (1983). "Digital Synthesis of Plucked String and Drum Timbres". Computer Music Journal. MIT Press. 7 (2): 43–55. doi:10.2307/3680062. JSTOR 3680062.

[7] Note that the highpass DC blocking filter we added earlier does not add any appreciable delay for the same reasons we explored in the highpass filter section of Chapter 7.

[8] You might enjoy the detuning effect as something a little more organic, and if so, it can liberate some quite enjoyable explorations into inserting multiple filters and filter types into the delay loop. A mix of a lowpass and several bandpass filters can produce some quite lovely multiphonic effects. If you are using resonant filters, you may also want to incorporate feedback limiting (saturation) as we did earlier in this chapter.

[9] Briefly, linear interpolation is a weighted average, and averaging tends to flatten out the fastest changes in a signal, which means losing information in the higher frequencies. The more our desired delay Is estimated between samples, the more we are relying on estimated rather than actual data, and thus the more the result loses higher frequency energy. This is why some pitches sound brighter than others. Unfortunately, switching to another built-in **delay** operator interpolation mode such as **@interp cosine** or **@interp cubic** doesn't help very much here; all of them have some kind of averaging effect.

[10] Many of the filter diagrams that we have looked at combine both feedforward and feedback paths, such as the allpass and biquad filters; the presence of a feedback loop is

likely to give these an infinite impulse response (IIR), unless the coefficients effectively cancel the feedback. The closest things to FIR filters we have seen so far in this book are the shift register based smooth random generator in chapter 4 (p. 115) and the weighted shift register sequencer in chapter 5 (p. 152).

Chapter 8: Frequent Modulations

[1] Scaling isn't the only way to make a bipolar signal unipolar. For example, we could send it through a **max 0** operator (this is also known as half-wave rectification) or an **abs** operator (which, in turn, corresponds to full-wave rectification) or a **fold 0 1** (a kind of wave-folding) etc. However, each of these operations will change the shape of the modulator waveform, and likely introduce a lot of aliasing harmonics. Scaling the waveform is the way to make it unipolar while preserving its original shape.

[2] The point of transition between events, rhythms, and timbre is particularly interesting, in that it does this at almost the same frequencies that can turn a series of still images into the perception of continuous motion in animation (the phi phenomenon at typically 20-30 frames per second).

[3] The use of the word *ring* in the name of this technique comes from the physical layout of diodes in a ring structure in the analog circuits that historically implemented this kind of modulation.

[4] According to Bill Schottstaedt (per https://ccrma.stanford.edu/software/snd/snd/fm.html), this is exactly how John Chowning accidentally discovered the technique, which was then developed by Yamaha in the renowned DX7 and other synthesizers. Unfortunately, it was marketed with the misnomer of frequency modulation (FM) when in fact these synthesizers implemented phase modulation. Since then many other synthesizers implementing phase modulation also called it "FM".

[5] Considering the **phasor** and *** twopi** carrier subcircuit as an angular integrator, we could think of both FM and PM as two kinds of "angular modulation", with the difference being whether the modulation is added into the *input* of the integrator (FM), or to its *output* (PM).

[6] Mathematically, the sideband intensities depend on Bessel functions, which are not very intuitive and are beyond what we cover in this book.

[7] https://cycling74.com/forums/carrier-and-harmonicity-in-fm-synthesis

[8] Actually, a sine wave shifted by a quarter turn phase difference, but we can't hear that difference!

[9] United States Patent US4249447A "Tone Production Method for an Electronic Musical Instrument" Norio Tomisawa, 1979 (Expired). Currently assigned to Yamaha Corp Nippon Gakki Co Ltd.

[10] Filters to block DC ("direct current") are sometimes called AC couplers ("alternating current"); both terms being inherited from equivalents in analog electronic circuits.

[11] Here is yet another intriguing connection with integration. In Chapter 6 (p. 209), we saw that a lowpass filter is a "leaky" integrator, and a highpass filter is the opposite operation (a kind of leaky differentiator). Earlier in this chapter, we pointed out how with FM, the modulation is integrated by the **phasor** operator (and vice versa). So perhaps it makes sense that correction to PM also requires the integration of a lowpass filter, whereas correction to FM requires the opposite operation!

[12] The issue is also present in FM, but is less noticeable, since a sudden jump of *magnitude* in the modulator leads to a sudden change of *slope* in the carrier. A change of slope isn't

as noticeable as a skip in phase, but it may still add a triangle wave-like sonority if the modulation is periodic.

[13] This also works with FM, with the difference noted earlier that the modulator signal is integrated before being waveshaped; so we hear the effect of the rate of change of the modulator instead.

[14] Through-Zero FM (TZFM) simply means that the analog oscillator has additional circuitry to be able to work with negative frequencies without running into difficulties. In contrast, for digital oscillators, negative frequencies pose no problems, and almost all of the FM patches in this chapter are linear TZFM.

[15] This idea was presented in J. A. Moorer, "Signal Processing Aspects of Computer Music: A Survey", Proceedings of the IEEE, 65 (8), pp.1108 - 1141 1977

[16] Carson, John R. "Notes on the theory of modulation." Proceedings of the Institute of Radio Engineers 10.1 (1922): 57-64.

[17] As you might imagine, the same principle of reading ahead / reading behind can be applied to reading audio from a **buffer** or **data** operator, and the same principles of PM and FM apply there too.

[18] However, for a more robust phase-modulated string model, the example at the end of Chapter 8 (p. 274) is recommended.

[19] Timoney, Joe, Victor Lazzarini, and Tom Lysaght. "A modified FM synthesis approach to bandlimited signal generation." Proceedings of the 11th International Conference on Digital Audio Effects (DAFx-08), Espoo, Finland. 2008.

Chapter 9: Navigating Waves of Data

[1] We recommended the **wave** operator here not just because it has these convenient sub-range inputs, but because it will also perform interpolation properly when wrapping over the edges of the sub-range. For example, if you set the range to be between 1000 and 1999, and at some point your phasor ramp is asking for the interpolated value at 1999.5, then it will output a blend between samples 1999 and 1000 (whereas the **sample** operator would have given you the blend between samples 1999 and 2000 – which is outside the sub-range!)

[2] The word *voxel* is a shortening of the term "volume element," similar to how the word "pixel" is a shortening of the term "picture element".

[3] If you're wondering why there are so many harmonics, it's because the sharp transition in a saw wave has theoretically infinite curvature, which produces an infinite series of harmonic frequencies. These are the frequencies that we cannot actually represent digitally, and what we need to filter away once they are above a reasonable range of hearing.

[4] Factum: The letters MIP in the name MipMap are an acronym of the Latin phrase *multum in parvo*, which means "much in little".

[5] Image courtesy of Wikimedia commons, at https://commons.wikimedia.org/wiki/File:Mipmap_Aliasing_Comparison.png#/media/File:Mipmap_Aliasing_Comparison.png, CC0 1.0 Universal (CC0 1.0) Public Domain Dedication

[6] If you wanted to save more computation, you could pre-bake the sinc filtering into a series of wavetables, one for each octave. This would make the playback patch a little more complex, but only slightly (it is analogous to what we did with the 2D wavetable set). However it also sacrifices the ability to modify the wavetable data dynamically.

---

[7] This relationship between effective resolution and harmonic limits might remind you of the mipmapping method we explored earlier in this chapter. It might be worth investigating terrains as an alternative way to help band limit wavetables.

[8] This technique of using regular polygons to generate audio output is documented in the paper "Continuous Order Polygonal Waveform Synthesis" by Christoph Hohnerlein, Maximilian Rest, and Julius O. Smith, in the Proceedings of the International Computer Music Conference, University of Michigan Library, 2016. It is also the basis of the Polygogo Eurorack module.

[9] If you're feeling ambitious, perhaps you might think about how to extend orbit generators to 3D, to drive a 3D wavetable oscillator for example – or even thinking about what a 3D terrain (and synthesizing trajectories through a voxel field) would work.

Chapter 10: Windows of Time

[1] Curtis Roads accounts for the use of "Pulsar" in this nomenclature in reference to the pulsars of astronomy – spinning neutron stars that emit periodic signals in the range of 0.25Hz to 640Hz, coincidentally a range of frequencies between rhythm and tone of central importance to pulsar synthesis. For an in depth exploration of microsonic techniques, including pulsar synthesis, see Roads, Curtis. Microsound. The MIT Press, 2004.

[2] If you wanted to set the pulsaret grain duration as a duty cycle between zero and one, rather than a division ratio of 1.0 or greater, all you need to do is take the reciprocal of the duty (using a **!/ 1** operator) to get the equivalent division ratio.

[3] This is analogous to Heisenberg uncertainty principle of particle physics: the more sharply we can position the event in time (due to a shorter window), the more uncertain or diffuse becomes its frequency (a wider spectrum), and vice versa, the more certainty we have over the spectral shape, the longer the window we need.

Remember also that windowing is a form of amplitude modulation (AM), and as we saw in Chapter 8 (p. 267), amplitude modulation introduces sidebands that depend on the modulator's frequency. Shortening the window duration will increase its frequency content, causing the sidebands to spread further apart. Moreover, the less smooth the window shape (and the more complex the carrier), the more sidebands will be produced.

[4] These and many other inspiring ideas can be found in Xenakis, Iannis. Formalized music: thought and mathematics in composition. No. 6. Pendragon Press, 1992.

[5] If this isn't clear, perhaps it helps to look at it the other way around. Imagine we have a sample counter that loops counting by ones from zero to ten. Since it counts by ones, the slope is 1. To get a phasor out of this we'd need to divide by the loop length (10). Then the slope would be 1/10 per sample. So, to get a sample counter back from a phasor we do the opposite: dividing by 1/10 is multiplying by 10, getting back to our original sample counter.

[6] The processing overhead is constant, regardless how many notes are actually playing, but this could be an advantage in some situations. For example, if we are designing an algorithm to export to an embedded hardware platform, a predictable computational cost can be preferable to an unpredictable one, as it is the maximum computational cost that determines whether the audio algorithm is viable or not.

[7] The fourth inlet to a **poke** operator sets the amount of the existing sound in a **data** or **buffer** to *retain*. By default this value is zero, which means the **poke** operator will by default overwrite and replace any existing sound. Setting it to 1.0 will preserve all of the existing sound *and* add the new sound to it. You can also think of it as a feedback gain control, if the **data** is being used as a delay.

[8] Another catch is that this algorithm only really works with integer delay times, since a **poke** operator can only write into one sample slot of the tape at once – it cannot interpolate. Since we can't smoothly modulate delay times this is perhaps less of a problem than it might seem.

[9] The method described here is different from but inspired by a method using box integrals in "Anti Aliasing Oscillators and Distortions with Pre-Integrated Wave Tables", Thierry Rochebois, 2016. The method described here avoids the complexity of the integrals themselves but reproduces equivalent waveforms.

[10] Of course, the physical reality isn't a straight line either (e.g. it can't sharply change directions), and depends on many factors, but this approximation is a lot closer than a step function, and easier to understand.

[11] We saw in Chapter 9 that using sinc interpolation can also suppress aliasing on general waveforms, and will see more methods in Book 2 that can do more precise antialiasing for specific waveforms. However, these benefits come at a price of greater computational complexity, and also latency in some cases

Acknowledgements

The authors would like to thank David Zicarelli and Darwin Grosse for keeping us on the path to this book, and for their support and encouragement along the way.

We are most grateful to those who read, commented, and offered good feedback as our book developed, including Sean Booth and Michael Zbyszynski as well as colleagues at Cycling '74 including Cory Metcalf and Isabel Kaspriskie, who helped us to refine our content with an eye toward new developments in Max. In addition to their reading of our text, we are particularly thankful to Luke Dubois, Robert Henke, and Jim O'Rourke for their kind words about it (which you'll find on the back cover).

Finally, our heartfelt thanks to our families — Haru Ji, Ina Ji Wakefield, and Jolanda Vanderwal Taylor — who were sources of advice, comfort, and joy. We hope they'll be seeing a bit more of us....

The Authors

Graham Wakefield was the primary author of gen~ while a doctoral student at the University of California Santa Barbara. Now an Associate Professor and Canada Research Chair, he directs the Alice Lab at York University and publishes research in journals and conferences spanning computer music, live coding, electronic arts, and mixed reality. With Haru Ji he also creates immersive bio-inspired *Artificial Nature* artworks, exhibited at venues such as the ZKM, Karlsruhe and la Gaîté Lyrique, Paris.

Gregory Taylor is the author of *Step by Step: Adventures in Sequencing with Max/MSP*. He creates and edits content for Cycling '74. He was trained as a visual artist, has studied central Javanese gamelan and electroacoustic music in the U.S. and the Netherlands, and hosts a radio program of contemporary audio on WORT-FM. His recordings are available on the Palace of Lights, c74, Clang, Nachtstück, Flood, Spectropol, Stasisfield, and ARTlevel labels.

Made in the USA
Columbia, SC
12 January 2024